QE
501.4
P 3
P 35

/QE501.4.P3P35>C1/

D1358366

AL

DATE DUE

MAY 0 5 1987 HAMILTON	APR 2 8 RECD		

DEMCO 38-297

A Publication of

The Society of Economic Paleontologists and Mineralogists

a division of

The American Association of Petroleum Geologists

FEB 16 1976

QE
501.4
P3
P35

PREFACE

Questions relating to the past distribution of faunas, floras and sediments, the meaning of the distributional patterns, and causes of changes in past distributions have greatly interested many scientists for more than a century. These problems take on added importance when viewed in the context of recent theories of plate tectonics and redistribution of crustal blocks. This volume presents the result of a Research Symposium on "Paleogeographic Provinces and Provinciality" sponsored by the Research Committee of the Society of Economic Paleontologists and Mineralogists, which was given at the annual meeting of the Society in Denver, Colorado, on April 18, 1972. The symposium featured fourteen papers presented in two half-day sessions and this volume includes nine of these and four additional papers which were included earlier in the planning of the volume. Particular thanks are due June R. P. Ross, Western Washington State College, for her help in processing the manuscripts.

The participants view paleogeographic provinces and provinciality over a broad spectrum. They were asked to examine from their own backgrounds the various aspects of provinciality based on available data. The resulting papers are most stimulating and thought provoking and, at the same time, so completely diverse in their approaches to the subject that their concepts and terminologies commonly contrast strongly. This situation projects the vigorous rejuvenation and reexamination of concepts and hypotheses in paleogeography and provinciality. I believe the reader will get as much delight and enthusiasm from perusing this collection of papers as the participants had in preparing the papers. Where future studies of paleogeography and provinciality will lead is difficult to foretell. However, we hope the ideas and thoughts presented here will contribute to a stimulating future.

CHARLES A. ROSS, *Editor*
Western Washington State College
Bellingham, Washington

108J0

CONTENTS

PALEOGEOGRAPHY AND PROVINCIALITY

CHARLES A. ROSS

Department of Geology, Western Washington State College, Bellingham, WA 98225

ABSTRACT—Segregation of Recent biotas into geographically restricted areas led, during the last hundred years, to investigation of factors that cause provincialism and the phenomena that restrict endemic species and evolutionary lineages to particular provinces. Biogeography as a discipline is a diversified subject that also includes synthesis from other biological and related sciences. Initial analyses in a biogeographic study usually examine the geographical distribution of different species and then attempt to determine similarities and differences in the distribution of each species in order to establish those which occur in the same area and those which do not. In addition, biogeography investigates phenomena giving rise to similarities or differences in these distributional patterns.

Biogeography is a many tiered science with several operational levels and paths of inquiry. When inter-specific relationships are examined using the present distributional patterns as a base, ecologic and geographic factors are the two primary sets of controls. Because many of the ecologic and geographic factors are constantly changing with time, distributional patterns and composition of component species also change. Introduction of a historical aspect broadens biogeography to include study of evolution of adaptive changes in species, in communities, the long term consequences of these changes, and geographic and climatological changes in barriers and corridors for dispersal that result from geological processes. Attempts to quantify differences in taxonomic composition between biogeographic areas lead to several equations. Analysis of diversity and stability in Recent ecosystems suggest an expansion of possible interpretations in paleobiogeography.

To date, paleobiogeography has combined the study of geographical distribution and morphological evolution (taxonomic change) into a historical framework. Development of ecological frameworks for past communities and interpretation of the adaptive significance of morphological changes in fossil groups have begun, and integration of geological processes and information, such as the wealth of sedimentological, climatic, paleogeographic, and structural data, into paleobiogeography has started.

INTRODUCTION

Our Recent biota is strongly segregated into geographically delimited areas, and, for more than a century, biologists have carefully investigated those factors that cause and maintain these strikingly demarcated distributional patterns, such as differences in climate, individual and community adaptations, barriers to dispersal, and history and duration of geographic isolation. These factors and their interrelations are clearly complex, difficult to analyze, and even more difficult to predict. The variety of concepts and terminologies used in the field of biogeography reflects the widely diverse avenues from which the subject has been approached and the resultant contrasting and, at times, almost contradictory philosophies that have developed. In introducing this symposium volume on *Paleogeography and paleogeographic provinces,* this brief review presents general concepts of Recent biogeography including terminology and contrasting points of view because the contributors to the volume have used or alluded to many of them in their approaches to their topics.

Early biogeographic studies investigating the geographic distribution of the myriad of organisms that form the world's biota, belong to the period of organized European explorations of the late 18th and early 19th centuries. Reports by Augustin De Candolle and Alexander Von Humbolt, Edward Forbes, Joseph Hooker and P. L. Sclater present a vast and interesting array of distributional data about new and unknown faunas and floras and provide some attempt to delimit those faunas having geographically similar distributions. Alfred R. Wallace (1876), also known for his contribution to the theory of natural selection with Charles Darwin, identified many of the processes and principles that control and effect these distributions and formulated the basic nomenclature and Recent faunal regions. During the later part of the 19th century interest in biogeography centered on the time and place of origin and subsequent dispersal of different members of the faunal and floral provinces. Debates and controversies by the vertebrate paleontologists, Cope and Marsh, enlivened much of this endeavor. Vertebrate paleontologists have continued to take a foremost place in evolutionary interpretation and paleobiogeographic analysis of their data as shown by Simpson's (1965) series of articles.

Another approach to biogeography originated from the gradual extension of ecology from analyses of autoecology to synecology and community organization, to community and biome geography, and to the evolution of ecosystems. In the succeeding outline of the principal schemes used in analyzing biogeographic distribution, the general overall agreement on how to partition the terrestrial areas of the World further emphasizes the distinctiveness of Recent biogeographic areas. Each scheme's approach to biogeography has different terminologies to exemplify the different concepts. Even strictly taxonomic studies of phytogeography and zoogeography use different terms and different boundaries for their major mapping units.

TAXONOMIC BIOGEOGRAPHICAL SCHEMES

Zoogeographic Areas.—Zoogeographers divide the Recent terrestrial world into three major geographical realms (fig. 1). The largest subdivision, the African-Eurasian-North American Realm, extends from South Africa around more than three-quarters of the globe to Central America. The next in size is the South American Realm and the third is the Australian Realm. Only the Middle American, West Indian, and Celebesian Transitions separate these realms.

Within each realm, regions and subregions are recognizable; the African-Eurasian-North American Realm is composed of African-Asian Tropical Region and an Arctic-Temperate Region. Each of these may be further divisible into subregions, such as the African Tropical Subregion, Asian Tropical Subregion, Arctic Subregion, North American Temperate Subregion and Eurasian-African Temperate Subregion. Both the Australian and the South American Realms are sufficiently similar internally that subdivision at the level of zoogeographic regions is not appropriate, although the contrast between Australia and New Guinea is equivalent to subregion level.

This subdivision of the terrestrial world into realms, regions and subregions is based mainly on geographical distribution of families and orders of the higher vertebrates, particularly Classes Aves (Schlater, 1857) and Mammalia (Wallace, 1876). Although other faunal groups may be as appropriate in establishing such subdivisions, when contrasted with other classes of terrestrial vertebrates, these two classes are by far the most diverse and widely adapted. They are also the most recently evolved classes and have either replaced or displaced many members of the older vertebrates in the Classes Amphibia and Reptilia.

The oceans are less easily subdivided into zoogeographical areas mainly because less is known of their faunas and because of depth and temperature stratification of faunas. Three sets of biogeographic subdivisions are commonly used. The earliest studied and most thoroughly known are the littoral realms which include the shore, shallow seas and shelves (fig. 2). Defined approximately by latitude and water temperature, they are named accordingly: Arctic, Antarctic, Boreal, Antiboreal, North and South Warm Temperate, and Tropical Realms (Zenkevich, 1949). Except for the Arctic and Antarctic Realms, these Recent littoral realms border and are isolated by major ocean basins and continents so that each is composed of separate regions; for example, the Boreal Realm is divisible into a European Atlantic Baltic Region and a North American Region, a Pacific Northwestern American Region and a Japanese Region. Most interest in marine biogeography has centered on identifying and delineating provinces within each littoral region. The present continental barriers, the Isthmuses of Panama and Suez, are relatively young geographic features of late Cenozoic age. The Panama Portal existed for most of the Cenozoic and this marine connection between the Caribbean and east Pacific was closed near the middle of the Pliocene Epoch (about 5 million years ago). As a result, warmer water biota of the western Atlantic Region has its closest relationship with that of the eastern Pacific and the faunas of the warm water Caribbean and Panamic marine Provinces have the most similarity, the Carolinian and Californian marine Provinces have less similarity, and the Boreal and Aleutian marine Provinces have the least similarity of these paired provinces.

The open oceans are known in broad outline, and the upper layer, or photic zone, is known far more thoroughly than the rest. The faunal regions of the oceanic photic zone (fig. 3) compare closely with surface temperatures (fig. 4) which are related to movements of surface water masses having characteristic temperature and salinity. The Northern and Southern Transition Regions are associated with shifting boundaries of cold and warm currents, each having contrasting faunas. These current boundaries are relatively stable on the western sides of oceans but are shifted by storms over considerable distances toward the eastern side of oceans.

Phytogeographic Areas.—Although phytogeography analyses parallel the zoogeographic approach and subdivide the world on the basis of distribution of plant taxa, the floral subdivisions and boundaries commonly do not coincide with the faunal units. These differences reflect the different adaptations, climatic tolerances, and means of dispersal between the higher forms of plants and animals, that is, the phytogeographic units are defined primarily on the basis of seed-bearing plants (spermatophytes) and the zoogeographic units on birds and mammals. These

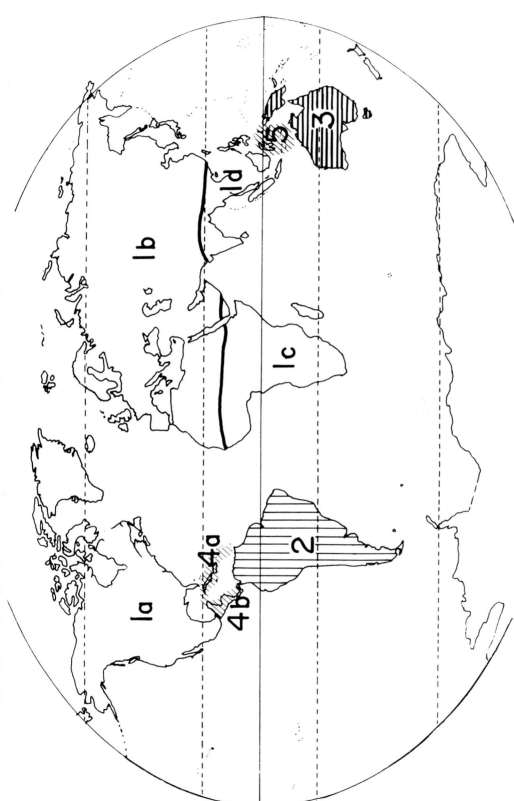

Fig. 1—Terrestrial zoogeographic subdivisions. 1, Eurasian-African-North American (Megagean or Arctogea) Realm; 1a, Nearctic Region, 1b, Palearctic Region, 1c, Ethiopian Region, 1d, Oriental Region; 2, Neotropical Realm, Region, and Subregion: 3, Australian Realm and Region; 4, Caribbean Transitions; 4a, West Indian Transition; 4b, Middle American Transition: 5, Celebesian Transition. (Data from Neill, 1969.)

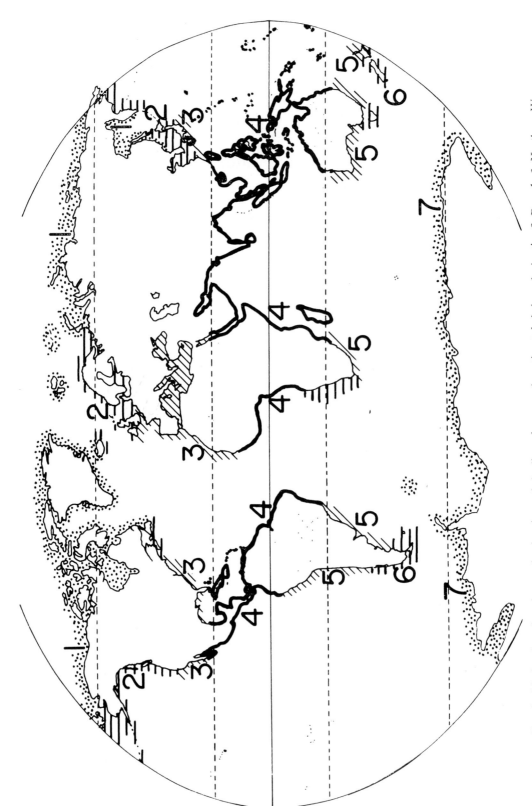

Fig. 2—Marine faunal regions and subregions of the littoral zone and continental shelves. 1, Arctic; 2, Boreal; 3, Northern Warm Temperate; 4, Tropical; 5, Southern Warm Temperate; 6, Antiboreal 7, Antarctic. (Based on data given by Ekman, 1953 and Hedgpeth, 1957.)

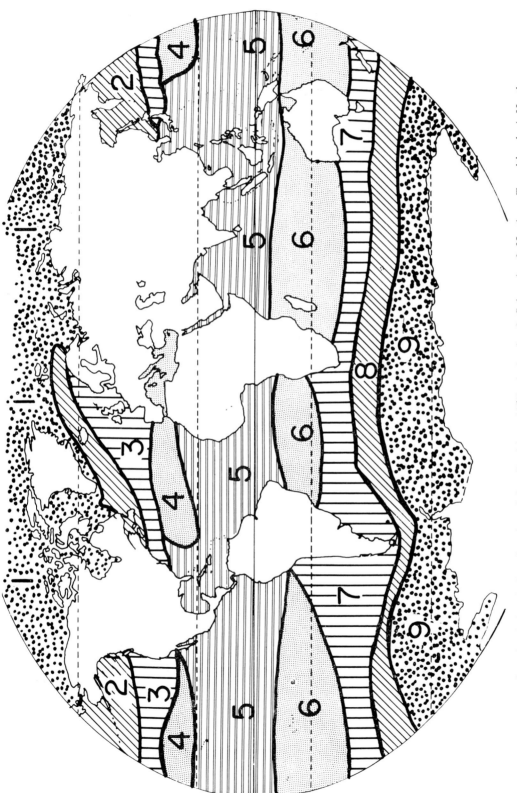

FIG. 3—Oceanic planktonic faunal regions (after Bradshaw, 1959). 1, Arctic; 2, Subarctic; 3, Northern Transitional; 4, Northern Subtropical; 5, Tropical; 6, Southern Subtropical; 7, Southern Transitional; 8, Subantarctic; 9, Antarctic. Compare with Text-figure 4 which shows surface water temperatures.

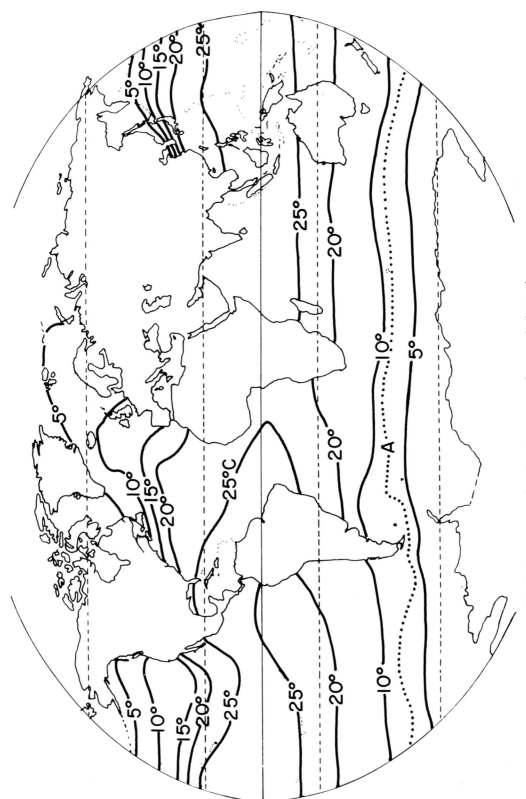

Fig. 4—Average annual surface temperature of oceans. A, Antarctic convergence. (Data from U.S. Navy, Marine climatic atlas of the world).

higher groups also differ appreciably in their geologic antiquity and their responses to events in their geologic history. These differences are sufficiently important that phytogeography uses another set of names for the different levels of geographic subdivision to contrast them with the zoogeographic levels and units.

There are six floral kingdoms (fig. 5): Australian, Cape, Antarctic, Palaeotropical, Neotropical and Boreal. The Palaeotropical is divisible into African, Indo-Malaysian, and Polynesian Subkingdoms. These and the other Kingdoms are divided into a large number of floral provinces (fig. 5). In contrast to zoogeographic subdivisions, major transitional areas between the largest units are not identifiable and boundaries in most places are more clearly defined. Few higher plants have adapted to marine conditions so, in contrast to zoogeography, no serious attempt has been made to subdivide the marine shore and shelves into phytogeographic units.

Phytogeographic kingdoms and zoogeographic realms are usually separated from one another by one or two provinces of high ecological stress or strongly contrasting physical environments. Commonly these are areas associated with orographic features or abrupt changes in climatic belts.

ECOLOGICAL BIOGEOGRAPHIC SCHEMES

Allen (1871) believed that the distribution of animals and plants was principally the result of two environmental factors, temperature and humidity. Hence, the distribution of species followed world-wide climatic zones and the mean yearly isotherms of 10° and 21°C and major oceanic barriers were used to divide the terrestrial areas into eight realms. Each realm was divided into regions which were further divided into provinces and, finally, into a number of floras and faunas. Although Allen's scheme was not accepted, a modification by Merriam (1892) was used for several decades in North America before it was eventually abandoned. Merriam (1892) held that plants and animals are limited in their poleward and altitudinal distribution because of the decreasing amount of heat available during their season of growth and reproduction and that they were limited in their southern distribution by the mean temperature during the hottest part of the year. Merriam studied the distribution of many plants and animals to find natural concentrations of range boundaries in order to define the limits of his life zones to appropriate isotherms. Although precipitation was added later as a criterion of less significance, so many other important ecological factors were not considered in Merriam's

life zone scheme that this approach to the problem was finally found untenable.

Biotic Provinces.—Biotic provinces, another type of biogeographic province, were initially recognized on the basis of characteristic species composition of both plants and animals (Vestal, 1914) and, therefore, were based on strictly taxonomic criteria. As the concept of biotic provinces developed, other criteria were introduced to include such nontaxonomic criteria as vegetation type, sere and climax vegetation, climate, physiography, and soil type (Dice, 1943). In areas of strong topographic relief, abrupt contrasts in physiography, climate, and altitude cause complex patterns and give rise to many more small provinces than in areas of low topography (fig. 6). Thus, biotic provinces are areas having distinctive modern environments and, at the same time, reflect an interval of endemic evolution. In theory, biotoic provinces are centers of ecologic dispersal and have arbitrary and quasistationary boundaries between them. This multifactorial approach in defining biotic provinces masks causes and effects, and it usually places undefined degrees of emphasis on different criteria. Only a few later studies have attempted to use the broad spectrum of criteria demanded by Dice's (1943) definition and most studies simplify the concept to emphasize faunistic uniformity and to describe the ecologic conditions in which that uniformity exists.

Vegetation Types.—Mapping vegetation types (i.e., types of plant cover) and analyzing these in relation to other factors in the environment is an ecological approach to biogeography that attempts to avoid the dependence on taxonomy for delimiting areas. The principal vegetation types, called biochores, result from morphological adaptation through evolutionary processes to similar environmental conditions and include only four categories: forest, savanna, grassland and desert. Biochores are subdivided into formation types (or formation classes) which appear to relate to the range and distribution of temperature and precipitation. The most common formation types are listed in table 1.

The geographical distributions of vegetation formation types are also referred to as *provinces,* a source of some confusion with province units used in phytogeographic, zoogeographic, and biotic description, therefore, Neill (1969) italicizes the vegetation formation type *provinces.* At present there are about 100 named vegetation formation type *provinces* in the world; each is an area important for its distinctive climate, vegetation type, and flora.

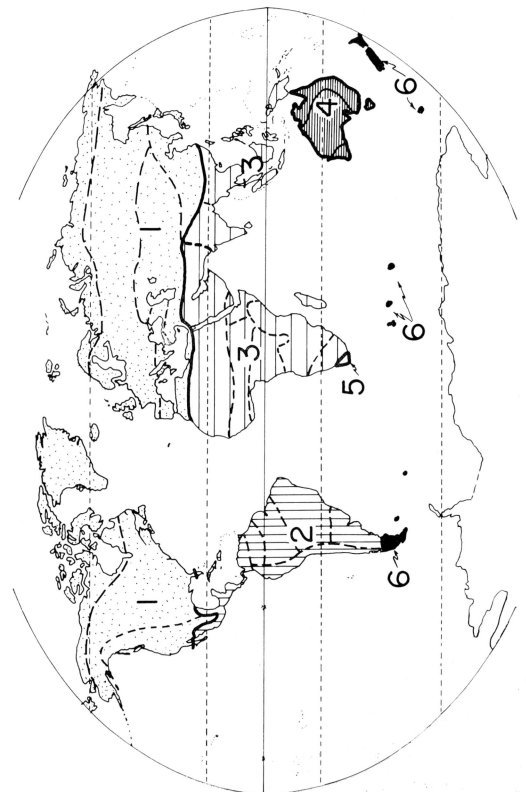

Fig. 5.—Phytogeographic subdivision. 1, Boreal Kingdom; 2, Neotropical Kingdom; 3, Palaeotropical Kingdom; 4, Australian Kingdom; 5, Cape Kingdom; 6, Antarctic Kingdom; dashed lines are province boundaries. (Data from Neill, 1969.)

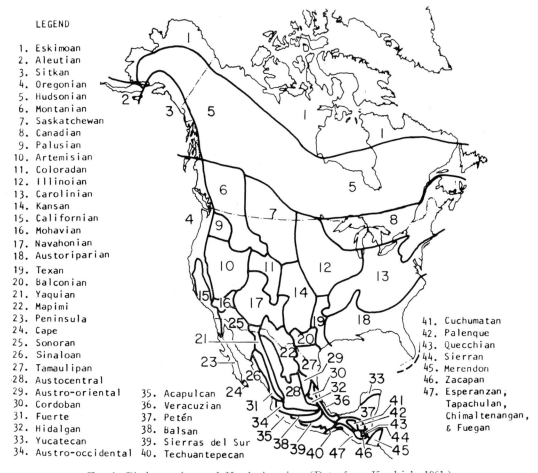

LEGEND

1. Eskimoan
2. Aleutian
3. Sitkan
4. Oregonian
5. Hudsonian
6. Montanian
7. Saskatchewan
8. Canadian
9. Palusian
10. Artemisian
11. Coloradan
12. Illinoian
13. Carolinian
14. Kansan
15. Californian
16. Mohavian
17. Navahonian
18. Austoriparian
19. Texan
20. Balconian
21. Yaquian
22. Mapimi
23. Peninsula
24. Cape
25. Sonoran
26. Sinaloan
27. Tamaulipan
28. Austocentral
29. Austro-oriental
30. Cordoban
31. Fuerte
32. Hidalgan
33. Yucatecan
34. Austro-occidental

35. Acapulcan
36. Veracuzian
37. Petén
38. Balsan
39. Sierras del Sur
40. Techuantepecan

41. Cuchumatan
42. Palenque
43. Quecchian
44. Sierran
45. Merendon
46. Zacapan
47. Esperanzan,
    Tapachulan,
    Chimaltenangan,
    & Fuegan

Fig. 6—Biotic provinces of North America. (Data from Kendeigh, 1961.)

The distributions of different kinds of plant cover (fig. 7) are largely the result of climate, but interaction with soils and topographic relief is also important and may help produce an environmental combination that results in a distinctive and unique plant cover. The area of distribution of a vegetation formation type is usually much broader than that of any single plant or animal confined to it. Because climates shift and vary, the boundaries of the vegetation formation types continually shift and small remnants may persist or pioneer colonies may invade small areas within other vegetation types. Comparison of the distributions of phytogeographic subdivisions and vegetation formation types shows some agreement, for example, evergreen hardwood forests characterize the Mediterranean and Southwest Australian Provinces and the Cape Kingdom.

Vegetation formation types are defined on the stable type of vegetation that will persist without further change in a particular province.

This stable vegetation is called the climax vegetation. However, before this stable vegetation cover is attained, the vegetation may have passed through a number of stages in which earlier groupings of plants prepare the way for the next successive stage. Only the climax stage is stable and the particular succession of stages leading to the climax is called a sere. Seres are frequently interrupted by many natural occurrences, such as fire, erosion, flooding, etc., so that the climax stage may not be attained, or not attained everywhere in the province at the same time, before its local destruction and the sere starts again. Because each stage in a sere alters its environment in such a way that it enables a succeeding stage to become established and to displace it, a sere represents an intricate adaptation among a number of plants that occupy or share the same vegetative province and, as such, the development of each sere must have a long evolutionary history. In the study of animal distribution,

TABLE 1—COMMON RECENT VEGETATION
FORMATION TYPES

Formation type	Dominant features
Tropical rainforest	Mostly evergreen hardwood trees, many species, no marked seasonal life cycles; constant warm temperature, consistent high rainfall
Subtropical rainforest	Similar to tropical rainforest, except that summer and winter seasons based on temperature and rainfall can be distinguished
Monsoon forest	Although tropical or subtropical, most rainfall arrives in warmer months and cooler months are dry; dominants are mostly deciduous hardwoods which drop leaves during cooler and dryer months
Temperate rainforest	Trees include hardwoods, conifers, and commonly tree ferns; high rainfall without a dry season; beyond the tropics so that there is a cool season.
Deciduous forest	Deciduous hardwoods and some conifers; precipitation distributed throughout years; winters include snow
Coniferous forest	Evergreen conifers, cold regions having long winters and abundant precipitation
Evergreen hardwood forest	Small trees with sharp brittle leaves; warm dry summers and precipitation during winters (Mediterranean-type climate)
Savanna	Scattered trees, thick tall grass, tropical to subtropical temperatures; strongly seasonal rainfall, long dry season
Thorn forest (scrub)	Small thorny trees and bushes; subtropical to warm temperate climates with seasonal and scant rainfall; special adaptations to prevent dessication
Prairie	Tall summer grasses; temperate climates precipitation mainly in summer
Steppe	Short clump grasses, temperate climates with scanty precipitation mainly in late fall and winter months
Semidesert	Scattered vegetation, dry summer and severely cold winters
Grassy tundra	Grasses and sedges; high latitudes or altitudes, brief thaw and short growing season
Cold desert	A few scattered plants around edges of permanent snow and glacial ice
Tropical desert	Virtually no vegetation, drifting sand
Subtropical desert	A few shrubs, small trees, ephemeral plants, scant irregular precipitation

plant succession becomes important because some animals are confined to particular stages of the sere or to the climax stage. The difference in animals in each stage is commonly a basis for different adaptions by the plants of the sere for seed distribution.

Biomes.—An integrative ecological scheme investigates and maps large biogeographic areas using a unit called the biome. These are areas characterized by particular maxima and minima temperatures, amount and distribution of precipitation, changes of seasons, and changes in length of daylight. These physical factors interact to give a biome a characteristic vegetation which in turn harbors a characteristic assemblage of animals. A biome has a series of developmental stages and is able to reach an equilibrium with the environment. Seven biomes are recognized in North America north of Mexico (fig. 8): arctic tundra, northern coniferous forest, montane forest, eastern deciduous forest, central grasslands, Californian chaparral, and southwestern deserts. When viewed on a world scale, several biomes show considerable similarities and they are grouped into the following major types of biomes: tundra, taiga, deciduous forest, grasslands, desert, high plateau, and tropical forest. The biome concept integrates a vast amount of data from broadly different fields. It is possibly the only integrative ecologic approach to biogeography that can be extended readily beyond the terrestrial areas into the shallow seas and oceans.

Biotic Communities.—Within its geographic range a species normally occupies a habitat (along with other species) that is defined by a particular environment. Vegetative types are the most convenient indicator of terrestrial environmental factors. Each area of distinctive vegetation has an associated characteristic assemblage of plants and animals that interact to form a biotic community. Although each community is mostly independent of other communities, they are not completely isolated and are separated by ecotones. A biotic community can be a climax or only one of the seres so that the developmental history of a community may become important. The climax stage of geographically adjacent communities having similar climatic conditions are grouped together into biomes (Clements & Shelford, 1939).

Associations.—Associations are smaller units than communities and are usually named for one or two dominant plant types. Associations commonly result from variation in different local soil types, topography, and drainage con-

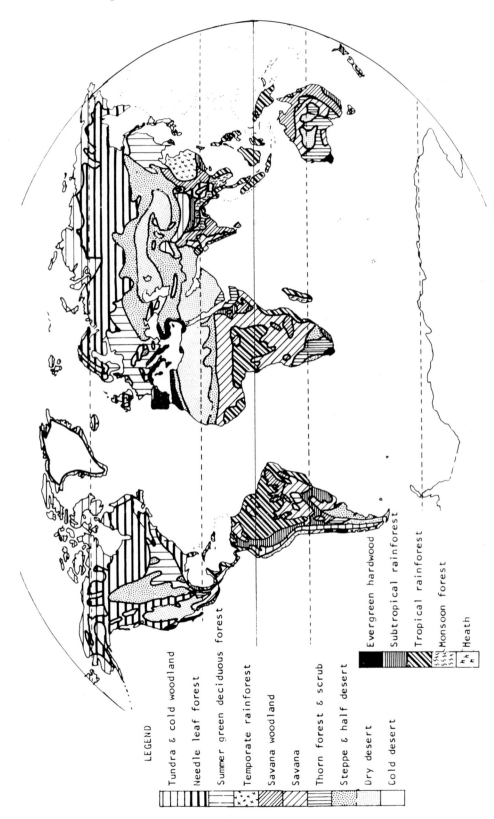

LEGEND

Tundra & cold woodland

Needle leaf forest

Summer green deciduous forest

Temperate rainforest

Savana woodland

Savana

Thorn forest & scrub

Steppe & half desert

Dry desert

Cold desert

Evergreen hardwood

Subtropical rainforest

Tropical rainforest

Monsoon forest

Heath

FIG. 7—Distribution of vegetation formation type *provinces*. (Data from Dansereau, 1957.)

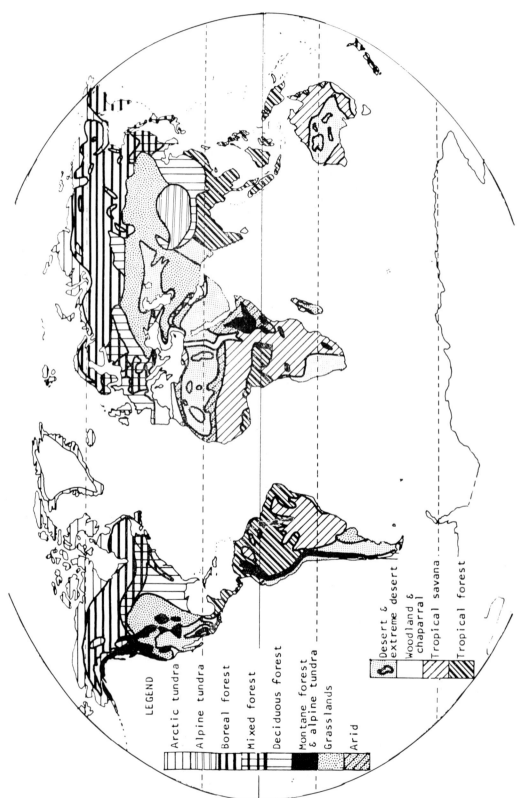

Fig. 8—Distribution of biomes. (Data from Kendeigh, 1961.)

LEGEND

Arctic tundra

Alpine tundra

Boreal forest

Mixed forest

Deciduous forest

Montane forest
& alpine tundra

Grasslands

Arid

Desert &
extreme desert

Woodland &
chaparral

Tropical savana

Tropical forest

ditions (i.e., flood-plains, sand dunes, hill slopes, uplands, etc.). Each association may be a sere or a climax and each contains its own distinctive plants and animals.

Biotopes.—The smallest biogeographic subdivision that displays environmental uniformity is the niche or biotope and is that place where a particular species of plant or animal occurs.

PHYLOGENETIC BIOGEOGRAPHY

Geographical and ecological approaches to the study of biotic distribution attempt to identify distinctive areas based on different levels of taxonomic relationships or ecological adaptions. The phylogenetic approach includes analyses from these two descriptive methods of study and combines them with phylogenetic or evolutionary history of each taxonomic group, analysis of the dispersal or distributional history of the different groups, and analysis of the geologic history (paleogeographic and paleoclimatic) of the areas. Two recent reviews of vertebrate zoogeography (Darlington, 1957; Simpson, 1965) illustrate the scope and deductive logic of phylogenetic biogeography and the intricate ramification of diverse data into broad convincing interpretations.

Phylogenetic studies of species, or taxa, and their distributions help to identify the length of time that provinces were isolated or adjacent and the type of barriers or boundaries that separated them. The phylogenetic history and success of individual species relate to the combination of many biological and environmental factors in the community or communities in which species is a member. A study of the geographic boundaries of all the species that are part of a community and study of changes of these boundaries with time become significant in determining the history of biogeographically defined areas. Because each boundary of a species range may be limited by different and strongly contrasting factors or conditions, the selection pressures and successful adaptations at different boundaries commonly produce different results. Under some conditions these adaptations are transmitted through the species ranges as a genetic gradient or cline so that opposing boundary adaptations are filtered out toward the center of the species range.

In general, species are best adapted to a set of optimal conditions or factors where species population densities are usually, but not always, highest. Much of the range of a species is in permissive conditions where its population densities are commonly lower. As environmental conditions or factors change in the species range, large parts of the original range may become uninhabitable and only local areas may remain permissive for the species and these local areas become refugia for relict populations.

The size, shape, continuity, and physical geography of a species range are also of considerable interest in establishing the phylogenetic history of related species populations. Discontinuous ranges are of two principal types, disjunct and dispersed ranges. Disjunct ranges include two or more widely separated geographic population ranges. Dispersed ranges are made up of many relatively small separate or semi-isolated populations. Separation time and mutation rates of isolated populations in disjunct or dispersed ranges, combined with differences in ecological stresses and modes of adaptation, initiate geographic speciation and the development of endemism and geographically distinctive biota.

Species ranges do not necessarily coincide with the geographic boundaries of communities and many species have geographic ranges through several communities, such as western hemlock and Douglas fir in western North America. Many other species have ranges that include only a portion of a community. The closeness of fit between species ranges and community ranges results from long term historical association, climatic and topographic gradients at the edge of the different ranges, homogeneity or heterogeneity of the biotope, and, of course, past changes and fluctuations in relationships and factors. Extinction may result when reduction in a species' geographic range falls below a certain minimum area and the population becomes too small for the species to reproduce a viable population. In theory, extinction may result from the inability of a species to adapt, by evolutionary change, to changing environmental conditions before the area it is able to inhabit is reduced to a size that the population falls below a critical minimum interbreeding level.

Patterns of distributions are repeated in widely different groups, such as bipolar, circumpolar, panboreal, and pantropic distributions, which emphasize temperature adaptations, and amphiamerican, amphipacific, and amphiatlantic distributions, which emphasize north-south dispersals. Arctic-alpine disjunct distributions ("glacial relicts") are common in northern hemisphere areas and are mainly related to Pleistocene climatic fluctuations. Similar patterns are also known for other disrupted distributions caused by Pleistocene climatic change in non-glaciated areas.

Intervals of strongly developed provincialism occur repeatedly during the phylogenetic history of many groups and strata within these time intervals are difficult to correlate from one province to another. Transitional areas having mixtures of biotas from two provinces, if located, and the occasional dispersal of some members of one biota into another province may be of extraordinary aid in establishing stratigraphic correlation between provinces (Ross, 1967, 1970). Although a certain degree of provincialism probably always has been a feature of the earth's biota, there were also intervals when provincialism gave way to nearly world wide cosmopolitan biotas (i.e., during Late Devonian and Early Mississippian time). The evolution of new species and development of distinctive communities in times of increasing provinciality is gradual and the threshold level for geographic isolation of separated segments of a species' populations is different for most species. Thus, provinciality is a matter of degree; the greater number of groups that show provincialism, presumably the greater are the ecologic barriers and the longer they have operated (Ross, 1973).

MEASUREMENT OF INTERREGIONAL RELATIONSHIPS

While biogeographers have recognized that different areas contain different biotas, the distinctivenes of biogeographic subdivisions varies widely. The need for an expression of the degree or a quantified measurement of the biotic similarity (or dissimilarity) between regions have resulted in a number of equations, each attempting to define certain relations or eliminate certain problems (Peters, 1955, 1968, 1971). The earliest attempts at quantification of biogeographic relationships involved calculation of the percentage of taxa shared, or not shared, by two or more areas and these have been summarized and analysed by Simpson (1960). Perhaps the most difficult statistical problem deals with biotas of very different numbers of taxa. The following commonly used formulae (Peters, 1968) outline various statistical approaches which attempt to solve problems of different statistical sample sizes. In these equations C is number of taxa common to both samples, N_1 is the number of taxa in the smaller sample and N_2 is the number in the larger sample.

1. Simpson Coefficient

$$= \frac{C}{N_1} \times 100 \text{ (Simpson, 1943)}$$

2. Jaccard Coefficient

$$= \frac{C}{N_2} \times 100 \text{ (Braun-Blanquet, 1932)}$$

3. Coefficient of Difference

$$= \left(1 - \frac{C}{N_2}\right) \times 100 \text{ (Savage, 1960)}$$

4. Burt Coefficient (a form of Pirlot's Index)

$$= \frac{2C}{N_1 + N_2} \times 100$$

5. First Kulczynski Coefficient

$$= \frac{C}{N_1 + N_2 - 2C} \times 100$$

6. Second Kulczynski Coefficient

$$= \frac{C(N_1 + N_2)}{2(N_1 + N_2)} \times 100$$

7. Otsuka Coefficient

$$= \frac{C}{N_1 + N_2} \times 100$$

8. Preston Resemblance Equation (solve for z)

$$= \left(\frac{N_1}{N_1 + N_2 - C}\right)^{1/z} + \left(\frac{N_2}{N_1 + N_2 - C}\right)^{1/z}$$

9. Preston Similarity (S) Formula $= (1 - z)$ $\times 100$ (see equation 8 for value of z)

10. Johnson Provincial Index

$$= \frac{C}{2(N_2 - C)} \text{ (Johnson, 1971)}$$

These equations are similar in that they compare numbers of species but differ mainly in the weight placed on the number of common taxa. They are widely used in zoogeographic and phytogeographic analysis because they emphasize taxonomic differences and each species or taxon is treated as if it is of equal importance.

Ekman (1940) introduced the principle that each endemic species or higher taxon characterizes to a certain degree the fauna in which it occurs, whereas, each taxon that appeared in both faunas being studied, has diminishing values. In Ekman's analysis each taxon is given a basic zoogeographical value based on its taxonomic rank; generic level taxa are worth twice the value of a species, and families are worth six times as much as genera in these comparisons. Another factor that Ekman (1940) attempted to quantify was the boundary between adjacent zoogeographic areas. He used a formula of greatest faunal change, $F = A + B/C$, in which A is the total positive zoogeographical values for fauna a, B is the total zoological value for fauna b, and C is the total of those taxa in common between a and b. In this analysis the total major geographical area is subdivided arbitrarily into subareas of approximately equal sizes and each compared with its neighboring area to determine the maximum values for F. Although Ekman's procedures of analyses have many subjective evaluations and involve lengthly computational procedures, they are convincing in theory and results. A more graphical approach for investigating problems of defining areas and boundaries is given by Schilder (1955, 1956) and illustrates the distribution of changes of faunas between two fixed end points and a number of intermediate points.

With the advent of computers, renewed attempts to define biogeographic areas through the use of statistical methods have appeared (Webb, 1950; Ryan, 1963; Huheey, 1965; Hagmeier and Stults, 1964; Hagmeier, 1966; and Goodall, 1954). Hagmeier (1966), after evaluating cluster analyses of faunistic affinity, established definition of North American faunal provinces, superprovinces, subregions and regions based on percentage of similarities between subareas and showed these various areas are closely related to ecological geographic units. Valentine (1966) applied this method of analysis to marine molluscan distributions and showed patterns that resemble water temperature distribution.

Diversity and Stability.—One difficulty of comparing the biota of different provinces is that the structure of their ecosystems may be markedly different and the number of species in a province may relate to the age, stability, and diversity of the trophic levels. Diversity in a biota commonly is indicated by the number of different species that occupy a particular area. As different species occupy different niches, number of species becomes more than an indicator of simple biotic diversity but rather of ecosystem sophistication, age, and evolutionary history. Udvardy (1969, p. 294) outlines many of the problems of using only numbers of species to classify diversity but points out that trends in species diversity in ecosystems are real and are identifiable. Thienemann (1918) related the small numbers of species which are able to adapt to extreme habitats to the harshness of environmental conditions. Although such an explanation is probably overly simplistic, in many groups of organisms a latitudinal diversity gradient does exist (Stehli, 1968) and more niches are available for occupancy in the lower latitudes than in higher latitudes. Many exceptions exist in smaller groups, such as coniferous trees and salamanders (MacArthur & Connell, 1966). Also related to the increased availability of niches is the increase in species number and species diversity as the size of the habitable area increases. Some increase in species diversity (as in the case of island populations) may relate to remoteness

from similar habitable areas, time, and "sweepstakes" chances of dispersal. However, in larger habitable areas, such as continental landmasses, different species may occupy the same niche if their respective populations are limited by different ecological factors.

Several ecological diversity studies suggest the problem of species diversity is not simply one of adaptation to harsh environmental conditions. In the tropics niches are more numerous and better exploited, shared, or divided by several species. Competition for space and food is more of a limiting factor in the tropics than in the higher latitudes where temperature is the principal limiting factor. Thus, different kinds of selection and adaptation pressures are at work which tend to increase further the number of available niches in tropical areas. Good (1964) gives the ratios of Recent cold, temperate, subtropical, and tropical vegetation belts as roughly $1:2:3:2\frac{1}{2}$ so that subtropical and tropical vegetation covers about twice the area of the combined cool and temperate belts. During the four Pleistocene glacial maxima, about 27% of the terrestrial areas were covered by ice or permafrost (in contrast to about 10% at present), and the cool and temperate belts were compressed proportionately more than the subtropical and tropical belts. For this reason the ecology and community relationships in the higher latitudinal belts were considerably more disrupted as indicated by the mixed niches of the North American eastern boreal forest.

Several theoretical generalizations have been proposed to explain diversity phenomena (summarized by Sanders, 1968; Bretsky & Lorenz, 1969): 1, older communities tend to be more diverse than younger ones; 2, heterogeneous physical environments support more complex and diversified biota; 3, stable climates and stable physical environments result in narrower niches and more species; 4, biologic competition and more complex ecosystems, rather than natural selection by physical environmental factors, accounts for greater diversity at low latitudes; 5, great productivity leads to greater diversity; and 6, because there are more predators in the tropics, there is less competition among the prey and more niches for the prey. Except for the last two of these statements, which may hold only for special examples, the rest appear to fit into a spectrum of ecosystems that range from strong physical stress conditions having low diversity to complexly interacting ecosystems having high diversity.

Measurement of diversity includes several aspects of the community, the number of species present, the relative proportion of these species, and their place and biomass in the trophic level of the ecosystem. Several equations have been proposed to measure these parameters of diversity and the modification of the Shannon-Weaver formula by Dickman (1968) approximates these conditions more closely than most others:

$$Hp = - \sum_1^n Pi \log_2 Pi,$$ where $Pi = pr/PR$ and is the ratio of productivity of a particular species (pr) to the total productivity of the sample (PR).

Stability in an ecosystem is also difficult to define and measure, and probably is not the same value everywhere within a community or range of a species. Therefore, some ecologists conceive of a center of stability within a community and less stable peripheral margins. Others (Preston, 1969) suggest that an ecosystem is stable when populations of all species are in balance (i.e., a time when no extinctions or plagues take place), although their populations may fluctuate. A number of approaches for measuring stability and degree of organization in ecosystems have been examined by Margalef (1969) who suggests comparing biomass and mortality rates of each species against diversity as given by the Shannon-Weaver formula.

Correctly interpreting fossil communities, their diversity, and their ecosystems eventually may lead to a more thorough understanding of the magnitude of biotic differences between communities, regions, and provinces. These approaches also may give clues for interpreting the history of an ecosystem, progressive changes in community structure, adaptive stress, and causes for extinctions and evolution of new species. Patterns of Recent diversity and productivity closely approximate the present temperature gradient which led Valentine (1967) to infer that past increases (or decreases) in the temperature gradient would result in an increase (or decrease) in ecologic niches, speciation, and provinciality but that the main effect of decreased provinciality would be more extinctions because of the small number of provinces.

CONCLUSIONS

Biogeography studies the distribution of the myriad of species that form the world's biota and the processes that control or affect these distributions. Although this field of investigation is more than 100 years old, most biogeographic studies have dealt with terrestrial biota and the current synthesis of biogeographic principles most readily applies to terrestrial situations. The principles and pecularities of marine biogeography and the ways they compare to terrestrial counterparts are less well understood. Recent distributions are the result of a complex series of ecologic and evolutionary interactions over a long interval of geologic time and include the adaptive history of each biotic lineage, the relation of these adaptations to changes in other lineages, in the physical environment, and in community structure.

Although paleogeographic provinces and the complicated processes that lead to provinciality have been known or observed for over a century, criteria for their interpretations and definitions are among the most difficult to establish quantitatively. In part this difficulty arises from the multiplicity of approaches used in analysis of biogeography. The earliest and most widely used methods compare the geographic distribution of endemic and cosmopolitan taxa in the higher forms of plants and animals. An outgrowth of this descriptive work has been the study of places of origin for various taxa, their morphologic evolution, and their patterns of dispersal. A third line of investigation originated from ecology and the study of vegetation types, their distribution, and their extension into the mapping of biomes and biotic communities based on ecosystems.

The theory of plate tectonics has brought a new perspective to the investigation of paleobiogeographic provinces. Structural, tectonic, geophysical, and sedimentological evidence adds to stratigraphic and fossil data in re-examining the various geologic regions that form our present continents to test other possible geographic distributions, spatial positions, and relationships to climatic belts and oceans basins.

REFERENCES CITED

ALLEN, J. A. 1871. The geographic distribution of animals. Bull. U.S. Geol. Geogrl. Survey 4:339–343.
BRAUN-BLANQUET, J. 1932. Plant sociology: the study of plant communities. (transl. H. S. Conard and G. D. Fuller) McGraw Hill, New York. xviii + 439 p.
BRADSHAW, J. S. 1959. Ecology of living planktonic Foraminifera of the North and Equatorial Pacific Ocean. Contr. Cushman Fdn. foramin. Res. 10:25–64.
BRETSKY, P. W., AND D. M. LORENZ. 1969. Adaptive response to environmental stability: a unifying concept in paleoecology. Proc. North Am. Paleont. Conv. E:522–550.
CLEMENTS, F. E., AND V. E. SHELFORD, 1939. Bio-ecology. Wiley, New York. viii + 825 p.
DANSERAU, P. 1957. Biogeography: an ecological perspective. Ronald Press, New York. viii + 394 p.
DARLINGTON, P. J. 1957. Zoogeography: the geographical distribution of animals. John Wiley, New York. xiii + 675 p.

DICE, L. R. 1943. The biotic provinces of North America. Univ. Mich. Press, Ann Arbor. 78 p.

DICKMAN, MIKE. 1968. Some indices of diversity. Ecology. 49:1191–1193.

EKMAN, S. 1940. Begründung einer statistischen Methode der regionale Tiergeographie. Nova Acta Reg. Soc. Sci. Uppsal. ser. 4. 12(2):1–117.

————. 1953. Zoogeography of the seas. Sidgwick and Jackson, London. xiv + 418 p.

GOOD, R. 1964. The geography of flowering plants. 3d ed. Longmans, London. xvi + 518 p.

GOODALL, D. W. 1954. Objective methods for the classification of vegetation: III. An essay in the use of factor analysis. Aust. J. Bot. 3:304–324.

HAGMEIER, E. M. 1966. A numerical analysis of the distributional patterns North American mammals II. Reevaluation of the provinces. Syst. Zool. 15:279–299.

————, AND C. D. STULTS. 1964. A numerical analysis of the distributional patterns of North American mammals. Ibid. 13:125–155.

HEDGPETH, J. W. 1957. Marine biogeography. Chapter 9. In J. W. HEDGPETH, Ed. Treatise on marine ecology and paleoecology; Ecology. Mem. Geol. Soc. Am. 67(1):359–382.

HUHEEY, J. E. 1965. A mathematical method of analyzing biogeographical data. I. Herpetofauna of Illinois. Am. Midl. Naturalist. 73:490–500.

JOHNSON, J. G. 1971. A quantitative approach to faunal province analysis. Am. J. Sci. 270:257–280.

KENDEIGH, S. C. 1961. Animal ecology. Prentice-Hall, Englewood Cliffs, N.J. x + 468 p.

MACARTHUR, R. H., AND J. H. CONNELL. 1966. The biology of populations. John Wiley, New York. xv + 200 p.

MARGALEF, R. D. 1969. Information theory in ecology (trans. W. Hall) Gen. Systems 3:36–71.

MERRIAM, C. H. 1892. The geographic distribution of life in North America with special reference to Mammalia. Proc. biol. Soc. Wash. 7:1–64.

NEILL, W. T. 1969. The geography of life. Columbia Univ. Press, New York. xiv + 480 p.

PETERS, J. A. 1955. Use and misuse of the biotic province concept. Am. Naturalist 89:21–28.

————. 1968. A computer program for calculating degree of biogeographical resemblance between areas. Syst. Zool. 17:64–69.

————. 1971. A new approach in the analysis of biogeographic data. Smithson. contr. Zool. 107:1–28.

PRESTON, F. W. 1969. Diversity and stability in the biological world. Symp. Biol. no. 22, Brookhaven Natl. Lab. Upton, N.Y. p. 1–13.

ROSS, C. A. 1967. Development of fusulinid (Foraminiferida) faunal realms. J. Paleont. 41:1341–1354.

————. 1970. Concepts in late Paleozoic corrrelations: In O. L. BANDY, Ed. Radiometric dating and paleontologic zonation. Spec. Pap geol. Soc. Am. 124:7–36.

————. 1973. Carboniferous Foraminifera. In HALLAM, A., Ed. Atlas of palaeobiogeography. Elsevier, Amsterdam, London, & New York. p. 127–132.

RYAN, R. M. 1963. The biotic provinces of Central America. Acta Zool. Mex. 6:1–54.

SANDERS, H. L. 1968. Marine benthic diversity: a comparative study. Am. Naturalist. 102:243–282.

SAVAGE, J. M. 1960. Evolution of a peninsular herpetofauna. Syst. Zool. 9:184–212.

SCLATER, P. L. 1857 (1858). On the general geographic distribution of the members of the class Aves. J. Linn. Soc. Zoology. 2:130–145.

SCHILDER, F. A. 1955. Statistische Methoden in der Biogeographie. Wiss. Z. Martin Luther-Univ. Halle-Wittenberg. 4:711–716.

————. 1956. Lehrbuch der allgemeinen Zoogeographie. Fischer, Jena. viii + 150 p.

SIMPSON, G. C. 1943. Mammals and the nature of continents. Am. J. Sci. 24:1–31.

————. 1960. Notes on the measurement of faunal resemblance. Ibid. 258A:300–311.

————. 1965. The geography of evolution. Collected essays. Chilton, Philadelphia and New York. xiv + 249 p.

STEHLI, F. G. 1968. Taxonomic diversity gradients in pole location: the Recent model. Chapter 6. In DRAKE, E. T., Ed. Evolution and environment. Yale Univ. Press, New Haven. p. 163–227

THIENEMANN, A. 1918. Lebensgemeinschaft und Lebensraum. Naturw. Wochenschr. N. F. 17:282–290, 297–303.

UDVARDY, M. D. F. 1969. Dynamic zoogeography with special reference to land animals. Von Nostrand Reinhold, New York. xviii + 445 p.

VALENTINE, J. W. 1966. Numerical analysis of marine molluscan ranges on the extratropical Northeastern Pacific shelf. Limnol. Oceanog. 11:198–211.

————. 1967. The influence of climatic fluctuations on species diversity within the Tethyan provincial system. In, ADAMS, C. G. AND D. V. AGER, Eds. Aspects of Tethyan biogeography: Syst. Ass. Publs. 7:153–166.

VESTAL, A. G. 1914. Internal relations of terrestrial associations. Am. Naturalist. 48:413–445.

WALLACE, A. R. 1876. The geographical distribution of animals. 2 vol. Harper, New York. xxiii + 503 p.; xi + 553 p. (reprinted 1962, Hafner, New York & London).

WEBB, W. L. 1950. Biogeographic regions of Texas and Oklahoma. Ecology. 31:426–433.

ZENKEVICH, L. 1949. La structure biologique de l'ocean: C. R. XIII Congr. Int. Zool. 522–529.

BIOMERIZATION: AN ECOLOGIC THEORY OF PROVINCIAL DIFFERENTIATION

CHRISTOPHER J. DURDEN
Texas Memorial Museum, Austin, TX 78705

ABSTRACT—Biotic provinces are centers of endemism surrounded by zones of coincidence of broad-ranged species. They form coherent units of association above the community level. Superimposed ranges are used to construct a surface contoured for provincial diversity. Provincial boundaries overlap. Frequencies of provincial components along boundaries vary seasonally and from year to year following patterns of selection. Relict provinces survive in these unstable zones.

In North America one major province is attributed to the Holarctic Realm, 11 to the Nearctic Realm, and 6 to the Neotropical Realm. Preliminary evaluation of world provinciality recognizes 63 major provinces in 13 realms of 4 realm groups. Density distribution of province heartlands reflects world thermal gradient configuration over the last 60 million years, rather than present conditions. Africa and Australia have fewer, and North America and Europe have more provinces than expected for their latitudes under present conditions.

Biomeres, as chronologic provincial units, are transgressive and regressive, and exhibit complex intertonguing in boundary regions. Faunal and floral zonal sequences are replicable within biomeres but are complicated by inversion and recurrence along boundaries where relicts persist. These anomalies are useful for locating boundary zones.

In Pennsylvanian and Lower Permian rocks, 10 terrestrial biomeres, based on insect faunal ranges and consistent with floral ranges, are found in Euramerica. Maps at approximately 5 million year intervals demonstrate the differentiation, spread and restriction of some provinces that are traced from origin to dissappearance. Consistent elongation of biomere distribution along arcs from 5 to 9 degrees inclined to the Westphalian paleomagnetic equator is attributed to biothermal latitudinal arrangement. Namurian restriction of redbeds, location of origin of new biomeres, diversity gradient, and organism size are criteria which locate the paleobiothermal equator. Distribution of provinces and latitudinal fluctuations on both sides of the paleobiothermal equator allow construction of a low latitude climatic curve. The variable r (redbed factor) permits inference of temperature; the variable e (angle of the ecliptic) permits inference of seasonality of climate.

Consideration of biomeric structure promises to facilitate fine correlation of distant zonal sequences, particularly those of coal areas remote from standard and type stratigraphic sections.

INTRODUCTION

Terrestrial biotic provinces have been informally recognized in the literature since the mid 19th century. Allen (1892), Dice (1943, 1952), Blair (1950) have used vertebrates, and Packard (1889), Van Dyke (1919, 1940), and Linsley (1940) have used insects to describe biotic provinces or equivalent units in North America. Biotic provinces have not received wide acceptance amongst ecologists, probably for two reasons. First, their boundaries are a gradual change in percentage of communities derived from the adjacent provinces and are thus difficult to represent on a map. Second, the life zone concept of Merriam (1898), so readily applied in some areas, is firmly entrenched in ecological theory, and seems on the surface to contradict the existence of biotic provinces. To solve the first problem, mapping diversity gradients for individual provinces is proposed. Province by province mapping is necessary because although Dice (1952) used a 50%–50% component line for delineating boundaries, this method tends to obscure reality where a rich province interfingers with a depauperate province, or where two provinces of different histories have comparable diversty in an intimate community mo-

saic over the same geographic region, such as the meeting of Neotropical communities including tropical evergreen forest, with Nearctic communities including cloud forest in eastern Mexico. To solve the second problem we must understand why life zones are so obvious in some areas and so obscure in others. Geographically, the best development of life zone structure is found in the boundary zones between provinces. This structure is weakest towards the center of diversity and endemism of a province. Merriam's classical areas are located in interprovincial zones. The San Francisco Peaks of Arizona involve interaction between communities of the Durangan and Coloradan provinces of the Nearctic Realm and the Sonoran Province and weakly developed Nevadian Province of the Neotropical Realm. The Spanish Peaks of Colorado involve interaction again between the Durangan and Coloradan Provinces with the addition of the Alleghenian, and with the Coahuilan and the weakly developed Kansan Provinces of the Neotropical Realm. In eastern North America, life zones are difficult to discern in the northern Appalachians of Gaspé and Maine, and in the southern Appalachians of Virginia and North Carolina; that is, crisp altitudinal lines cannot be drawn between life zones. Conversely in the middle Appalachians of Pennsylvania and in the Catskills, where Canadian Province interdigitates with Virginian Province, crisp altitudinally bounded life zones can be seen. Why should this be so?

Centrally in a province, all the species are accustomed to coexistence because they have been together for a long time. An intricate network of interdependence within and between communities has had time to develop. Any single species is expected to have developed ecological tolerances as broad as its edaphic and biotic matrices have permitted, given adequate time for the attainment of selective quasi–equilibrium. The genetic segregates that accompany this broad tolerance are, if modal (i.e., if the niche is dumbell-shaped), termed ecotypes. A species represented by several ecotypes in the heartland of a province may range to the provincial boundary on all sides. Because of climatic gradients, physiographic differences, and differences of geologic substrate, the species will not be accompanied by all its ecotypes at the provincial periphery. Stated another way, the gene pool is expected to be broadest in the area of longest occupancy, for strictly historical reasons of selective survival and adaptation to gradient and interdependant conditions. We may expect that different ecotypes will occur in different parts of the periphery according to local conditions. Thus communities at the periphery, composed of ecotypically narrow species will have lesser tolerances as a whole, and will tend to give way without stragglers to adjacent communities, particularly to those derived from other provinces, to the coexistence with which the adjacent components have had neither time nor genetic latitude to adapt.

WHAT ARE BIOTIC PROVINCES?

A biotic province is a region occupied by a set of communities and their component species, which differ at least specifically from those of an adjacent region. Their stability is achieved through adaptation of their components to a set of conditions that have been present for a period of time. Provinces of different origin may come to overlap through detailed partitioning of available habitat by their respective communities. In the literature there seems to have been confusion between biotic structural units and taxonomic (or differentiate) units. For example, Shelford (1963, p. 16) discusses the *association* as ". . . identified by the presence of characteristic climax dominant or index species" and roughly equated by him with "region" or "faciation" of authors, and thus roughly equivalent to the *biotic province*. However, he classes

the association as a subunit of the *Biome* or "formation" which is a structural unit not equivalent to the *realm,* of which the biotic province is a subunit.

MAPPING BIOTIC PROVINCES

Attempts to map provinces have, until recently, been made under the assumption that boundary *lines* are necessary (Van Dyke, 1919, 1940; Dice, 1943, 1952; Blair, 1950). Analysis of range-end characteristics initiated by Hagmeier and Stults (1964) has opened up new possibilities, and is responsible for stimulating the work presented here.

If provinces are real we should be able to identify all but the most opportunistic of species as constituents of a province. Theoretically, it should be possible to plot diversity as the number of species occurring in a unit area (e.g., quadrangle census), contour the density and classify the anomalous highs as intrinsic or extrinsic. Intrinsic highs are to be expected from the coincident occupancy by a large number of species of an historically persistent area, being there by right of survival over a long period of time. Because specific diversity is high and because ecotypy within species is rich, these areas may be called optimal. Here we shall refer to them as central areas or heartlands. Extrinsic highs are to be expected in zones where communities of different provinces meet. Here different comunities of similar group tolerances compete for the same terrain. Intracommunity symbiotic homeostasis retards intercommunity mixing of species, so the community competition tends to be mutually exclusive and to hinge on rather small variables. This should effectively double the diversity in interprovincial regions (fig. 1). It is in these zones where the biotic mosaic is composed of community tiles of different provincial color of the same tolerance shape, where one color is not at a consistent or persistent advantage, that other colors may be present. These are either the remnant communities of former provinces, surviving in this zone of indecisive advantage, or are the vanguard communities of intruding provinces. Endemics located along the Appalachian piedmont fall line and inner cuestas from New Jersey and Delaware through Georgia, Mississippi to southern Oklahoma, outline such boundary zone endemism. Their component species are found to be old, often of monotypic genera, or are new segregates of biota invading from the southwest or north.

Obviously we cannot make the perfect map, using the distribution data of all species. The ranges of many species are not yet documented, and indeed not all species are yet described. We

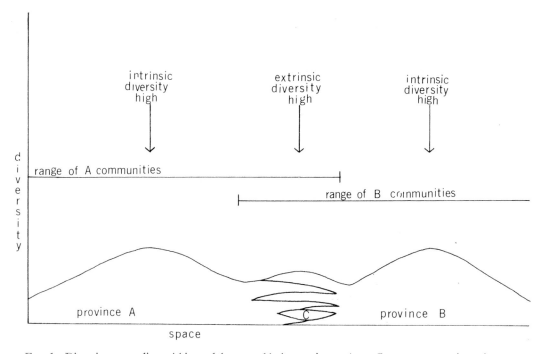

Fig. 1—Diversity anomalies within and between biotic provinces. Area C represents an intrusive tongue or relict occurrence of a third province in the interprovincial zone of uneven or fluctuating selective advantages.

must sample. The sample may be either taxonomically random or may be functionally biased. In order to map modern provincial structure in its setting of Cenozoic orogeny and climatic change, we must employ taxa that contain strong ecological averagers. Vertebrates, the traditional sample taxon for provincial mapping, do their averaging by "running around," being in general, little tied biochemically to the community (e.g., not strongly dependent on a single food plant) and very mobile (e.g., migratory birds, and large feline individual ranges). Most vertebrates are not the best measure of long-term community history (plethodontid salamanders are a fine exception). At the other extreme, the most stable components are the long-lived, large, sedentary woody plants epitomized by the redwood and bristle cone pine. Practically the mapping of provinces using woody plants is impossible until the data bank of the Flora North America Project is more complete. Initially it is possible to prepare estimates of provincial distribution and diversity by selecting a higher taxon for analysis of known specific ranges and using these as a sample. For this purpose the orders Coniferales (pines, cedars and allies) and Fagales (oaks, birches and allies) were chosen to run two independent analyses of North American provinces. Superimposed species ranges were plotted to determine diversity highs. These diversity highs were assigned convenient geographic names as labels. A species was scored according to the diversity highs that occur within its range. Diversity highs were classified according to their degree of relationship by comparing species lists. The "central" area or heartland of a province was identified by its higher count of species co-occurring in adjacent highs. The ranges for the species listed for the heartland were then used to construct an overlapping range map for the province. On this map were then plotted iso-diversity lines for number of coincident species, producing a contoured surface of diversity. All of these operations were done manually, much of the work by inspection. The results are thus but a first approximation, to be improved mechanically when a fully informed data bank is available. The remarkable, but in retrospect, logical result of these plots is that the same set of provincial centers was discovered independently using different sample orders. This in itself demonstrates the strength of the province concept, because although the components mapped are drawn from diverse different communities, the elements act in concert to form the provincial patterns.

Examining the configuration of these provinces (figs. 2 and 3), they are found to resemble most closely those described by Van Dyke

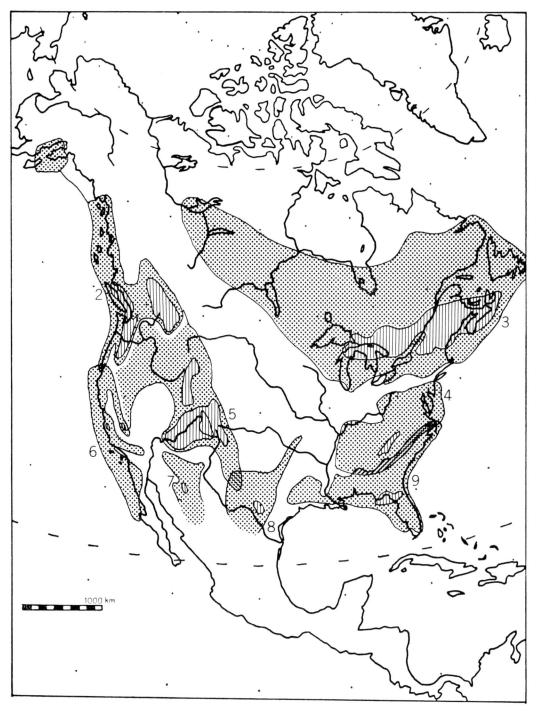

FIG. 2—Location of diversity modes for North American Coniferales. 2. Vancouveran, 3. Canadian, 4. Virginian, 5. Coloradan, 6. Californian, 7. Durangan, 8. Balconian, 9. Georgian.

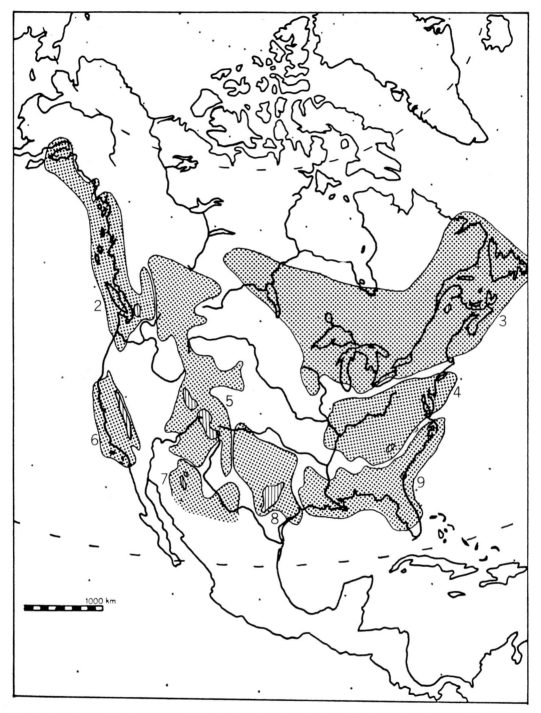

Fig. 3—Location of diversity modes for North American Fagales (oaks, birches and relatives). 2. Vancouveran. 3. Canadian, 4. Virginian, 5. Coloradan, 6. Californian, 7. Durangan, 8. Balconian, 9. Georgian.

(1940) and by Linsley (1940) using insect ranges. The finer-grained provincial units of Dice (1943, 1952) and Blair (1950) must be grouped for comparison. This probably reflects the more rapid adjustments made by the mobile vertebrate faunal components to fluctuation of conditions within a province. Fidelity of insect provinces, based on beetle ranges, suggests that other groups may be used. The beetle taxa originally analysed; Cerambycidae (longhorn beetles) are directly dependent upon the woody plants as hosts for their boring larvae; and the Carabidae (ground beetles) are mostly members of the cryptic (Lawrence, 1953) or litter and crevice component of communities which, with their carnivorous habits are far removed from direct dependence upon the woody plant matrix of the community.

Community stability, the infrequency with which succession is initiated in a community, is higher towards the heartland of a province. Peripherally, accidents of climatic change and competitive foreign biota frequently unbalance community stability. A substructure is to be expected within the province, in which species well adapted to mature associations are more frequent centrally and species best adapted to life in the earlier stages of succession will tend to be more frequent peripherally. As an oversimplified example, natural "weeds" (e.g., the hawthorns—*Crataegus*) are more diverse in the "Prairie Triangle" of the Midwestern United States than they are in the provincial heartlands of the northern and southern Appalachians.

Provinciality of North American cockroach distribution was analysed. Such mapping is very imprecise without the use of a central data bank of all records, because of the large number of unpublished records reposing in scattered collections. A future North American Invertebrate Survey along the lines of the currently active European Invertebrate Survey, would remedy this situation. Without such a resource, somewhat incomplete maps were prepared from data in the literature (Hebard, 1917; works listed by species in Princis, 1961). Because of the physiological intolerance of cockroaches to hard frost, only the provinces of the warmer regions that were discovered from woody plant data, are matched by diversity highs in cockroach distribution. The marginal areas of these provinces do however differ in detail. This is probably because cockroaches, with few exceptions, are members of associations early in succession while many of the Coniferales and Fagales are the largest, and thus the structural determinants of mature communities. The midwestern and piedmont diversity highs of cockroach distribu-

tion may be ascribed to the edge enrichment effect by early successional components.

As well as showing the provincial diversity highs coincident with highs determined from the mapped woody plant ranges of Nearctic taxa, cockroaches show another set of diversity highs. Upon inspection these are centers of provinces that may also be described using woody plant taxa of Neotropical affinity, such as Caesalpinaceae. Leguminosae, and Cactaceae. Many component cockroach genera of this second set of provinces have a more or less wide range in Central and South America.

The major biotic provinces of North America (fig. 4) include 1 province from the Holarctic Realm, 11 from the Nearctic Realm, and 6 or possibly 10 from the Neotropical Realm. From the Holarctic Realm the *Mackenziean Province* (Eskimoan + Hudsonian + Aleutian of Dice, 1943; Tundran Biome of Shelford, 1963) (figs. 5 & 6) has been periodically displaced from its heartland in Mackenzie and Yukon territories, its component communities surviving in the Central Alaskan Refugium, and a few in the Montana-Wyoming Rocky Mountains; in the Wisconsin driftless area; and apparently in Appalachian Pennsylvania, during glacial times. Western refugia are documented by relict populations of plants and animals, eastern refugia are inferred from plant fossils in Connecticut (Durden, unpublished ms; Flint, 1965) and Massachusetts (Argus & Davis, 1962) in postglacial deposits. Components of this peculiar province of the Holarctic Realm have close relatives in bordering provinces, and the province appears to have arisen in eastern Asia and northern North America during Pleistocene time as an impromptu melange of opportunistic colonists drawn from provinces displaced by the continental ice sheets (fig. 5).

Eleven well differentiated provinces are recognized in the Nearctic Realm, the Canadian, Vancouveran, Californian, Coloradan, Virginian, Georgian, Balconian, Durangan, Hidalgan, Mexican, and Cuban. In addition indications are that in preglacial times the Sitkan and northern Great Plains (Manitoban) regions had more diverse provincial biota that are now reduced to a few anomalous endemic species. There may have been more differentiation, with the presence of lowland communities in the biota now assigned to the polycentric Mexican Province, prior to the late Tertiary influx of Neotropical forest biota.

The heartland of the *Canadian Province* (Allen, 1892; Dice, 1943; Beech-Maple + Maple-Basswood + Hemlock-White Pine-Northern Hardwoods Forest Regions of Braun, 1950;

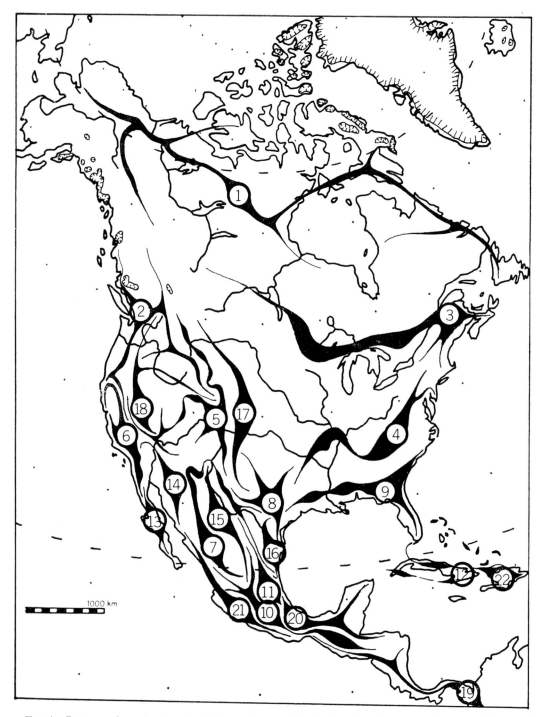

Fig. 4—Centers and trends of major biotic provinces of North America. Trends are the crests of areas of modal diversity. Holarctic–1. Mackenziean; Nearctic–2. Vancouveran, 3. Canadian, 4. Virginian, 5. Coloradan, 6. Californian, 7. Durangan, 8. Balconian, 9. Georgian, 10. Mexican, 11. Hidalgan, 12. Cuban; Xeric Neotropical–13. Vizcainian, 14. Sonoran, 15. Coahuilan, 16. Tamaulipan, 17. Kansan, 18. Nevadan; Mesic Neotropical–19. Darienian, 20. Veracrusian, 21. Riobalsan, 22. Antillean.

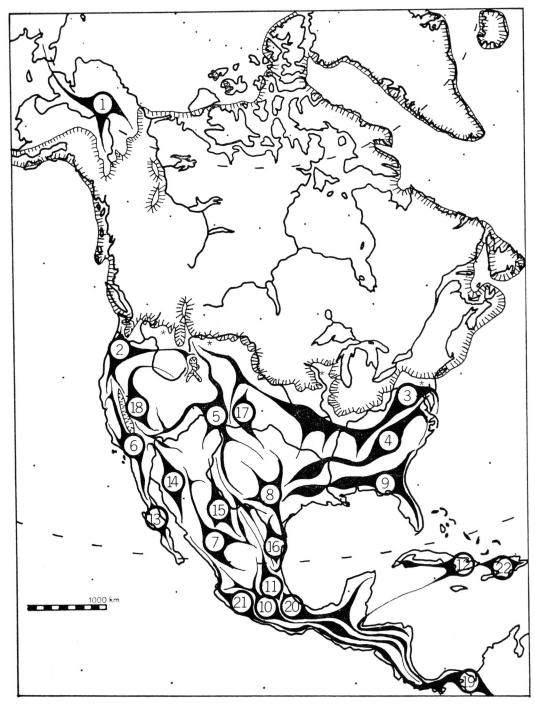

FIG. 5—Inferred centers and trends for biotic provinces during Pleistocene glacial maxima. Provinces are numbered as in figure 4. Pleistocene (probably early) connection between Cuba and Mesoamerica appears to have been *via* the Cayman Rise rather than *via* Yucatan. Asterisks indicate refugial areas for some communities of the Mackenziean Province (1) inferred from fossils and isolated populations.

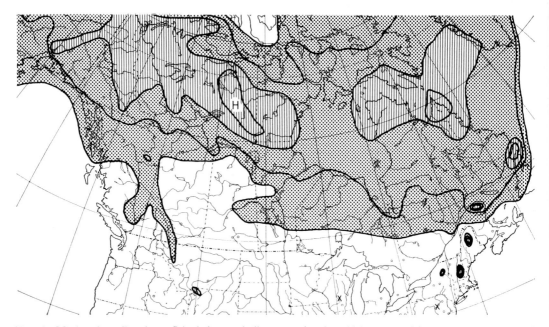

Fig. 6—Mackenziean Province. Stippled area indicates region in which communities contain at least 30% of Mackenziean biota. Lines indicate regions with at least 60% of Mackenziean biota in some communities.

Temperate Deciduous Forest Biome, Northern (part) + Boreal Coniferous Forest of Shelford, 1963) (fig. 7) was displaced during glacial episodes, from its present location in the Gaspé-Maine Appalachians, but probably no farther south than southern Pennsylvania (Clench and McCrady, Maps A and B, *in* Guilday and others, 1964), (figs. 4 and 5). The province is strongly developed from northern West Virginia to northern Alberta (fig. 7). Fossil assemblages and relict communities indicate former importance in Pennsylvania, southern West Virginia, Iowa, Missouri, South Dakota, and down the Rocky Mountains Front Range to central Colorado (Missouri watershed only).

The heartland of the *Vancouveran Province* (Van Dyke, 1919; Linsley, 1940; Oregonian + Sitkan + Montanian of Dice, 1943; Montane Coniferous Forest (part) + Northern Pacific Coast Rainy Western Hemlock Forest Biome of Shelford, 1963) (fig. 8) was also glacially displaced from its present location in southwestern British Columbia to the Coast Ranges of Washington and Oregon. A large segment, located along the Idaho-Montana boundary, was probably isolated at times, because it contains autochthonous components. Disjunct occurrences suggest that elements of this province extended at times to the Sierra Nevada (possibly also the San Bernardino Mts.) mountains of northeastern Nevada and Colorado (fig. 8).

Fossil plant assemblages indicate that Tertiary location of the province lay to the south (Axelrod and Ting, 1961) and that it had begun to differentiate in the southern Great Basin by Miocene-Pliocene time (Axelrod, 1962).

There is no indication of Pleistocene shift in location of the heartland regions of the polycentric *Californian Province* (Van Dyke, 1919; Linsley, 1940; Dice, 1943; Broad Sclerophyll-Grizzly Bear Community of Shelford, 1963) (fig. 9). The three most strongly developed high diversity-high endemism areas in California suggest the long, *in situ* history of this province that is amply documented in the Tertiary record. Its former extent is documented by faunal disjunct relicts northeast to the Wasatch Moutains of Utah, east to southeastern Arizona, and south far into Baja California. Some of the endemic plants of the offshore islands have been found in fossil deposits of the mainland.

The heartland of the *Coloradan Province* (Coloradan + Navahonian + Palusian of Dice, 1943; Montane Coniferous Forest (part) of Shelford, 1963) (fig. 10) is a high diversity area remarkably poor in endemic species, which probably remained in situ in Colorado through glacial episodes, hence loosing its endemics through extinction. The present total composition of the biota and the ecological position of invading communities of other provinces in the periphery suggest that during late Cenozoic time the whole province was subjected to trun-

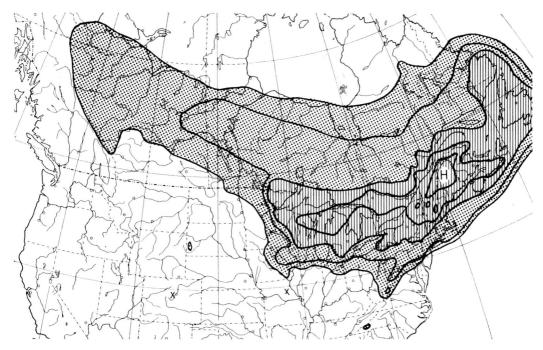

FIG. 7—Canadian Province. Stipple–30% of biota, ruled–60% of biota.

cation of its mesic communities. This may account to some extent, for the low degree of endemism, notable exceptions are the salamanders *Aneides hardii* and *Plethodon neomexicanus,* most other mesic endemics having become extinct. Alternatively the whole provincial biota may be of relatively recent origin, having been drawn from opportunist colonists derived from the Vancouveran, Californian, and Virginian Provinces, which filled territory vacated by the Balconian Province when this was displaced to the south under cooler climates of the late Cenozoic. Supporting greater age of the Coloradan Province are the well developed shrubland communities, rich in endemics peripherally, particularly arthropods. Considerable history of boundary interaction with the Vancouveran Province is indicated by the zone of relict distribution in western Wyoming and northwestern Colorado which contains a number of intrusive species, subspecifically distinct from their closest relatives in Eurasia, and by a few endemic species with their closest relatives in Eurasia. Elements of the high altitude fossil assemblage at Creede, Colorado, suggest the beginning of differentiation of the Coloradan Province as early as Oligocene time.

The heartland of the *Virginian Province* (Alleghenian Province of Wallace, 1876; Van Dyke, 1919; Linsley, 1940; Carolinian Province

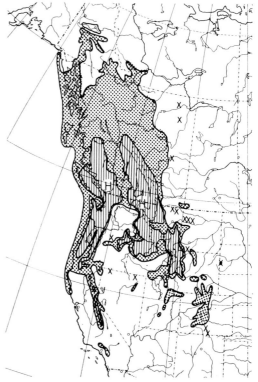

FIG. 8—Vancouveran Province. Stipple–30% of biota, ruled–60% of biota.

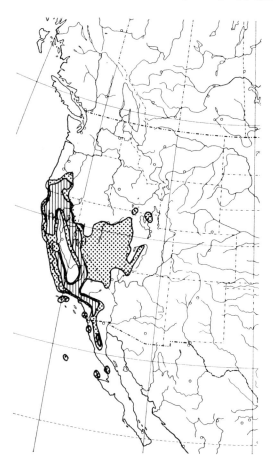

The Virginian Province is well developed as far southwest as the Ouachita Mountains of Oklahoma. Fossil occurrence of components of this province in Canada, such as those in the Don Valley Beds at Toronto, and the occurrence of relicts today in the Black Hills of South Dakota, in eastern New Mexico, and in central Texas, record former positions of the provincial periphery.

The heartland of the *Georgian Province* (Austroriparian of Dice, 1943; Oak-Pine + Southeastern Evergreen Forest Regions of Braun, 1950; Temperate Deciduous Forest Biome (Southern) of Shelford, 1963) (fig. 12) lies in northern Florida and southeastern Georgia where two diversity highs are also centers of endemism. One center on the lower Altamaha River in Georgia is famous for the monotypic tree genus *Franklinia,* now extinct outside of cultivation, and the only recently extinct tree genus. The other center, on the lower Appalachicola River in Florida, is famous for its nearly extinct endemic species of the evergreen yewlike tree *Torreya.* These two centers are

Fig. 9—Californian Province. Stipple–30% of biota, ruled–60% of biota.

of Dice, 1943; Temperate Deciduous Forest Biome (Upland) of Shelford, 1963; Mixed Mesophytic + Western Mesophytic + Oak-Hickory + Oak-Chestnut Forest Regions of Braun, 1950) (fig. 11) is located on the Blue Ridge of southwestern Virginia and appears to have remained *in situ* for a long time because of the clear diversity high and endemism cluster of such a sedentary group as the plethodontid salamanders. The term Alleghenian is not used because the heartland is located in the Appalachian Blue Ridge and not the Allegheny Plateau and because the term Alleghenian has a history of time stratigraphic and time usage for Pennsylvanian biota dating from 1840. The term Carolinian is not used, to avoid confusion with the widespread use of this name for a Merriam life zone. A subregion of Virginian endemism is present on the coastal plain north of Chesapeake Bay but this may be composed of remnants of a different, more ancient province, because of the number of monotypic genera present.

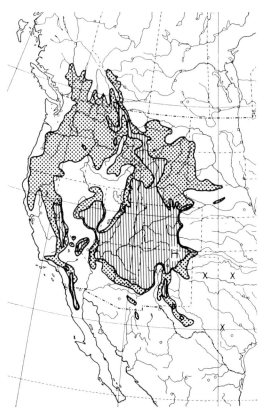

Fig. 10—Coloradan Province. Stipple–30% of biota, ruled–60% of biota.

contained in the diversity high for Nearctic
cockroaches. The province extends in a well developed state from the Dismal Swamp of Virginia to the Florida Everglades and west to
central Texas. The Pleistocene record suggests
that the province was restricted during glacial
times but persisted *in situ* in some areas where
pollen and megafossil records indicate proximity of northern genera, as in east-central
Texas and Louisiana.

The *Balconian Province* (Blair, 1950; Co-
manchean (part) + Texan of Dice, 1943) (fig.
13) is strangely depauperate in endemic trees
except in its southern diversity high in Nuevo
Leon, but is very rich in shrubland species,
especially insects. Two centers of insect endemism are present and these are reflected also
in the cockroach diversity pattern. The western
center of endemism is located in the canyons
of the Edwards Plateau, Pedernales and Guade-
lupe River region and the taxa such as the
snakefly *Agulla* sp. and the shrub *Mahonia
swaseyi* have their closest relatives in the Durangan and Coloradan Provinces. The other
center of endemism follows the wooded and
ravine cut Eocene sandstone cuesta between
Bastrop and Bryan, the insect taxa having their
closest relatives in more mesic communities of
the Californian Province. Resemblance between
the components of the Balconian Province and
some of the insects and woody plants described
from the Oligocene of Florissant, Colorado, is
remarkable. Communities of this province are
found from southeastern Colorado to southern
Tamaulipas; and from Van Horn, Texas, to the

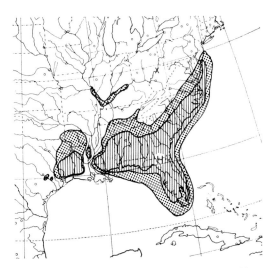

FIG. 12—Georgian Province. Stipple–30% of biota,
ruled–60% of biota.

Piedmont of Georgia and Ozarks of southwestern Missouri.

The center of diversity of the *Durangan
Province* (Dice, 1943; Ecotone Woodland and
Bushland Communities of Shelford, 1963) (fig.
14) is located in southern Durango, with centers of endemism in the major mountain regions of the province, the polycentry implying
considerable age. Its communities are found
well developed in the Western Cordillera of
Mexico, to southeastern Arizona, through southern New Mexico and western Texas, east as
far as the Edwards Plateau with piñon and

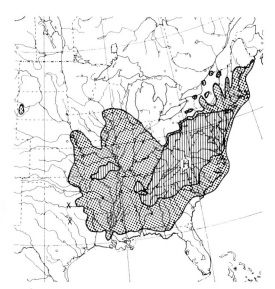

FIG. 11—Virginian Province. Stipple–30% of biota,
ruled–60% of biota.

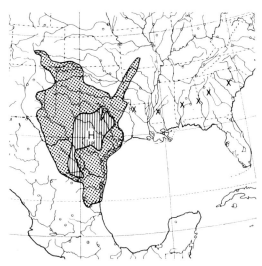

FIG. 13—Balconian Province. Stipple–30% of biota,
ruled–60% of biota.

FIG. 14—Durangan Province. Stipple–30% of biota,
ruled–60% of biota.

madroñe communities, and south through eastern Coahuila to the Sierra de Tamaulipas. Subspeciation and endemism in the eastern outposts suggests a long history of *in situ* isolation. Identification of some of these eastern elements as Durangan or Balconian components is difficult and possibly the two components are derived from the xeric and mesic communities noted in the Florissant Oligocene biota (MacGinitie, 1953; Durden, 1966).

The *Hidalgan Province* (?Potosian of Dice, 1943) (fig. 15) of the Eastern Cordillera of Mexico is remarkable for its combination of

genera of Virginian affinity, such as *Fagus, Picea,* and *Liquidambar,* with ancient holotemperate genera, such as *Podocarpus,* in a well developed cloud forest community with treeferns (Martin and Harrell, 1957). The lack of similar Virginian affinities in the vertebrates and their rarity in the insects implies great age of separation. The diversity high and major center of endemism appears to be located (using ranges of *Pinus* from Martinez, 1948) on the eastern slopes of the mountain ranges of Hidalgo in a region still poorly known biotically. Communities of this province occur as disjuncts in mountain ranges from the Sierra del Carmen, just south of Big Bend National Park, to southwestern Vera Cruz.

The rich *Mexican Province* (fig. 16) runs the length of the Transverse Volcanic Belt of Mexico and Guatemala, with several diversity and endemism highs in Mexico State, Oaxaca, Chiapas, and in Guatemala. Communities composed of Nearctic elements occur as far south as central Columbia, but no provincial structure is recognizable in these disjuncts unless provincial status is assigned to each mountain "island" with its high degree of local endemism.

The *Cuban Province* (fig. 17) contains a high diversity area with endemism in the mountains of eastern Cuba. Lowland relict communities, for the most part of wide-ranged species with Nearctic affinities, from the Bahamas to Honduras are assigned to the province. Lowland communities of pine and live oak woodland and savanna are well developed in western Cuba and Isle of Pines.

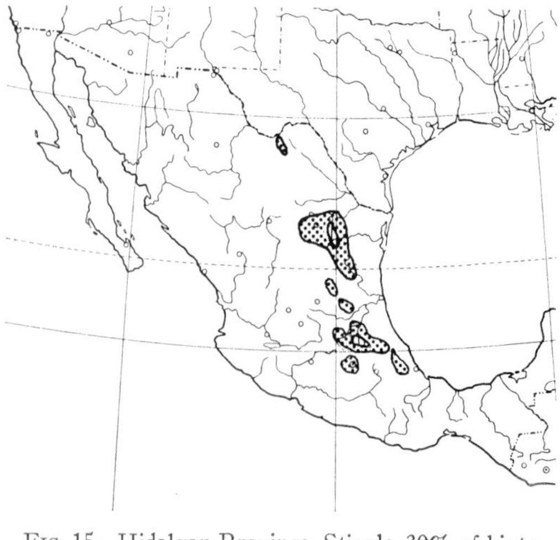

FIG. 15—Hidalgan Province. Stipple–30% of biota,
ruled–60% of biota.

FIG. 16—Mexican Province. Stipple–30% of biota,
ruled–60% of biota.

The Neotropical Provinces fall into two groups. A northern group of 4 to 6 provinces composed of xeric communities with many species of Andean affinities, characterized by a very high degree of endemism, has probably been in North and Central America since Paleocene or latest Cretaceous time. A southern group of two or four weakly differentiated provinces of tropical forest communities of high diversity but little endemism above the subspecific level, probably entered Central America no earlier than Pliocene time.

The xeric group of Neotropical provinces (fig. 18) includes the Vizcainian, Sonoran, Coahuilan, and Tamaulipan Provinces as well as the Nevada and Kansan Weak Provinces. The *Vizcainian Province* (Sanlucan of Dice, 1943; Vizcaino Desert of Shelford, 1963) of Baja California is especially rich in endemics, especially the arthropods. The *Sonoran Province* (Van Dyke, 1919; Linsley, 1940; Sonoran + Mohavian of Dice, 1943; Mojave + Colorado + Arizona–Sonora Desert of Shelford, 1963) has subregions of diversity and endemism in the Sonoran and Mojave Deserts with many monotypic genera. The *Coahuilan Province* (part of Comanchian + Chihuahuan + Apachian of Dice, 1943; Southern Temperate Grassland Biome + Chihuahuan Desert of Shelford, 1963) with its heartland just south of the Big Bend Region of Texas, extends the length of the Mexican Interior Plateau from just north of Mexico City to central New Mexico with local areas of endemism in the mountains of the western edge of the plateau. A broad extension composed of cold tolerant communities crosses Texas to southwestern Oklahoma and

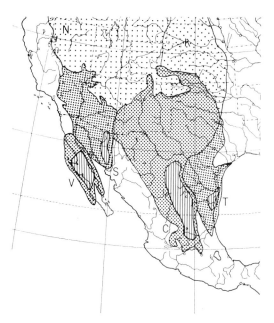

Fig. 18—Neotropical Provinces, older xeric group. Stipple–30% of biota, ruled–60% of biota, open stipple–relict and depauperate biota. V–Vizcainian Province, S–Sonoran Province, C–Coahuilan Province, T–Tamaulipan Province, K–Kansan Province, N–Nevadan Province.

southeastern Colorado. The *Tamaulipan Province* (Dice, 1943) with its own diversity high along and south of the lower Rio Grande Valley, is distinguished from the Coahuilan Province only by its degree of endemism. To the north are often recognized a *Nevadan Province* (Artemisian of Dice, 1943; Cold Desert and Semidesert of Shelford, 1963) and a *Kansan Province* (Dice, 1943; Northern Temperate Grassland Biome of Shelford, 1963). These are certainly real in terms of provincial structure, but are so depauperate in species as to be conspicuous by their endemism rather than by diversity. They probably represent climatically truncated remnants of Neotropical Provinces that had greater diversity in pre-Pleistocene time, having been decimated probably not by cold but by periodic increase in moisture during Pleistocene time. Communities of the Kansan Province are found as far north as southeastern Alberta; communities of the Nevadan Province are found as far north as the Okanagan Valley of British Columbia.

The *Mesoamerican Province* ("tierras calientes" of Godman and Salvin, 1879; Tropical Rain Forest + Tropical Deciduous Forest of Shelford, 1963) (fig. 19) is tenuously divisible into Riobalsan, Veracruzian and Darienian Provinces on the basis of weak diversity highs

Fig. 17—Cuban Province. Stipple–30% of biota, ruled–60% of biota.

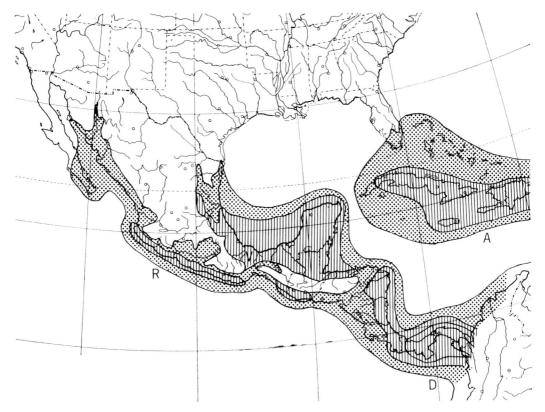

Fig. 19—Neotropical Provinces, younger mesic group. Stipple–30% of biota, ruled–60% of biota. Meso-american Province: R–Riobalsan Subprovince, V–Veracrusian Subprovince, D–Darienian Subprovince; A–Antillean Province.

and low clusters of endemism, barely above the subspecific level. The Mesoamerican Province reaches its northern limit in southern Tamauli-pas where its insect fauna is found to be far richer (Durden, 1971, 1972a) than was formerly supposed, although differentiation is only at the subspecific level when compared with the Vera-cruzian and Darienian biotas.

The *Antillean Province* (fig. 19) because of its island location contains much more endem-ism than the Mesoamerican Province, but the biotic matrix is one of wide-ranged species, barely distinguishable from those of the Meso-american Province, and then only at the sub-specific level. Faunal disjuncts of dense forest recluse genera indicate a previous land connec-tion between Cuba and Mesoamerica. Other species appear to have entered from the Orino-can Province by "island hopping" across the Windward Islands. The bulk of the biota could have entered either way, probably no earlier than the Pliocene. Certain elements of xeric communities indicate Tertiary contact with a precursor of the Tamaulipan or Coahuilan Province.

INTERPROVINCIAL INTRUSIVE TONGUES

Numerous communities of the earlier stages of succession are not characteristic of a par-ticular province but are found in the zone of meeting between provinces (fig. 20). Insects as-sociated with prairie and marshland communi-ties frequently have a "prairie triangle" or "transition zone" range. Ranges typical of the *Prairie Triangle Interstitial Tongue* are fre-quently less than 500 km wide but extend from New Jersey to the upper MacKenzie River. *Lycaena thoe* is a butterfly species representa-tive of this range pattern.

Another kind of interstitial region is the *East-ern Plains Intrusive Tongue* (fig. 21), composed of "southwestern" fauna and flora that extends from central Texas through eastern Kansas to Minnesota and South Dakota. Unlike the Prairie Triangle Tongue, this intrusive tongue contains a high proportion of annual immigrant Neo-tropical species. Typical of this distribution pattern are a large number of butterflies nor-mally considered to be tropical, such as *Papilio anchisiades, Ascia monuste, Appias drusilla,*

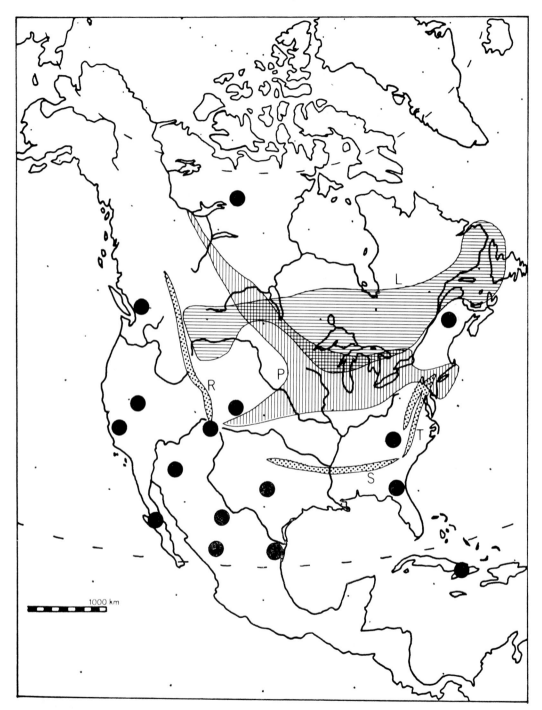

Fɪɢ. 20—Interstitial tongues and interprovincial relict zones. P–Prairie Triangle, R–Rocky Mountains Relict Zone, T–Tryon-Piedmont-Shale Barrens Relict Zone, S–Southern Piedmont and Cuesta Relict Zone, L–Laurentian ("Nunatak") Relict Zone. Spots locate provincial heartlands.

Kricogonia castalia, Anteos maerula, Phoebis agarithe, Mestra amymone. Some of these seasonally intrusive species veer eastwards when they encounter the Prairie Triangle and range along it as far as the Finger Lakes Region of New York State, between the Canadian and Virginian Provinces. All these species are rare but some are found every year, indicating the persistence of conditions amenable to colonization, given the immigrants. There is some establishment of breeding colonies along this tongue and rare survival through exceptionally mild winters, especially in the south. Any amelioration of winter climatic extreme during the Pleistocene probably rendered this tongue biotically important. The Eastern Plains Intrusive Tongue is really an unusual temperate climate manifestation of the tropical phenomenon of vadose communities, well developed in south Texas. Here in early successional communities that are continually rejuvenated by an irregular series of moist and killing drought years, the fauna is always rich, but the taxonomic structure changes from season to season and from year to year depending on minute changes in biotic advantages. Similar conditions exist in southern Arizona and a much weaker *Great Basin Intrusive Tongue* is recognized passing between the Californian and Coloradan Provinces and between the Coloradan and Vancouveran Provinces as far as southern Montana (Clarksfork and Bighorn Basins). Such butterflies as *Phoebis sennae marcellina* and *Brephidium exilis* sporadically colonize along this route.

Coastal communities, because of their physiographic and climatic setting, are constantly being rejuvenated and thus include a higher proportion of early successional stages than do inland sites. In this biotically unsaturated condition, they are analogous to the interstitial regions (fig. 21). Tropical fauna pass north along a *Pacific Coastal Intrusive Zone* reaching points north of San Francisco and include insects such as *Urbanus* spp. and in southern Alaska, *Erebus odora*. Tropical fauna pass north along a *Texas Coastal Instrusive Zone* to reach Galveston and include insects such as *Chioides zilpa* and *Papilio thoas*. Occasionally it reaches as far as southwest Louisiana. Intermittent tropical colonization occurs and persists, sometimes for decades, in the *Gulf Coastal Intrusive Zone* between New Orleans and Mobile (e.g., the butterfly *Anartia jatrophae*). The source of these Gulf colonists is not known but is presumably either Cuba or Yucatan. Antillean fauna sporadically colonize coastal habitats in southern Florida with some species persisting for many

decades. Many of the south Florida established species of Antillean affinity are occasionally found in coastal sites as far north as Long Island, New York State, along the *Atlantic Coastal Intrusive Zone,* (e.g., *Strymon columella* and *Anartia jatrophae*).

A number of interprovincial relict zones are recognized on the basis of both floral and faunal disjuncts and endemics (fig. 20). The *Rocky Mountains Relict Zone* contains a number of species with their closest relatives in eastern Asia and Alaska. These are differentiated at the subspecific level (e.g., *Boloria napaea halli*) or at the specific level (e.g., *Coenonympha haydenii*—cf. *C. oedippus* of Eurasia; *Erebia callias* —cf. *E. tyndarus* of Eurasia). This relict zone apparently records the route taken by many more successful Pleistocene intrusives from the Old World (such as *Heodes cupreus*—cf. *H. alciphron* of Eurasia) that have since successfully colonized through subspeciation in the Californian (*H. c. cupreus*), the Vancouveran (*H. c. henryae*) and the Coloradan (*H. snowi*) Provinces.

The *Tryon-Piedmont-Shale Barrens Relict Zone* contains an interesting series of endemics (e.g., *Pyrgus wyandot*—cf. *P. loki* of the Coloradan Province) and disjuncts of western species (e.g., *Lycaeides melissa*). This zone in its Piedmont portion is interstitial between Virginian and Georgian Provinces but extends for edaphic reasons inland to the shale barrens of the Great Valley of the Appalachians. Guilday, McCrady, and Hamilton (pers. comm.) have found vertebrate elements of this zone well developed in Sangamon or possibly mid-Wisconsin interglacial or interstadial time (the two are difficult to separate) with elements of the Coloradan Province such as pika (*Ochothonus*) and grizzly bear, and elements of the southwestern Balconian Province such as the extinct peccary (*Mylohyus*) and extinct armadillo (*Dasypus bellus*). Coloradan elements probably passed along the Prairie Triangle (cf. relict populations of *Lycaeides melissa* from Wisconsin to New York) where Sangamon or mid-Wisconsin interstadial deposits bear *Ephedra* and *Artemisia* pollen in Michigan. Balconian elements possibly entered along the Southern Piedmont and Cuesta Relict and Intrusive Zone.

The *Southern Piedmont and Cuesta Relict and Intrusive Zone* lies between the Virginian and Georgian Provinces from South Carolina (e.g., disjunct Balconian species *Amblyscirtes belli*) and northern Georgia (e.g., endemic *Megathymus harrisi*) through central Alabama and Mississippi with disjunct and endemic plant species, and extends westward between the

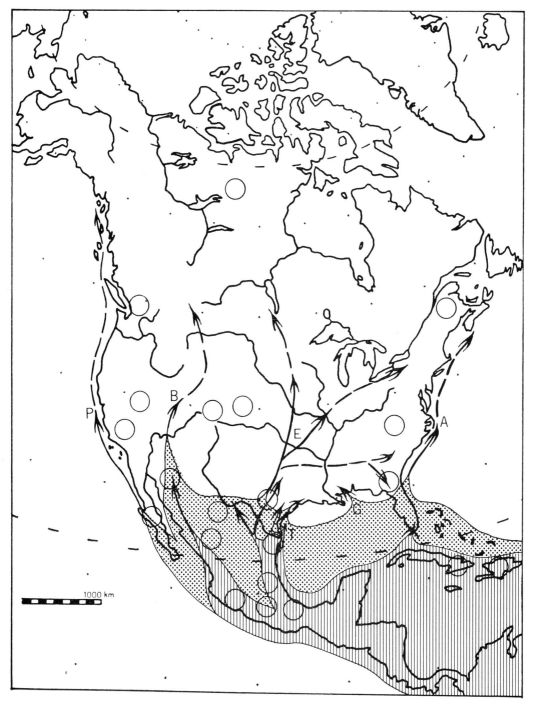

FIG. 21—Neotropical intrusive tongues. E–Eastern Plains Intrusive Tongue, B–Great Basin Intrusive Tongue, P–Pacific Coastal Intrusive Tongue, T–Texas Coastal Intrusive Tongue, G–Gulf Coastal Intrusive Tongue, A–Atlantic Coastal Intrusive Tongue. Open circles represent provincial heartlands.

Virginian and Balconian Provinces as far as the Criner Hills of southern Oklahoma (e.g., *Alnus maritima*). The degree of speciation attained amongst the plants suggests considerable age for this zone, which is still sporadically active as an intrusive zone because of records of Mesoamerican elements, normally found in south Texas, such as *Celotes nessus*, *Erynnis funeralis*, and *Urbanus dorantes* found in Georgia and Florida.

The *Laurentian Relict Zone* corresponds roughly with the zone of "nuntak" relics proposed by Fernald (1925) and ably interpreted by Rousseau (1953). Although this zone lies completely within the former ice margin it must have existed several times during interglacial episodes, with some of its components successfully surviving in refuges to the southeast. This zone is recognized from Montana and southern Alberta to Gaspé and Newfoundland and is widest in the Great Lakes Region, where it extends from northern Ontario to Green Bay, Wisconsin, and the northern part of the southern peninsula of Michigan. Organisms with this distribution include a few endemics and many disjuncts and intrusives. Endemics are frequent among the herbaceous plants (Fernald, 1925; Scoggan, 1950; Rousseau, 1953) and to a lesser extent among insects (e.g., *Papilio brevicauda*, *P. khali* and *P. nitra*). Such endemics probably spent at least one glacial episode in isolated refuges. Many of these probably could not have survived in the unglaciated sites of the Gulf of St. Lawrence unless the glacial climate of the area was less extreme than it is today. A southern group of disjuncts, barely differentiated at the subspecific level from their relatives in the Coloradan Province, may have entered the area during the cool dry postglacial phase, for they are in general associated with xeric habitats [e.g., *Ocneis chryxus strigulosus* closest to *O. c. chryxus* of Colorado; *Speyeria cybele* var. *krautwurmi* which appears from both male and female characters to be an ecotype derived from the gene pool of *S. c. leto* but existing in balanced polymorphism with *S. c. novascotiae* and forming from 1 percent (Carleton Co.) through 60 percent (Nippissing District) to near 100 percent (Kirkland Lake) in Ontario]. A northern group of disjuncts, also barely differentiated at the subspecific level from their relatives in the Vancouveran Province, probably entered the area relatively recently (*Everes amyntula* is supposed to have spread from Manitoba to Gaspé in the last 50 years); for, in general, they occupy mesic lowland, usually calcareous habitats, which were inundated by the postglacial Tyrrell Sea (extension of Hudson-James Bay over the lowlands) until 4,000

to 5,000 years ago (emergence continuing today). Some of these latecomers are: *Hesperia borealis* which is probably only subspecifically distinct from *H. colorado*; *Oeneis chryxus calais* which is very close to the subalpine race of Montana and quite distinct from *O. c. chryxus*; *Erynnis borealis* which is possibly an active intrusive; *Erebia discoidalis* and *E. disa mancina* which are of Holarctic origin; *Euchloe ausonides*, *Callophrys eryphon*, *Everes amytula*, *Plebeius saepiolus* and *Pieris occidentalis* which are all apparently recent intrusives from the Vancouveran Province.

DYNAMICS OF DIVERSITY IN
INTERPROVINCIAL ZONES

Since July, 1968, the author has conducted a year-round survey of seasonal diversity change and the attendant apparent provincial aspect change in the insect fauna of central Texas, using butterflies as a systematically well known sample taxon. The survey area is bounded by a circle of 90 km radius around Austin, Texas. Sample size (to January 1, 1972) is 8109 specimens, of 142 species (Durden, 1969, 1970, 1971, 1972b). Similar faunal sampling of diversity structure is being conducted at intervals in a temperate montane region (Beartooth Mountains of Montana and Wyoming, since 1964) and a tropical montane region (Sierra Madre Oriental of southern Tamaulipas, "Sierra de Guatemala," since 1970). Early in the central Texas sampling project, subjective week by week summary indicated pronounced seasonal shifts in apparent provinciality. Species of Georgian affinity appear to predominate in winter, Virginian in spring (May), and Balconian in fall (October) when moisture supply is above normal. Tamaulipan species predominate in winter, Coahuilan in spring and fall when the weather is consistently hotter and drier than normal. The question is what does a fossil insect assemblage preserved in a single event (as many Palaeozoic assemblages appear to have been) tell us about the provincial affinity of the sampled area?

Diversity was analysed using 10 day class intervals for a 3 year period, assigning a provinciality weight of 1 to each occurring species. Surprisingly no significant seasonal change was indicated by diversity alone. It seems that some provincial representatives become common and some become rare, but the species are present always in roughly the same provincial proportions. This is probably dependent upon the long term damping effect of the seasonally stable components of the community. For example, *Celtis* spp. (hackberry trees) may suffer frost-drought die-back of foliage, poor fruiting, or low seeding survival, but the mature trees rarely die. Adults of *Asterocampa* spp. (with Georgian, Balconian, and Tamaulipan representative species in the area) are dependent upon these trees as structural components of individual territories, and larvae utilize the leaves as food. *Asterocampa* spp. fluctuate wildly in population size; one species and now another predominates and occasionally all species are rare. If a large sample is taken all the species are found to be present. Thus the apparent seasonal variation in provincial aspect is due to the relative proportions of individuals of each species rather than to any short term shift in diversity. It is rather a measure of immediate success of community facies than a measure of community change. From a paleontological point of view, provincial aspect in an interprovincial region determined from the diversity (species count) of a small sample will err in its heavy dependence on the population size of each species (because of different probabilities of sampling each species). The diversity of a large sample will approach the long term composition of the biota and give a reliable picture of interprovincial location. A succession of small samples at one site may be used to demonstrate interprovinciality if the provincial aspect determined from apparent diversity shows rapid change or recurrence.

ZONES OF HYBRIDIZATION

The biogeographic importance of wild interspecific hybrids has been recognized for some time in both animals and plants (Anderson, 1949; Hovanitz, 1949). Wild hybrids are expected to be at a selective disadvantage when in competition for a station in the niches of the parent species. Niche requirements of the hybrid are likely to be an unusual combination of those of the parent species, and thus not usually satisfied in the local habitat. Usually where both parent species are well adapted to the occupancy of niches in available communities, hybrids, although they may occur naturally, will not be recognized because they do not survive selection before maturity. This situation may vary from year to year dependent upon the climatic effects on community "success." The two lycaenid butterfly species, *Callophrys (Mitoura) castalis* and *C. (M.) smilacis*, overlap broadly in central Texas. Most years, although there is broad overlap of flight time and mating possibility, no intermediates are found. The few intermediate individuals (presumed hybrids) found so far have occurred at times of relative scarcity of both species. This suggests survival of disadvantaged individuals (one of the hybrids is both a somatic mosaic and gynandromorph) under

low conditions of intraspecies competition for sites, existing in the unsaturated niche after a selective event has decimated the populations of both species. Occurrence of interspecific hybrids in *Speyeria* (Beartooth Mountains, Durden, unpublished data) is frequent away from the modal flight time of each parent and infrequent during the modes. Under these conditions of 2 to 5 percent interspecific hybrid survival, the individual hybrid apparently must be offset temporally during its ontogeny, in order to survive competition with larvae of the parent species. The occurrence of wild hybrids in the adult state may then be taken as an indicator of unsaturated niches.

When occurrences of wild animal hybrids are mapped (Hovanitz, 1949; Remington, 1968) they are found to be more frequent in regions recognized here as the interprovincial zones between biotic provinces. Short (1969, 1970) and Uzzel and Ashmole (1970) discussed Remington's "suture-zones" and his reliance on allopatric speciation theory to interpret these areas as recent phenomena. Examples of intrarange hybridization zones in broadly coincident species suggest that the recent meeting of closely related species, that have not yet evolved isolating mechanisms, is not the major reason for patterned distribution of wild hybridization. The butterfly genus *Limenitis* has been used to map zones of hybridization in North America (Hovanitz, 1949; Remington, 1968) and species of this genus demonstrate natural hybridization in the zones of meeting of species of different provinces. One problem species, however, that has been avoided is *Limenitis archippus* (the "viceroy" mimic of the "monarch," *Danaus plexippus*). The range of this species is crossed by bands of its hybrid occurrence with other *Limenitis* spp. These bands fall in interprovincial areas. Although hybridization may occur between individuals drawn from the heart of a province as several successful laboratory crosses have indicated, the progeny in the wild do not reach maturity in the provincial heartland but only in the interprovincial region. *L. archippus* is well adapted for niche saturation within each province that it occupies, in several cases, having a distinct provincial subspecies (*L. a. archippus*—Virginian; *L. a. floridana*—Georgian; *L. a. watsoni*—Balconian; *L. a. hoffmani*—Tamaulipan; *L. a. obsoleta*—Durangan; and *L. a. lahontani*—Nevadan). In transition from one province to another, from one regional ecotype to another, niche saturation is not possible, and selection is relaxed permitting hybrids with other species to reach maturity. Combinations that have been reported from wild caught hybrids are with *L. arthemis rubrofas-*

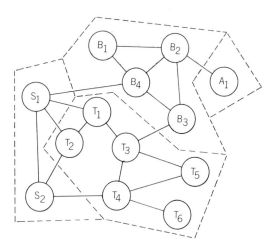

FIG. 22—Relationship of realms by component taxa. Palaeaustral Realm Group: S1–Afraustral Realm, S2–Australian Realm; American Realm Group: A–Neotropical Realm; Boreal Realm Group: B1–Holarctic Realm, B2–Nearctic Realm, B3–Oriental Realm, B4–Palaearctic Realm; Palaeotropical Realm Group: T1–Afrotropic Realm, T2–Malagasian Realm, T3–Indotropic Realm, T4–Papuotropic Realm. T5–Polynesian Realm, T6–Austral Realm.

ciata (Vancouveran–Canadian Zone), with *L. arthemis* and *L. astyanax* (Canadian–Virginian Zone), with *L. astyanax* (Virginian–Georgian Zone and Balconian–Virginian–Georgian Zone), with *L. weidemeyerii* (Coloradan–Virginian Zone, and Coloradan–Durangan Zone, and Coloradan–Californian Zone) and with *L. lorquini burrisonii* (Vancouveran–Coloradan Zone). Backcross of these wild hybrids in areas of unsaturated niche may balance intraprovince selection against hybridization, and a quasi-equilibrium condition over a long period of time is conceivable.

WORLD-WIDE OCCURRENCE OF BIOTIC PROVINCES

On the basis of animal distribution, principally of vertebrates, Beaufort (1951) presents revised boundaries of 6 Wallacean Realms; recognizing Palaearctic, Ethiopian, Indo-Malayan, Australasian, Nearctic and Neotropical. Good (1964), on the basis of plant distribution, recognizes 130 floristic provinces in 37 regions of 6 kingdoms (Boreal, Palaeotropical, Neotropical, South African, Australian, and Antarctic). Schilder (1956) recognizes 24 provinces in 8 regions of 4 realms, based on animal distribution. In this paper two sample groups drawn from plants and animals have been used to determine the locations of diversity highs. Woody plant distribution (data chiefly from Bader, 1960) and cockroach distribution (data chiefly from Princis, 1961) have been used to recognize 63 major provinces in 13 realms of

4 realm groups. Relationship between the realms may be represented by evaluation of the relationships of their higher taxa as in figure 22, or as a diagram indicating present contact and interaction in figure 23. Relationship between provinces within each realm may be represented by dendrograms based on taxonomic similarity (fig. 24). These dendrograms are rough approximations based on few taxa and will be much improved by thorough analysis of more segments of flora and fauna. Figure 25 is a world map showing the location of the heartlands of the 63 major provinces.

PENNSYLVANIAN AND PERMIAN BIOMERES

The biotic province, thus far in this paper, has been discussed as a unit of ecological structure as found in the modern biota. Former differences and fluctuations in the location of provincial peripheral zones, possible derivation of two or more provinces out of a common biota, and survival of provincial remnants in the boundary zones between major provinces also have been discussed. The province through time appears to be a biostratigraphic unit above the level of the biofacies. Where the biofacies is, strictly speaking, the time integral of the community, the biomere (Palmer, 1965) is the time integral of the province (Durden, 1967), and the geobiota (cf. the geoflora) is the time integral of the realm. A pattern of biomeric succession has been described from the Cambrian of the Great Basin by Palmer (1965) on the basis of trilobite fauna. "The biomere, although it is in historical succession with other biomeres

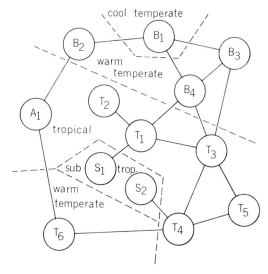

FIG. 23—Present interaction of realms. Symbols as in figure 22.

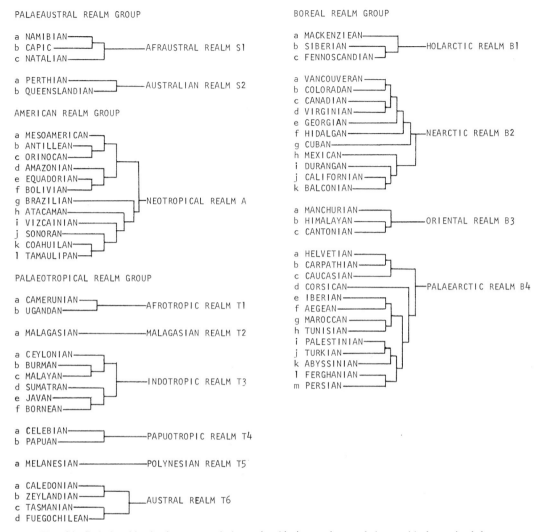

PALAEAUSTRAL REALM GROUP

a NAMIBIAN
b CAPIC
c NATALIAN — AFRAUSTRAL REALM S1

a PERTHIAN
b QUEENSLANDIAN — AUSTRALIAN REALM S2

AMERICAN REALM GROUP

a MESOAMERICAN
b ANTILLEAN
c ORINOCAN
d AMAZONIAN
e EQUADORIAN
f BOLIVIAN
g BRAZILIAN — NEOTROPICAL REALM A
h ATACAMAN
i VIZCAINIAN
j SONORAN
k COAHUILAN
l TAMAULIPAN

PALAEOTROPICAL REALM GROUP

a CAMERUNIAN
b UGANDAN — AFROTROPIC REALM T1

a MALAGASIAN — MALAGASIAN REALM T2

a CEYLONIAN
b BURMAN
c MALAYAN
d SUMATRAN — INDOTROPIC REALM T3
e JAVAN
f BORNEAN

a CELEBIAN
b PAPUAN — PAPUOTROPIC REALM T4

a MELANESIAN — POLYNESIAN REALM T5

a CALEDONIAN
b ZEYLANDIAN
c TASMANIAN — AUSTRAL REALM T6
d FUEGOCHILEAN

BOREAL REALM GROUP

a MACKENZIEAN
b SIBERIAN
c FENNOSCANDIAN — HOLARCTIC REALM B1

a VANCOUVERAN
b COLORADAN
c CANADIAN
d VIRGINIAN
e GEORGIAN
f HIDALGAN — NEARCTIC REALM B2
g CUBAN
h MEXICAN
i DURANGAN
j CALIFORNIAN
k BALCONIAN

a MANCHURIAN
b HIMALAYAN — ORIENTAL REALM B3
c CANTONIAN

a HELVETIAN
b CARPATHIAN
c CAUCASIAN
d CORSICAN
e IBERIAN
f AEGEAN
g MAROCCAN — PALAEARCTIC REALM B4
h TUNISIAN
i PALESTINIAN
j TURKIAN
k ABYSSINIAN
l FERGHANIAN
m PERSIAN

FIG. 24—Relationship dendrograms of the major biotic provinces of the world, determined from similarity of component taxa. Symbols refer to figure 25.

at any geographic locality and has a unique faunal content, does not have a unique age. Either or both boundaries may be diachronous" (Palmer, 1965). In a three dimensional representation where two dimensions map the province succession and the third, time, integrates the biomere, we expect the biomere to appear as a streamlined base heavy solid with its long axis parallel to time, because communities and biomeres are notoriously persistent, taking a long time to die out after becoming rare and old provinces tend to be small. Is it possible to reconstruct such solid figures using provinces plotted over short time intervals?

Modern provinces can be mapped based on cockroach distribution and the possibility exists for using the late Paleozoic cockroach-like insects for the same purpose. Mapping the distribution of late Paleozoic winged insects gives a unique opportunity for observing from their first appearance the geographic spread and differentiation of a major group of organisms (subclass Pterygota) over a time interval sufficiently long that some of the biomeres can be observed from origin to extinction.

In correlating eastern Canadian Pennsylvanian insect faunas (Durden, 1967, 1972c) the pronounced presence of European elements, first noted by W. A. Bell (1938) among the plants, is apparent. There is even some conspecificity between assemblages of the Stellarton Coalfield of Nova Scotia, South Wales Coalfield

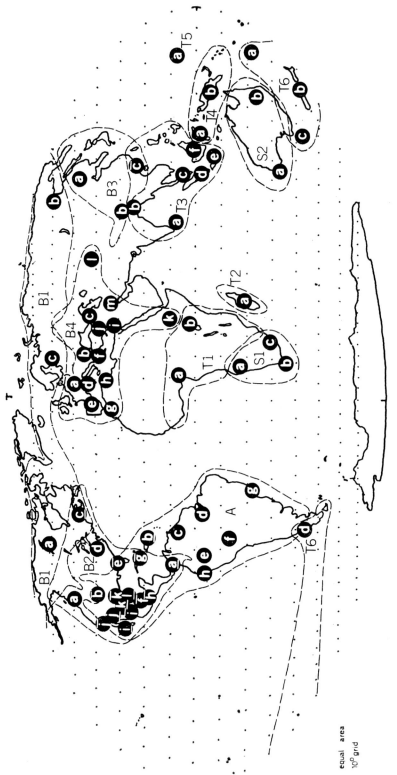

Fig. 25—Heartlands of the major biotic provinces of the world. Symbols as in figure 24.

equal area
10° grid

and Coalfield of Northern France (Durden, 1972c). Because these European elements occur sporadically in assemblages to the west (Durden, 1967, 1969) and because American elements extend sporadically to the east, at least as far as France (Durden, 1972c), these two faunas may be provincially differentiated rather than physiographically separated. Because late Paleozoic fossil insects were evolving generically at rates comparable to those of Tertiary mammals, most assemblages can be dated precisely by zonation within time units that appear to be on the order of 2.5 million years (Durden, 1969). Data from described assemblages, most of the old unstudied collections and newly collected material from localities between the Rhine Valley and Portugal and north-central Texas and Colorado have been assembled. Recurrent associations of genera have been tentatively recognized as representative of provincial biotas. Maps of the distribution of these provincial biotas have been prepared at approximately 5 million year intervals, as far as current potassium-argon age determination permits.

The oldest winged insects, which belong to the order Protoptera (Sharov, 1966), have been found in the Namurian B or possibly Namurian A of central Europe (Kukalova, 1958). They first appear in western Europe and North America in the Namurian C (fig. 26) about 320 myBP. These early winged insects, although they include the oldest members of several orders are all more or less closely related and appear to form an autochthonous fauna which is here termed the *Pocahontan Biomere,* after its occurrence in rocks of the Pocahontas Group of the southern Allegheny Plateau. In South Wales, associated with this fauna, are the first elements of a fauna of small blattoid insects of later importance. Because, contrary to numerous textbook statements, cockroaches *have* changed considerably since the Carboniferous, to use the term Pennsylvanian cockroach is as misleading as calling a dinosaur a Mesozoic lizard, and the Palaeozoic ancestors of cockroaches are referred to as blattoids (loosely translated as leaf-like or pinnule insects).

In Westphalian A (Morrowan) time at about 315 myBP (fig. 27), the Pocahontan Biomere shifted slightly to the south, extending from Arkansas through northeast Alabama (Pratt Group), West Virginia, the Northern Anthracite Field of Pennsylvania (Campbells Ledge Black Slate), New Brunswick (Little River Group), Nova Scotia (Riversdale Group) and South Wales to Northern France and eastward into central Europe. To the north the *Brabantian Biomere* with its fauna of small blattoids

that appeared earliest in South Wales, had spread westwards to Pennsylvania and western Maryland. By Westphalian B time the advancing western tongue of the Brabantian Biomere had differentiated to the extent that mixed assemblages of Brabantian and Alleghenian elements are found in western Pennsylvania and a mixture of Brabatian and Iberian elements are found in western Missouri.

In Westphalian C (early Desmoinesian) time about 310 myBP (fig. 28) a most complex pattern of provincial differentiation followed the widespread orogeny from the Ouachitas to western Europe. The Pocahontan Biomere is still represented in Central Europe as far west as the Saar Basin and in northern Georgia. From its first appearance in Missouri the *Iberian Biomere* spread eastward as far as Maryland in the interprovincial zone north of the Pocahontan Biomere. From its first appearance in western Pennsylvania the *Alleghenian Biomere* spread westward as far as southeastern Oklahoma, mostly to the north of the Iberian Biomere. Eastward the Alleghenian Biomere spread along or just north of the Brabantian Biomere with elements appearing in the upper parts of the sections of the South Wales and Northern France Coalfields. South of the Brabantian Biomere, but north of the Iberian Biomere, a new biota appeared, the *Mazonian Biomere*. From its systematic affinities the Mazonian Biomere appears derived by differentiation of an eastern tongue of the Alleghenian Biomere, probably augmented by non–blattoid elements adopted from the Pocahontan Biomere. At this time the Mazonian Biomere extended from Maryland and the Southern Anthracite Field of Pennsylvania, through Cape Breton Island to the Saar Basin. To the north the Brabantian Biomere flourished with great diversity in Northern France and the Stellarton Basin of Nova Scotia. Brabantian elements are found in mixed assemblages as far west as Missouri.

Westphalian D (mid-Desmoinesian) time about 305 myBP (fig. 29) appears to have been a time of provincial restriction. No remnants of the Pocahontan Biomere have been found this late, but this may be due to lack of localities. The Iberian Biomere greatly expanded to the east as far as Portugal, Spain, and southern France. Iberian elements are found in mixed assemblages in Maryland, Rhode Island, and Cape Breton Island. The Mazonian Biomere was restricted in the east and is found no farther east than Cape Breton Island. To the west the Mazonian Biomere extended into the Illinois Basin and is found at several localities in Indiana and Illinois including the famous Mazon

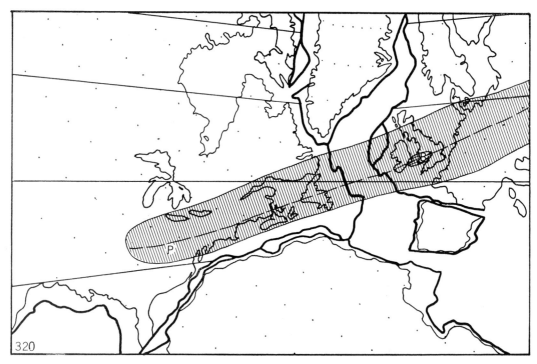

FIG. 26—Distribution of biotic provinces in Namurian C time (about 320 myBP). P–Pocahontan Biomere, B–Brabantian Biomere. Dashed line indicates the inferred biothermal equator. Configuration of the continents after Bullard and others (1965), except that the European block has been rotated counter-clockwise with respect to North America to bring the American and European late Westphalian paleomagnetic equators into line.

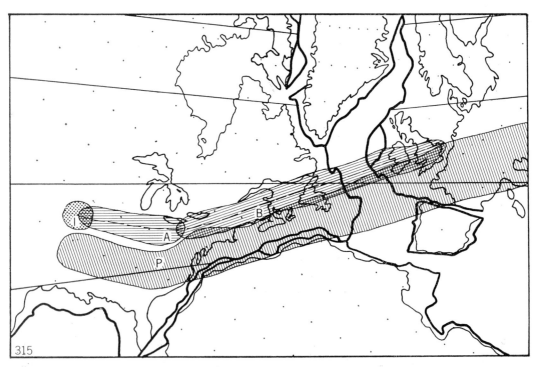

FIG. 27—Distribution of biotic provinces in Westphalian A (Morrowan) time (about 315 myBP). P–Pocahontan Biomere, B–Brabantian Biomere, A–Alleghenian Biomere, I–Iberian Biomere.

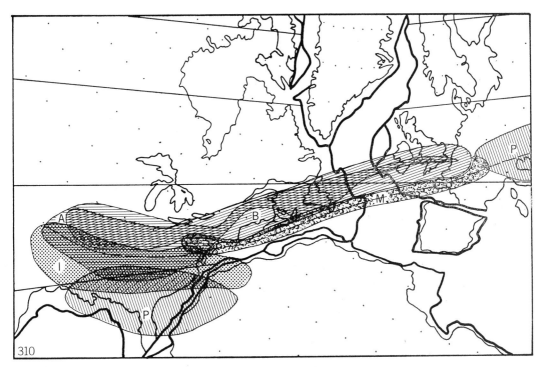

Fig. 28—Distribution of biotic provinces in Westphalian C (early Desmoinesian) time (about 310 myBP). P–Pocahontan Biomere, B–Brabantian Biomere, A–Alleghenian Biomere, M–Mazonian Biomere, I–Iberian Biomere.

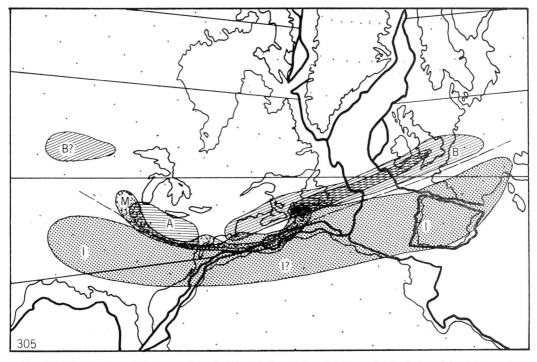

Fig. 29—Distribution of biotic provinces in Westphalian D (medial Desmoinesian) time (about 305 myBP). B–Brabantian Biomere, B?–disjunct occurrence of Brabantian biota inferred from later derivatives (location unknown), A–Alleghenian Biomere, M–Mazonian Biomere, I–Iberian Biomere, I?–African occurrence not known.

Creek Nodule area of Morris and Grundy Counties. Alleghenian elements are found in mixed assemblages from South Wales to Cape Breton Island and in Maryland and Illinois. They form pure Alleghenian assemblages in western Pennsylvania. The Brabantian Biomere, found from the Saar Basin to Rhode Island, has been displaced farther west. Later appearance of the earliest elements of the Zavjalovian and Lebachian Biomeres, presumed derivatives of the Brabantian on systematic grounds, suggests a disjunct remnant or remnants of Brabantian biota survived somewhere to the west or north of the Illinois Basin.

The Cantabrian of Spain and the Freeport Group of the type Pennsylvanian, at about 300 myBP (fig. 30) represent a time interval which correlates with the Asturian orogenic phase of Europe, between the Westphalian and Stephanian Epochs (as currently defined). Although its fauna is mostly of Westphalian aspect, the Cantabrian-Freeport interval is arbitrarily attached to the lower Stephanian because it is younger than the Tonstein 60 upper boundary of the revised type Westphalian. During this time the Iberian Biomere is well developed in Portugal and is, in North America, represented in mixed assemblages of western Pennsylvania. The Mazonian Biomere shrank to a few elements of mixed assemblages of the Southern Anthracite field of Pennsylvania. From Maryland westward, apparently a western tongue of the Mazonian differentiated sufficiently to be recognized as the beginning of the Ottweilerian Biomere. The inferred western relict occurrence of the remnants of the Brabantian Biomere, probably differentiated into two segments about this time; one, somewhere north of Pennsylvania, destined to become the Lebachian Biomere; the other, somewhere north or west of Kansas, destined to become the Zavjalovian Biomere.

In Stephanian A (late Desmoinesian, early Conemaughan) time at about 295 myBP (fig. 31), the Iberian Biomere is well developed in Portugal and southern France and enters mixed assemblages of the Glenshaw Group in western Pennsylvania. The strange assemblage of Commentry in France (Brongniart, 1893) is usually cited as late Stephanian. The blattoids, however, include genera found in the Freeport and Glenshaw Groups of Pennsylvania and the degree of specialization of the Commentry species of *Spiloblattina* suggests an age no older than early Glenshaw (Mason) and no younger than late Glenshaw (Duquesne) unles the assemblage represents a pocket of relict persistence. The non-blattoid elements are so unlike those of contemporaneous faunas elsewhere that

they probably represent a biomere of a different geobiota. Where did they come from? Possibly elements of the early Pennsylvanian Pocahontan Biomere, isolated on another land mass probably no later than Namurian C (for no unusual blattoids are present at Commentry), were unable to interact with the Euramerican geobiota until Stephanian time. The Ottweilerian Biomere, which appeared in Freeportian time in Maryland, expanded as far east, at least, as the Saar Basin and as far west as western Missouri. In western Missouri it is mixed with relict elements from the Brabantian Biomere which are suggestive of the beginnings of the Zavjalovian Biomere. Because this stage of differentiation has been reached, the Brabantian relict, presumed to occur somewhere north of Pennsylvania, is certainly isolated by this time.

In Stephanian B (Missourian to earliest Virgilian) time about 290 myBP (fig. 32), the Iberian Biomere was still present to the south of the Ottweilerian Biomere. Iberian elements occur in mixed assemblages in the Southern Anthracite field of Pennsylvania and Missouri. Typical Iberian assemblages of Stephanian age in Portugal may be this young. A single posttillite assemblage in Brazil, which appears to contain Iberian elements, may be this old. The Ottweilerian Biomere remains typically developed at this time from eastern Germany through the Saar Basin to Pennsylvania. In Kansas Ottweilerian elements occur in the mixed assemblages at Garnett and Lawrence, and also in central Colorado. The *Zavjalovian Biomere* is predominant in the mixed assemblage at Lawrence, Kansas, while the first appearance of elements of the Elmoan Biomere occur in the Garnett assemblage. Like the assemblage at Commentry, France, non-blattoid elements of the Elmoan Biomere are so different from Euramerican non-blattoid elements that their origin in a different geobiota is presumed. This was probably located somewhere to the north and west, because the Elmoan Biomere is most similar to the later Permian faunas of Siberia (such as the Kuznetsk).

In Stephanian C through Autunian A (early through mid Virgilian) time about 285 myBP (fig. 33), the Iberian Biomere is represented in Texas. The Ottweilerian Biomere extended from Wettin, Germany, through Pennsylvania probably as far as Colorado. Indication of the transitional Brabantian-Lebachian fauna and the Elmoan fauna have not yet been found, but few insect localities are known from this time interval. The Zavjalovian Biomere is represented in the mixed assemblages at Wettin, Germany, and the rich development of this biomere in the Upper Balakhonsk Formation of the

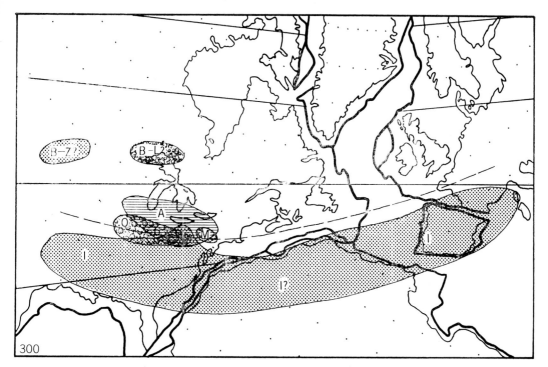

Fig. 30—Distribution of biotic provinces in Cantabrian (Freeportian) time (about 300 myBP). A–Alleghenian Biomere, M–Mazonian, O–Ottweilerian Biomere, I–Iberian Biomere (African occurrence not established), B-Z? and B-L?–postulated disjunct Brabantian relicts inferred from later occurrence of derivatives, location not known.

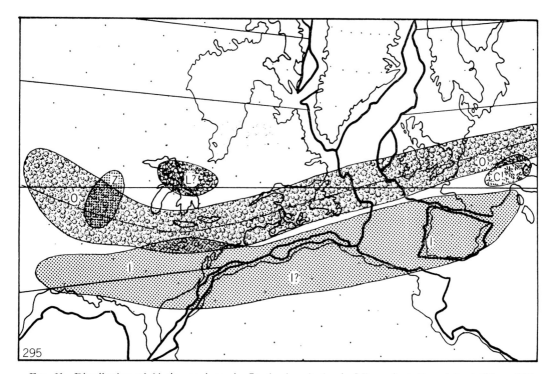

Fig. 31—Distribution of biotic provinces in Stephanian A (early Missourian) time (about 295 myBP). O–Ottweilerian Biomere, Z–Zavjalovian Biomere (of Brabantian origin), L?–postulated Brabantian relict, I–Iberian Biomere (African occurrence not established), C–Commentry fauna of unknown provenance. The Commentry fauna is an unique occurrence of diverse elements of "Permian aspect" but it contains blattoid lineages of Alleghenian affinity which from their degree of specialization (mylacrid, hemimylacrid and spiloblattinid lineages) indicate an early Stephanian age at slight variance with the late Stephanian age inferred from the associated flora.

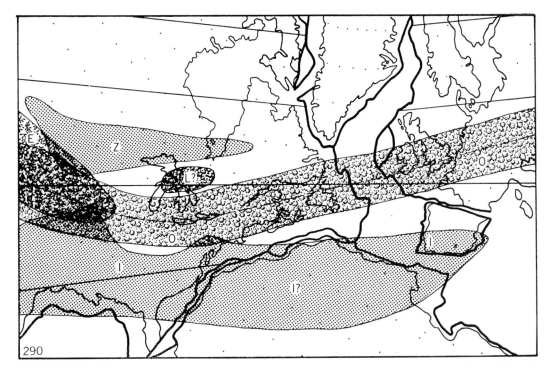

Fig. 32—Distribution of biotic provinces in Stephanian B (Missourian) time (about 290 myBP). O–Ottweilerian Biomere, Z–Zavjalovian Biomere, L?–postulated Brabantian relict, I–Iberian Biomere (African occurrence not established), E–Elmoan Biomere of "Permian aspect."

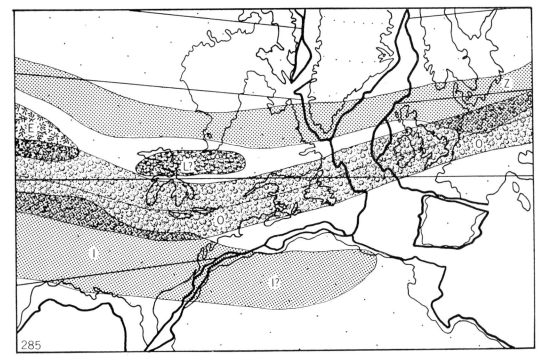

Fig. 33—Distribution of biotic provinces in Stephanian C through Autunian A (early and medial Virgilian) time (about 285 or 280 myBP). O–Ottweilerian Biomere, Z–Zavjalovian Biomere, L?–postulated Brabantian relict, I–Iberian Biomere (African occurrence not established), E–Elmoan Biomere of "Permian aspect."

Kuznetsk Basin, Siberia, is probably contemporaneous.

In Autunian B (late Virgilian and early Wolfcampian) time about 275 myBP (fig. 34), the Iberian Biomere persisted in Texas, where, in the Newcastle Coal Zone of Jack Co., it occurs in mixed assemblage with Lebachian elements. The rich and remarkably widespread *Lebachian Biomere* has so far been identified only in assemblages of this interval except for a few younger stragglers in the Wichita Group of Texas and the Wellington Group of Kansas. This biomere is well developed in the Lebacher Schichten of the Saar Basin and occurs to the north at Löbejün near Halle. It is represented by over a thousand specimens of several genera and numerous species from Cassville West Virginia. The Cassville collection was made from the upper parting of the Waynesburg Coal of the Monongahela Series and from the Cassville Shale or roof shale of the same coal in the Dunkard Series. In this assemblage the only Ottweilerian remnants are species of *Spiloblattina,* but they are quite different from the Conemaughan species. In the Sangre de Cristo Formation ("Maroon" of some authors) at its northern edge in South Park, Colorado, an assemblage contains Lebachian, Ottweilerian, and Zavjalovian elements in a diverse Elmoan fauna. The type and other species of *Spiloblattina* are intermediate between those of the Upper Balakhonsk Formation of Siberia and the last known representative of the genus, an undescribed diminutive species from Elmo, Kansas. They are also morphologically intermediate between the Cassville species and that of Elmo, suggesting an age for the Fairplay assemblage slightly younger than Cassville. Zavjalovian elements are also present in the Löbejün assemblage, near Halle, Germany, indicating the wide extent of this biomere in the northern hemisphere.

In Sakmarian (late Wolfcampian and early Leonardian) time about 265 myBP (figs. 35, 36), the Iberian Biomere flourished in Texas. An element of this biomere is found in the roof of one of the highest coals (Black Mine Vein) of the Southern Anthracite Field of Pennsylvania, and also known from Henrietta, Texas, in the upper Admiral Formation. Minor constituents of assemblages in the Belle Plaines and Clyde Formations of the Wichita Group and in the Elmo assemblage of the Wellington Group indicate local persistence of a few Lebachian elements. The Elmoan Biomere is well developed at several localities in Kansas and Oklahoma but has not been found south of the Wichita and Arbuckle Mountains. Conversely Iberian elements have not been found to the

north of these ranges at this time. Zavjalovian elements are not present in known North American assemblages but presumably persisted to the east as their derivatives appear in later Permian faunas of the Ural region and Siberia. The presence in Rhodesia of *Rhodesiomylacris* indicates that Iberian biota persisted well after Permian time in some parts of the southern hemisphere. Only a single occurrence of *Pareinoblatta* (the earliest Triassoblattidae) in the Cassville assemblage foreshadows the rich Mesozoic blattoid faunas, which first appear well developed in the late Permian-early Triassic of Australia.

CLIMATIC AND GEOGRAPHIC INFERENCE

When considered with paleomagnetic evidence, the pattern of distribution of Pennsylvanian and early Permian biomeres may be used for some climatic interpretation. In North America, through much of Pennsylvanian time the paleomagnetic equator passed diagonally through the northern end of the Gulf of California, the Great Lakes, and northern Newfoundland (fig. 37). In Europe it passed south of Ireland, through Brittany and Italy. Euramerican insect deposits of the Pennsylvanian and early Permian all lie within 15 degrees of this magnetic equator, suggesting that the thermal equator was located nearby. Provincial elongation, most noticeable where several biomeres are involved, is assumed to be latitudinal by analogy with modern patterns in regions of low relief. The differences between thermal and magnetic equators (fig. 37) compare with a present difference of almost 20 degrees and, on meridians where the thermal equator is strongly warped away from the rotational equator, this difference appears larger. Supporting the Pennsylvanian-Early Permian determination of thermal equator location is the late Namurian-early Westphalian restriction of redbeds to within 8 degrees of the same line. The modern distribution of red soils is generally within 38 degrees of the equator. Many of these modern red soils are, from fossil content, of Pleistocene age (cave clays in particular) and apart from special desert sites with summer rain regime, modern hematitogenic soils may not be forming much north of 31 degrees (8 degrees north of the tropics). This restriction of redbeds in the early Pennsylvanian indicates that the tropics of Cancer and Capricorn were displaced towards the equator and that the earth suffered no pronounced temperature seasonality. Independent support for this finding comes from the absence of growth rings in the wood form-genus *Dadoxylon* in the Pennsylvanian of Euramerica and the presence of growth rings in *D. indicum*

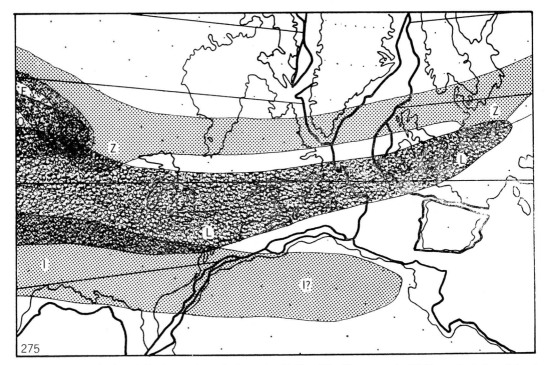

FIG. 34—Distribution of biotic provinces in Autunian B (late Virgilian or early Wolfcampian) time (about 275 or 270 myBP). O–Ottweilerian Biomere, Z–Zavjalovian Biomere, L–Lebachian Biomere, I–Iberian Biomere (African occurrence not established), E–Elmoan Biomere of "Permian aspect."

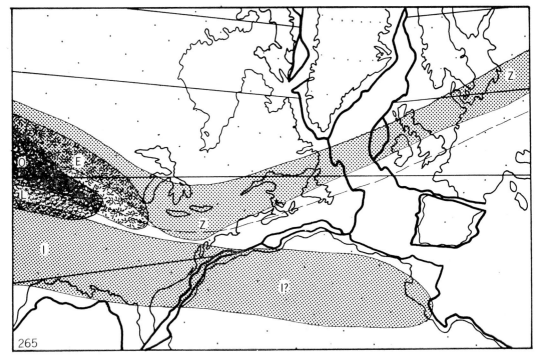

FIG. 35—Distribution of biotic provinces in Sakmarian (late Wolfcampian) time (about 265 myBP). O–Ottweilerian Biomere, Z–Zavjalovian Biomere, L–Lebachian Biomere, I–Iberian Biomere, E–Elmoan Biomere.

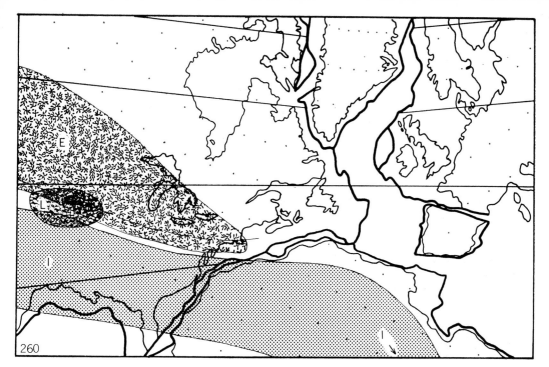

FIG. 36—Distribution of biotic provinces in Artinskian (early Leonardian) time (about 260 myBP). L–Lebachian Biomere, I–Iberian Biomere (African occurrence in Rhodesia), E–Elmoan Biomere.

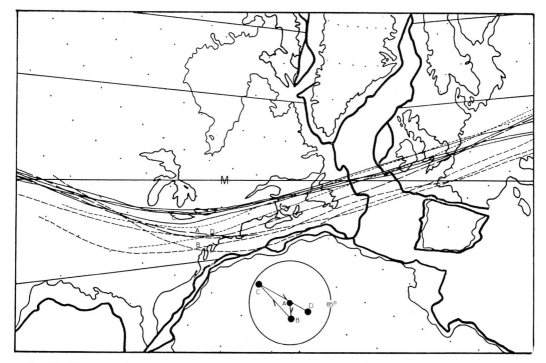

FIG. 37—Clusters of biothermal equators determined from biotic provincial distributions. Cluster A for 320 and 315 myBP, cluster B for 310, 305 and 300 myBP, cluster C for 295, 290, 285 and 275 myBP, cluster D for 265 and 260 myBP. M–paleomagnetic equator determined from redbeds of late Westphalian age (about 305 myBP) in western Europe and eastern North America. The axis of elongation of biomeres indicates differences between thermal and magnetic equators for cluster A of 7°, cluster B of 9°, cluster C of 5° and cluster D of 7°. Inset circle of the polar region shows polar wandering determined from shifts in equatorial location and clustering. Shifts appear to be rapid: A–B (about 312 myBP) is contemporaneous with Ouachitan and Variscan orogenies, B–C (about 297 myBP) is contemporaneous with Asturian orogeny, and C–D (about 270 myBP) is contemporaneous with Saalian orogeny and orogeny in the ancestral Rocky Mountains.

(Seward, 1933; fig. 73) of the Permian of India, and in several other stems from Australia and South America cited by Seward. A similar restriction of the tropics appears to have occurred in latest Ordovician-earliest Silurian time (Ashgillian and Whitewater through early Llandoverian and Edgewood time), when redbeds are restricted to a narrow band almost coincident with the magnetic equator of that time. Many species distributions are elongate along this zone (e.g. *Dalmanella edgewoodensis*, and *Mendacella uberis*). This tropical restriction may have been synchronous with continental glaciation on North Africa, then far removed to the south relative to North America just as the Namurian-Westphalian tropical restriction is contemporaneous with at least part of the Gondwanan glaciations of South America and Australia.

The narrow tropical belt of the Pennsylvanian encloses a number of small biomeres, while the extensive temperate belts contain few widespread biomeres (figs. 38, 39). The pattern today (fig. 25) appears unusual because the heartlands of 36 major provinces are located outside the tropics and only 27 centers are located in the tropics. At least in North America, the origins of most of the provinces may be traced back to middle and early Tertiary time and, therefore, the location of heartlands should be considered in relation to the early Tertiary location of the tropics. Using that basis the situation is reversed and 43 heartlands are located within the tropics and only 20 in temperate latitudes. Tertiary tropical areas (fig. 25) which now are temperate, such as eastern and southern North America, Europe, and Australia–New Zealand, are disproportionately rich in provin-

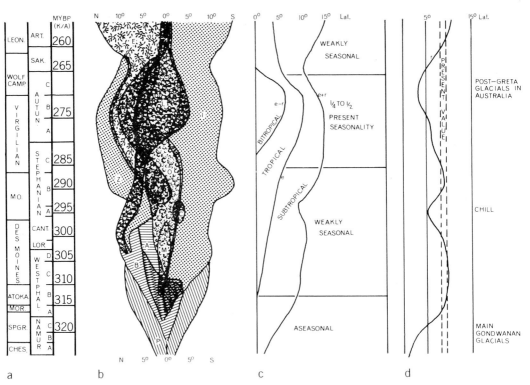

FIG. 38—Paleoclimatic interpretation. *a*–Time scale. In North America the younger boundary of the Pennsylvanian is usually placed at the end of the Virgilian Epoch, the older boundary at the beginning of the Springeran Epoch. In Europe the younger boundary of the Upper Carboniferous is usually placed at the end of the Stephanian Epoch, occasionally at the end of the Autunian Epoch, the older boundary is placed at the beginning of the Namurian Epoch. *b*–Projection of the biomeres on a meridian (horizontal axis) through time (vertical axis). Scale given in degrees of latitude. P–Pocahontan, B–Brabantian, A–Alleghenian, M–Mazonian, I–Iberian, C–Commentryan, O–Ottweilerian, Z–Zavjalovian, L–Lebachian, E–Elmoan. Stipple and lines indicates biomeres thought to be subtropical, strong patterns indicate tropical biomeres. *c*–Seasonality inferred from biotic provincial distributions. e–angle of the ecliptic and latitude of the tropic line. r–maximum solar incident angle from zenith, under which red soils will form on open lowland sites given adequate moisture (an indirect measure of solar strength. *d*–Relative temperature curve for low latitudes. r–redbed index (see above–*c*).

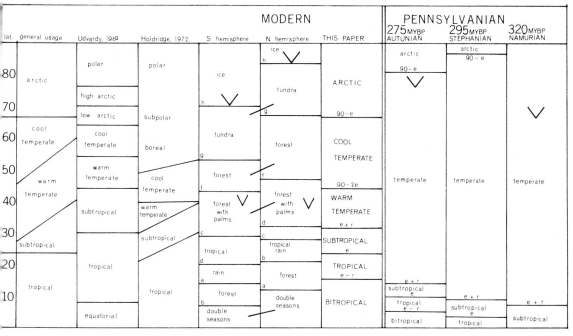

FIG. 39—Climatic zonal interpretation. From the left—Column 1–latitude, Columns 2, 3, and 4–comparison of climatic zonal classifications, Columns 5 and 6–latitudinal limits of biotic indicators: a–limit of double-season equatorial rain forest, b–mode of limits of tropical rain forest on all continents, c–extreme limit of tropical rain forest, d–mode of limits of palm distribution on all continents, f–extreme limit of palms, g–mode of limits of forest on all continents (modal "tree-line"), h–extreme limit of vascular plants, Column 7–climatic zonal classification based on causal parameters: e–angle of the ecliptic, r–redbed index (see fig. 38c), Columns 8, 9 and 10–inferred climatic zonation of 3 Pennsylvanian epochs. Note variation in value of r and in location of arctic and tropic circles from just under half the present value to coincident with pole and equator. Chevrons indicate latitude reached by polar glaciation. Narrow chevrons of Columns 5 and 6 indicate latitude reached during maximum Pleistocene glaciation. The curve of figure 38d suggests that a low value of r (less than 5 degrees of latitude) is correlated with the occurrence of glaciation while Columns 5 and 6, and 8 and 10 show that neither low nor high values of e appear correlated with glaciation.

cial heartlands. Tertiary temperate regions which now are tropical, such as middle South America and Africa, are disproportionately poor in provincial heartlands. This historic effect is also preserved in the species counts of some groups of organisms, such as the butterflies, where the diversity high for the superfamily is located in Central America and northern South America with a secondary high in the Malaya to Papua region. Europe and Australia are disproportionately rich for temperate faunas while Africa is disproportionately poor for a tropical region.

One other independent indicator of tropicality of Pennsylvanian blattoid faunas is their relative size. As in some other poikilotherms the average size of tropical species is smaller than that of the temperate species. In modern blatoids the largest average individuals are in faunas in subtropical and warm temperate areas and, individuals tend to be smaller both toward the equator and into the cool temperate regions.

In the late Paleozoic blattoids average size increases with latitude.

A curve indicating the inferred temperature changes at the thermal equator may be derived from the expansion and contraction of biomeres based on the estimated amount of tropical versus temperate adaptation for individual provinces. A curve for Pennsylvanian and Early Permian time (figs. 38, 39) shows a gradual warming from the cool Namurian (tillites dated by both spore and marine faunal evidence, in southern South America and Australia) into mid-Westphalian time. A minor chilling appears to have occurred in early Stephanian time to be followed by a warming in Stephanian time concomitant with the first appearance of redbeds in the Pennsylvanian type section and a rapid expansion of the equatorial Ottweilerian Biomere. The warmest episode of the Pennsylvanian appears to have occurred either in mid Stephanian time or in mid-Westphalian time. The relationship of the Lebachian Biomere to the

Brabantian Biomere suggests a late Autunian chilling, possibly contemporaneous with the youngest tillites in Australia. The rapid disappearance of the Ottweilerian biota from most of Euramerica in Autunian time certainly indicates an important climatic change. The Sakmarian configuration of biomeres, although poorly known, suggests an abrupt shift of the thermal equator, but there are not enough sample points for this time interval to determine a clear axis of provincial elongation.

CONCLUSIONS

Biotic provinces and their time integrals, biomeres, may be mapped using single taxa at or near the ordinal level as a source of sample generic ranges. For modern provinces, the results of diversity mapping are repeatable when the sample ranges are drawn independently for several orders. Deviation from normal provincial pattern, shown by a few taxa, particularly of mammals and birds, may be attributed either to the extreme mobility of the members of the taxon or to their niche position usually being in the earlier or "weedier" stages of succession. Pennsylvania biomeres are comparable in size to modern biotic provinces. They differ in having extreme latitudinal elongation, probably because the Pennsylvanian continent of Euramerica was latitudinally elongate, whereas modern North America is meridionally elongate. Pennsylvanian Euramerica was apparently of low relief, while modern North America is divided meridionally by mountain ranges. Modern North American biotic provinces are latitudinally elongate in the east but are irregularly complex and interdigitate in the mountain west.

Pennsylvanian Euramerican biomeres are neatly arranged latitudinally during times of orogenic quiescence but are divided and complexly interdigitate during times of orogeny, such as at the end of the Atokan.

New biomeres arise as segregates of old ones by adaptation to special local conditions. When climate changes these new biomeres are available to replace old biomeres. Frequency of appearance, spread, and disappearance of biomeres along the inferred thermal equator in Pennsylvanian time suggests that significant climatic change involved worldwide temperature fluctuations. Details of shifts in provincial boundaries can be used to construct a relative temperature curve for the tropical zone, although no values may be attached to the curve, other than those limits that can be inferred from the presence or absence of laterization and shifts in the angle of the ecliptic.

During rapid climatic change determination of short time intervals is necessary for mapping the successive provincial patterns that make up the biomere. Five million-year intervals seem to be adequate for resolving detail of Pennsylvanian biogeography; longer intervals (perhaps 15 million years) may be permissible during less eventful periods such as the Cambrian.

The hypotheses of biomeric dynamics, advanced here to explain the properties of provinces, biomeres, and their boundary relations, are difficult to evaluate experimentally because of the slow time scale of the processes involved. Only careful description of biogeographic structure in the fossil record, using small chronologic and geographic units, can overcome these limitations.

REFERENCES CITED

ALLEN, J. A. 1892. The geographic distribution of North American mammals. Bull. Am. Mus. nat. Hist. 4: 199–242.

ANDERSON, E. 1949. Introgressive hybridization. John Wiley, New York. 109 p.

ARGUS, G. W., AND M. B. DAVIS. 1962. Macrofossils from a late-glacial deposit at Cambridge, Massachusetts. Am. Midl. Nat. 67:106–117

AXELROD, D. I. 1962. A Pliocene Sequoiadendron forest from western Nevada. Univ. Calif. Publs. geol. Sci. 39:195–268, pls. 38–50.

———, AND W. S. TING. 1961. Early Pleistocene floras from the Chagoopa Surface, southern Sierra Nevada. Ibid. 39:119–194, pls. 25–37.

BADER, F. J. W. 1960 Die Verbreitung borealer und subantarktischer Holzgewächse in den Gebirgendes Tropengürtels. Nova Acta Leopoldina. n.s. 148:1–544.

BEAUFORT, L. F. DE. 1951. Zoogeography of the land and inland waters. London. 208 p.

BELL, W. A. 1938. Fossil flora of the Sydney Coal Field, Nova Scotia. Mem. geol. Surv. Brch. Can., 215:1–334. pls. I–CVII.

BLAIR, W. F. 1950. The biotic provinces of Texas. Tex. J. Sci. 2:93–117.

BRAUN, E. L. 1950. Deciduous forests of eastern North America. Facsimile reprint 1964, Hafner, New York and London. 596 p.

BULLARD, E., J. E. EVERETT, AND A. G. SMITH. 1965. The fit of the continents around the Atlantic. Phil. Trans. R. Soc. Lond. 258:41–51.

DICE, L. R. 1943. The biotic provinces of North America. Univ. Mich. Press, Ann Arbor. 78 p.

———. 1952. Natural communities. Univ. Mich. Press, Ann Arbor. 547 p.

DURDEN, C. J. 1966 Oligocene lake deposits in Central Colorado and a new fossil insect locality. J. Paleont. 40:216–219.

——. 1967. Faunal affinities of the Acadian Upper Carboniferous insects. Geol. Ass. Can.–Mineralog. Ass. Can. Int. Mtg. (Kingston, Ont.). Abstr. Pap.: 25–26.

——. 1969. Pennsylvanian correlation using blattoid insects Can. J. Earth Sci. 6:1159–1177.

——. 1970. Records of butterflies collected in Texas. In, FREEMAN, H. A., Season's Summary for 1969, Zone 14: Great Plains. Lepid. News. 15 April 1970: 11–12.

——. 1971. Records of butterflies collected in Tamaulipas. In, E. C. WELLING M., Season's Summary for 1970, Northern Neotropics Region. Lepid. News. 1 March 1971:8.

——. 1972a. Records of butterflies collected in Texas, In FREEMAN, H. A., Season's Summary for 1971, Plains Area. Lepid. News. 15 March 1972:6–7.

——. 1972b. Records of butterflies collected in Tamaulipas, In E. C. WELLING M., Season's Summary for 1971, The Northern Neotropics. Lepid. News. 15 March 1972:15.

——. 1972c. Systematics and morphology of Acadian Pennsylvanian blattoid insects (Dictyoptera-Palaeoblattina) : a contribution to the classification and phylogeny of Palaeozoic insects. Yale Univ. Ph.D., dissertation: 408 p., 142 fig., 18 pls.

FERNALD, M. L. 1925. The persistence of plants in unglaciated areas of Boreal America. Mem. Am. Acad. Sci. 15:239–342.

FLINT, R. F. 1965. The surficial geology of the New Haven and Woodmont Quadrangles. State Geol. Nat. Hist. Surv. Conn. Quad. Rep. 18:42 p. + map.

GODMAN, F. D., AND O. SALVIN. 1879. Insecta, Lepidoptera-Rhopalocera. Biologia Centrali-Americana. 1:1–487.

GOOD, R. 1964. The Geography of the flowering plants. 3rd. ed. John Wiley, New York. 518 p.

GUILDAY, J. E., P S. MARTIN, AND A. D. McCRADY. 1964. New Paris No. 4: a late Pleistocene cave deposit in Bedford County, Penn. Bull. Natn. speleol. Soc. 26:121–194.

HAGMEIER, E. M., AND C. D. STULTS. 1964. A numerical analysis of the distribution patterns of North American mammals. Syst. Zool. 13:125–155.

HEBARD, M. 1917. The Blattidae of North America north of the Mexican boundary. Mem. Am. ent. Soc. 2: 1–284.

HOLDRIDGE, L. R., W. C. GRENKE, W. H. HATHEWAY, T. LIANG, AND J. A. TOSI, JR. 1971. Forest environments in tropical life zones. Pergamon, Oxford. 780 p.

HOVANITZ, W. 1949. Increased variability in populations following natural hybridization. In JEPSEN, G. L., E. MAYR., AND G. G. SIMPSON, Eds. Genetics, Paleontology and Evolution. Princeton Univ. Press p. 339–355.

KUKALOVA, J. 1958. Paoliidae Handlirsch (Insecta-Protorthoptera) aus dem oberschlesischen Steinkohlenbecken. Geologie. 7:935–959.

LAWRENCE, R. F. 1953. The biology of the cryptic fauna of forests. A. A. Balkema, Capetown and Amsterdam. 408 p.

LINSLEY, E. G. 1940. The origin and distribution of the Cerambycidae of North America, with special reference to the fauna of the Pacific slope. 6th Pac. Sci. Congr. (1939) Proc. 4:269–282.

MacGINITIE, H. D. 1953. Fossil plants of the Florissant beds, Colorado. Contr. Paleont. Carnegie Inst. Wash. Publs. 599:1–198.

MARTIN, P. S., AND B. E. HARRELL, 1957. The Pleistocene history of temperate biotas in Mexico and eastern United States. Ecology. 38:468–480.

MARTÍNEZ, M. 1948. Los Pinos Méxicanos (2ª. ed.). Ediciones Botas, México. 361 p.

MERRIAM, C. H. 1898. Life zones and crop zones in the United States. Bull. U.S. Dep. Agri. 10:1–79.

PACKARD, A. S. 1883 A monograph of the phyllopod Crustacea of North America, with remarks on the Order Phyllocarida. U.S. Geol. Surv. Terr. Rept. 12:295–592 + map.

PALMER, A. R. 1965. Biomere, a new kind of biostratigraphic unit. J. Paleont. 39:149–153.

PRINCIS, K. 1961. Blattaria. Orthopterorum Catalogus. Pars 3, 4, 6, 7: 394 p.

REMINGTON, C. L. 1968. Suture-zones of hybrid interaction between recently joined biotas. In, DOBZHANSKY, TH., M. K. HECHT, AND W. C. STEERE., Eds. Evolutionary Biology. 2:321–428.

ROUSSEAU, J. 1953. The value of botany as indicator of unglaciated areas. 7th Pacif. Sci. Congr. (1949) Proc. 5:178–186.

SCHILDER, F. A. 1956. Lehrbuch der Allgemeinen Zoogeographie. G. Fischer Verlag, Jena. 150 p.

SCOGGAN, H. J. 1950. The flora of Bic and the Gaspé Peninsula, Québec. Bull. Nat. Mus. Can. 115:39 p.

SEWARD, A. C. 1933. Plant life through the ages. Facsimile reprint 1966, Hafner, New York. 603 p.

SHAROV, A. G. 1966. Basic arthropodan stock, with special reference to insects. Pergamon. Oxford. 271 p.

SHELFORD, V. E. 1963. The ecology of North America. Univ. Illinois Press, Urbana. 610 p.

SHORT, L. L. 1969. "Suture-zones," secondary contacts, and hybridization. Syst. Zool. 18:458–460.

——. 1970. A Reply to Uzzel and Ashmole. Syst. Zool. 19:199–202.

UDVARDY, M. D. F. 1969. Dynamic zoogeography. Van Nostrand Reinhold Co., New York. 445 p.

UZZEL, T., AND N. P. ASHMOLE. 1970. Suture-zones: An alternative view. Syst. Zool. 19:197–199.

VAN DYKE, E. C. 1919 The distribution of insects in western North America. Ann. ent. Soc. Am. 12:1–12 + map.

——. 1940. The origin and distribution of the coleopterous insect fauna of North America. 6th Pacific Sci. Congr. (1939) Proc. 4:255–268.

WALLACE, A. R. 1876. The geographical distribution of animals. Facsimile reprint 1962, Hafner, New York. 1: xxiii + 503 p. 2: xi + 553 p.

ANCIENT GEOSYNCLINAL SEDIMENTATION, PALEOGEOGRAPHY, AND PROVINCIALITY: A PLATE TECTONICS PERSPECTIVE FOR BRITISH CALEDONIDES AND NEWFOUNDLAND APPALACHIANS

FREDERIC L. SCHWAB

Department of Geology, Washington and Lee University, Lexington, VA 24450

ABSTRACT—The mechanisms and constraints of plate tectonics, sea-floor spreading, and continental drift can be invoked to reinterpret the characteristics and distribution of the sedimentary successions in the British Caledonides and Newfoundland Appalachians. Such an approach indicates that the basal (late Precambrian) deposits in both areas are continental clastic wedge sequences which accumulated in a series of graben-like tensional fault block basins produced during the initial rifting of a Precambrian supercontinent. The axis of rifting and later spreading cut haphazardly across the trends of older orogenic belts and did not coincide with the spreading axis of the present Atlantic Ocean. Overlying Cambrian sediments accumulated symmetrically along the paired trailing edges of passively drifted continental segments as continental terrace (shelf) and continental rise deposits which flanked a growing Protoatlantic Ocean basin. Late Cambrian (in Great Britain) and Early Ordovician (in western Newfoundland) underthrusting of oceanic lithosphere beneath the adjacent continental blocks converted Atlantic-type continental margins into Western Pacific and Andean marginal types. The Protoatlantic Ocean began to close, and episodes of deformation, volcanism, metamorphism, and intrusion genetically related to this convergence consolidated the Orthotectonic Belts of western Newfoundland and Scotland. The continued closure of the Protoatlantic during the Silurian generated several "intrageosynclinal" source areas, a number of trenches, troughs, island arcs, and continental rise regions, and the bulk of the structures which constitute the present Paratectonic Belts in central Newfoundland, England, and Wales. Finally, Devonian collision of the original marginal continental segments reconsolidated the original, but now enlarged supercontinent. Subsequent tensional rifting generated a series of internal rift-block molasse basins while isostatic subsidence along the southern margin of the supercontinent produced continental terrace and continental rise regions in which the basal deposits of the Hercynian Geosyncline accumulated.

These global tectonics basin models indicate that the conventional models proposed to explain major geosynclinal sedimentary provinces may be inaccurate, emphasize the need for reinterpreting the origin and evolution of distinct faunal provinces, and suggest that the paleogeographic setting which is commonly envisioned for evolving mobile belts is misleading. At the same time plate tectonics provides reasonable solutions to many of the unsolved problems posed by conventional geosynclinal theory. The major geosynclinal provinces are actualistic; they *can be,* but not necessarily *must* be interpreted as composites of discrete, but interrelated continental margin and ocean basin deposits (continental shelf, continental rise, inland sea, trench, abyssal plain sequences) which are superimposed upon one another laterally and vertically by the divergence and convergence of lithospheric plates. Geosynclinal belts originate by the lateral rifting of continents. Crustal mobility is due initially to normal isostatic subsidence along continental margins but is subsequently maintained by subduction. Consumption of oceanic lithosphere (and the sediments deposited on it) can readily generate the necessary large volumes of "intrageosynclinal" sialic source areas and can also explain the nature and distribution in time and space of geosynclinal orogeny, volcanism, intrusion, and metamorphism.

Progressive widening of newly generated ocean basins may laterally displace sialic "borderlands" and also lead to the development of distinct faunal provinces. Subsequent closure of ocean basins may result in the physical juxtaposition of sedimentary provinces, source areas, and faunal provinces which originally developed in widely separated areas. The stratigraphic and structural differences and similarities along and across individual geosynclinal belts (and the distinctions between supposedly once-contiguous belts) can arise simply because the exact nature, location, and timing of initial rifting, subsequent spreading, conversion from one continental margin type to another, and continental collision can all vary appreciably along single plate margins and between opposite margins of ocean basins. Consequently the orogenic history of individual belts is complex, and though locally episodic, can regionally appear almost continuous. The application of plate tectonics to an understanding of ancient geosynclinal belts emphasizes the need for wider use of palinspastic reconstructions, for clearer understanding of the characteristics of modern continental margin and ocean basin sedimentary assemblages, and for a re-evaluation of conventional models for continental evolution.

INTRODUCTION

Classical geosynclinal theory provides a general conceptual model which genetically relates the ancient orogenic belts of the world to linear subsiding belts of the Earth's crust in which thick sequences of sediment accumulated. The progressive transformation from a simple eugeosynclinal-miogeosynclinal basin couple into a deformed, metamorphosed, and intruded mountain belt purportedly proceeds in a series of systematic stages. The distribution of sedimentary rock types in time and space is a function both of their locus of deposition within the geosynclinal basin as well as the prevailing tectonic framework.

Because no viable alternative theory existed,

the geosynclinal explanation for mobile belts has persisted, despite the fact that it left a number of problems unresolved. What and where are the modern analogues of ancient geosynclinal basins? What produced the original crustal subsidence and how was crustal mobility maintained over long periods of time? Why were some geosynclinal belts located along continental margins whereas others were apparently intracontinental? Why did segments of individual geosynclinal belts evolve similarly, but not simultaneously? What were the major source areas for geosynclinal sediments?

The new theories of sea-floor spreading and plate tectonics bring fresh insight to these problems and are rapidly altering our thinking on the nature, timing, and location of orogeny, the geographic framework of geosynclines, and the probable characteristics of geosynclinal sedimentary provinces. This paper reinterprets the major patterns of sedimentation in two ancient geosynclinal belts, the British Caledonides and Newfoundland Appalachians, in light of plate tectonics theory in order to demonstrate the new perspectives which global tectonics models impose on our earlier understanding of geosynclinal sedimentation, paleogeography, and provinciality.

GLOBAL TECTONICS THEORY: HISTORY AND MAJOR PREMISES

Plate tectonics theory was originally devised to explain the present worldwide distribution of seismic activity, volcanicity, mid-oceanic ridges, island arcs, ocean trench systems, and sea-floor magnetic anomaly patterns. All these features were related to large scale displacements of thick (50–100 km) rigid lithospheric plates which are generated by mantle rising along mid-ocean ridges, spread laterally as a growing sea-floor, and ultimately descend beneath adjacent plates near continental margins producing ocean trenches, seismic zones, deformation, and intense volcanism (Le Pichon, 1968; Isacks and others, 1968; Vine and Matthews, 1963).[1] Later studies such as those of Drake and others (1959), Dietz (1963), Dietz and Holden (1966), Gilluly and others (1970), and Mitchell and Reading (1969, 1971) related lateral and vertical changes in the composition, texture, and thickness of sedimentary assemblages accumulating along present-day continental mar-

[1] General references are cited individually in the text and listed under "References Cited: General." The numerous references on which the figures discussed are based are not cited within the text, but are listed at the end of the paper as "References: Specific Cross-sections."

gins (modern geosynclines) to the relative movement of lithospheric plates. Finally Wilson (1966), Dewey (1969), Dewey and Horsfield (1970), Dewey and Bird (1970), Bird and Dewey (1970), Hamilton (1969), Ernst (1970), Gilluly (1971, Hsu (1971) and others applied the mechanisms of plate tectonics to the understanding of sedimentation, metamorphism, magmatism, and deformation of ancient (pre-Triassic) mobile belts.

The above studies and a review of the major precepts of plate tectonics (Bott, 1971; Menard, 1971; Wyllie, 1971) suggests that if the mechanics of plate tectonics are invoked to govern and explain the evolution of ancient geosynclinal belts, the following major constraints apply:

(1) Geosynclinal sedimentary assemblages approximate "half oceans," for example, they are composites of the sedimentary assemblages which accumulate along continental margins, in ocean trenches, and to a debatable extent on the abyssal plains of the deep ocean floor.

(2) The three types of fundamentally distinct continental margin types which exist presently (Mitchell and Reading, 1969) must have ancient analogues in now deformed geosynclinal belts (fig. 1). These continental margin types include: (a) Atlantic-type (aseismic) margins, where continental terrace (miogeosynclinal) and continental rise (eugeosynclinal) assemblages accumulate along the trailing edges of passively drifting continental blocks (i.e., continental and oceanic crust are coupled); (b) Andean-type margins, developed where oceanic lithosphere descends beneath an overriding continental block producing a trench (eugeosynclinal) marginal to a narrow continental shelf (miogeosynclinal) and a volcanically active andesitic orogenic belt; and (c) Western Pacific-type margins (island arc-Japan Sea), where the descent of oceanic lithosphere beneath an adjacent continental block produces an exterior subsiding trench (eugeosynclinal), a volcanic island arc-tectonic land complex, and an interior inland sea (miogeosynclinal).

(3) Geosynclinal sediments initially accumulate as continental terrace and continental rise assemblages developed along newly-formed Atlantic-type continental margins produced by the rifting and lateral separation of older consolidated continental blocks.

(4) The lateral accretion of new ocean floor at mid-ocean ridges (*diverging* plate boundaries) produces a progressively larger

Continental margin types

1.   ATLANTIC   TYPE

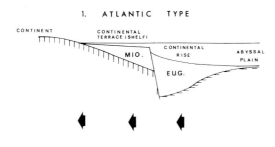

2.   JAPAN   SEA- ISLAND   ARC   TYPE

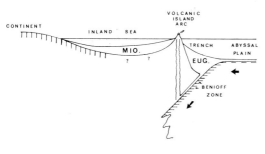

3.   ANDEAN   TYPE

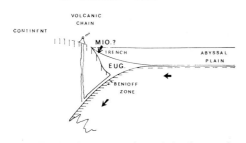

Fig. 1—Schematic cross-sections of the three major modern continental margin types indicating components equivalent to ancient miogeosynclines (mio.) and eugeosynclines (eug.). Arrows indicate relative motions of lithospheric plates.

ocean basin whose growth separates the earlier-formed deposits. Sediments continue to accumulate principally along Atlantic-type margins, but additional sediments are deposited on abyssal plains of the growing ocean floor.

(5) Because there must be a global balance between the generation and destruction of lithospheric plates, oceanic lithosphere is eventually uncoupled from the adjacent continental blocks, descending beneath them along Benioff Zones. This underthrusting defines new *converging* plate boundaries

along which ocean trench systems, island arcs, and inland sea areas are generated. As a consequence, Atlantic-type margins are transformed into Andean and Western Pacific continental margin types.

(6) Converging plate boundaries are areas where destruction of oceanic lithosphere occurs by subduction. An oceanic plate (including its sedimentary cover) must either be consumed by melting into the mantle and/or laterally and vertically accreted to the continental crust by the processes of deformation, metamorphism, and migmatization.

(7) Continued convergence of lithospheric plates must ultimately lead to the closure of ocean basins, the eventual collision of marginal continental segments, and episodes of final geosynclinal orogeny which reconsolidate an enlarged supercontinental block.

The current geological literature makes it evident that stratigraphers and sedimentologists will increasingly use these concepts primarily to: (1) compare the overall distribution of sediments in ancient mobile belts of the world which *are* presently disjunctive across ocean basins, *were* presumably once proximal and contiguous, and consequently *should* exhibit a similar structural and stratigraphic framework; and (2) analyze and reinterpret evolutionary changes in the lithology, thickness, depositional environments, and source areas of ancient geosynclinal sediments by analogy with present-day continental margins and lithospheric plate boundary types. The first approach largely attempts to verify the existence of sea-floor spreading and continental drift since the Triassic; the second approach tests the applicability of plate tectonics prior to that time. This paper demonstrates both such approaches by example from the Northern Appalachians (Newfoundland) and the British Caledonides.

BRITISH CALEDONIDES AND NEWFOUNDLAND
APPALACHIANS: GENERAL COMPARISONS

A generalized tectonic map of the Newfoundland Appalachians and British Caledonides (fig. 2) shows, as a number of studies have pointed out, that both orogenic belts can be subdivided into a similar series of stratigraphically and structurally distinct belts:

(1) a stable northwestern foreland belt (the Western Platform of Newfoundland; the Northwest Foreland of Scotland);

(2) a central orogenic belt (the Central Mobile Belt of Newfoundland; the Caledonian Orogenic Belt of Britain) which can be fur-

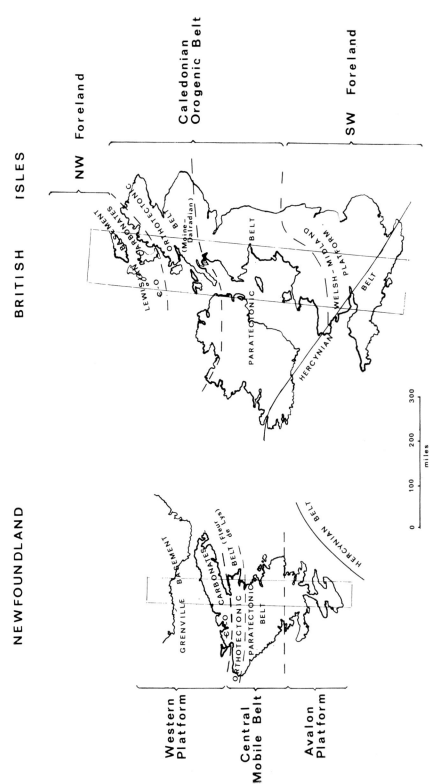

Fɪɢ. 2—Generalized tectonic map of Newfoundland and Great Britain emphasizing the similarity between major structural and stratigraphic belts (Dewey and Kay, 1968; Daliel, 1969; Rodgers, 1970). Zoned areas are regions on which cross-sections are based.

ther subdivided into a Northern Orthotectonic Belt and a Southern Paratectonic Belt;

(3) a stable southwestern foreland belt (the Avalon Platform of Newfoundland; the Midland Platform of England and Wales).

Figure 2 also shows the general areas on which the stratigraphic cross-sections drawn for the late Precambrian, Cambrian, Ordovician, Silurian, and Devonian are based (figs. 3, 4, 5, 6, and 7). These cross-sections include my own interpretations as well as those of a number of other workers, particularly Dewey (1969), Dewey and Bird (1970). All cross-sections are drawn using two major constraints imposed by accepting an actualistic[2] plate tectonics model for geosynclines:

(1) lateral contrasts in sediment composition, texture, and thickness are represented by analogy with changes in the distribution of sediments accumulating along present-day continental margins, for example, in a series of subparallel lithofacies belts (sedimentary provinces) designated as continental terraces, continental rises, continental slopes, inland seas, trenches, and abyssal plains);

(2) most secular changes (and many lateral changes) in the distribution of sediment are related to an evolving paleogeographic setting in which both source areas and depositional areas are produced and maintained by periodic separation, underthrusting, overriding, and collision at lithospheric plate boundaries.

Therefore all the cross-sections are schematic and conceptual with only general lithology and major stratigraphic units identified. The detailed effects of metamorphism, magmatism, and deformation are not shown. Because the width of the inferred Protoatlantic can not be finally determined, only a probable minimum width is shown.

The remainder of this paper first deals in greater detail with each of these cross-sections in sequence, retracing the sedimentary history of the Appalachian-Caledonian geosyncline in terms of plate tectonics theory. Finally I attempt to point out the wider implications involved if such an approach is to be generally applied in reinterpreting other ancient geosynclinal sedimentary assemblages.

[2] "Actualistic model: a model in which a modern situation is used as a guide to an ancient one" (Garrels and Mackenzie, 1971, p. 321).

LATE PRECAMBRIAN

Tectonics

Figure 3 suggests the the Appalachian-Caledonian geosyncline originated as a series of linear intracontinental rift-block basins produced by the distension and eventual rupture of an older Precambrian supercontinent. The late Precambrian axis of continental rifting becomes the later axis of spreading for a Paleozoic Protoatlantic ocean basin. Both axes cut haphazardly across the trends of older Precambrian orogenic belts which have been discriminated in the shield areas flanking the present Atlantic Ocean (Wynne-Edwards and Hasan, 1970; Semenenko, 1970). If the plate tectonics models described are valid, the bulk of the sediments which constitute the Appalachian and Caledonian orogenic belts accumulated along the margins of and within a lower and middle Paleozoic ocean basin whose axis of spreading did not coincide with that of the present Atlantic Ocean. Therefore the name "Protoatlantic Ocean" used in this paper is misleading.

Sedimentary Facies and Provinces

The late Precambrian stratified assemblages are interpreted as a composite of nonmarine clastic wedges and marine continental terrace and continental rise deposits. The clastic wedges presumably accumulated in downfaulted basins developed during the earlier stages of rifting. They include the coarse clastic alluvial fan, channel, floodplain, deltaic, and coastal plain sediments which now constitute the Torridonian of Scotland, marginal parts of the Welsh Longmyndian succession, most of the Musgravetown, Hodgewater, and Cabot Groups of the Avalon Platform, and parts of the lowermost Gander Lake Group in the Central Mobile Belt of Newfoundland.

Continued rifting would presumably produce an embryonic ocean basin along whose flanks paired Atlantic-type continental margins could develop. The now-metamorphosed shallow marine sandstone, siltstone, and shale successions which together constitute parts of the lowermost Fleur de Lys and Gander Lake Groups of Newfoundland, portions of the lower and middle Dalradian Series of Scotland, and the bulk of the Longmyndian of Wales are shown as continental terrace prisms. Adjacent parts of the lowermost Fleur de Lys, Gander Lake, and lower and middle Dalradian successions, as well as parts of the Moine Series (Scotland) and all of the Monian Series (Wales) are shown as continental rise prisms.

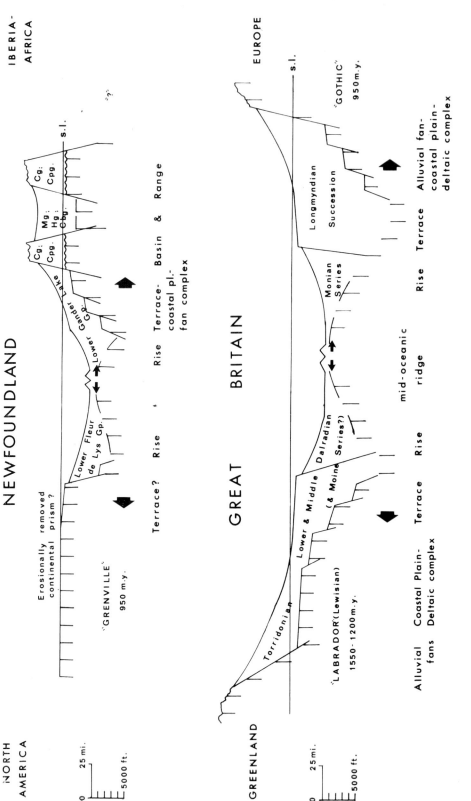

Fig. 3—Late Precambrian deposition in continental rift block basins which widened to produce the Protoatlantic Ocean. Approximate age of Precambrian basement is indicated. Faulting has separated eastern Newfoundland successions into a series of separate blocks and erosion may have removed clastic wedge deposits equivalent to the Torridonian from western Newfoundland. Large arrows show relative movement of continental segments and small arrows locate center of spreading. Vertical ruling (continental crust); Cg (Conception Group) ;Cpg (Connecting Point Group) ; Mg (Musgravetown group) ; Hg (Hodge-water Group) ; Cbg (Cabot Group).

Paleogeography and Provenance

Sedimentary structures indicate principal directions of transport perpendicular to the inferred axis of rifting. Therefore almost all of the late Precambrian material must be derived from source areas located along both margins of the rift zone. Overall dispersal was transverse to the axis of the growing Protoatlantic Ocean. In terms of the proposed model, these "borderland" sources were simply the topographically high, fragmented segments of the original Precambrian supercontinent (North America and Greenland on the northwest; Europe and Iberia-Africa on the southeast).

CAMBRIAN

Tectonics

Figure 4 extends the model proposed above to a logical next stage. The continued growth of new ocean floor must laterally separate the marginal continental blocks and produce progressively larger abyssal plain areas. As long as continental and oceanic crust remain coupled, the continued development of simple paired continental terrace-continental rise prisms along the trailing edges of both continental blocks is promoted. However, because plate construction must be matched globally by plate destruction, it is also necessary to hypothesize the eventual uncoupling of oceanic plates from adjacent continental lithosphere. This must dramatically change the framework of sedimentation by converting Atlantic-type margins into Western Pacific and Andean continental margin types.

The lithology and thickness of Cambrian sediments in Newfoundland and Great Britain suggest that Atlantic-type marginal sedimentation did in fact persist throughout most of Cambrian time. However, evidence of Late Cambrian and Early Ordovician deformation, volcanism, and metamorphism argues persuasively that although the later stage of plate uncoupling and margin-type conversion did occur near the Cambrian-Ordovician boundary, its exact nature and timing varied greatly from place to place.

Sedimentary Facies and Provinces

Figure 4 shows that the Cambrian stratigraphic units can be conveniently related to four Atlantic-type sedimentary provinces: continental terraces, continental rises, continental slopes, and abyssal plains. The earliest deposits of the inferred continental terrace prisms consist of basal transgressive quartzose sandstone and conglomerate (Labrador Group and Random Formation of Newfoundland, Eriboll Quartzite of Scotland, and the Caerfai, Wrekin,

and Malvern Quartzites of Wales). Deposition of these units was preceded by the erosional bevelling of the late Precambrian sedimentary and crystalline basement complex and the local extrusion of plateau basalts. The rest of the Cambrian sections in the western continental terraces are shallow marine carbonate bank deposits (upper part of Labrador and lower part of St. George Group of Newfoundland, the Durness Sequence and parts of the upper Dalradian of Scotland). The rest of the Cambrian sections in the eastern continental terraces are marine (and nonmarine?) fine-grained sandstone, siltstone, and shale (Adeyton and Harcourt Groups in the Avalon Platform, *Lingula* Flags and Menevian Series in the Welsh-Midland Platform).

The eastern edge of the western continental terrace areas is clearly marked by a series of limestone slump breccias (Cow Head Breccia, Newfoundland; portions of the Tayvallich Limestone, Scotland). These bank-edge deposits may delineate more specifically than is possible elsewhere ancient continental slope areas. Their texture suggests topographically abrupt carbonate bank margins similar to those bounding the present Bahama Banks.

The thick sequences of now-metamorphosed graywacke and shale exposed along the margins of the central orogenic belt (lower part of Humber Arm, Fleur de Lys, Mings Bight, and Gander Lake Groups of Newfoundland, the upper Dalradian of Scotland, and the Harlech Beds of Wales) are shown as continental rise prisms which developed adjacent to the continental terrace areas. Thinner, finer-grained marine clastics and submarine lavas of possible Cambrian age in central Newfoundland (lower part of Lushs Bight, Wild Bight, and Tea Arm Groups), in the English Lake District (lowermost part of Skiddaw Slates), and in the Isle of Man (lowermost part of Manx Slates) conceivably represent portions of the original ocean crust and the sequences of abyssal plain muds deposited on it.

Paleogeography and Provenance

Directional structures in most of the Cambrian sediments are oriented perpendicular to the spreading axis of the inferred Protoatlantic. This suggests that most material was derived from marginal source areas, interpreted by this model as being the topographically low segments of the original rifted supercontinent. Some "deeper water" deposits have directional structures which indicate transport parallel with the presumed ocean axis and this is a common feature of modern continental rise and abyssal

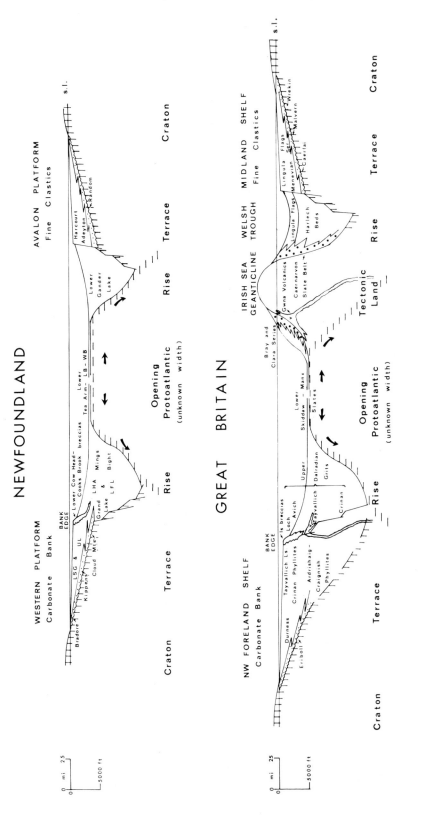

Cambrian

Fig. 4—Cambrian depositional framework: paired Atlantic-type margins in Newfoundland; paired Atlantic-type margins in Britain through the Middle Cambrian with Late Cambrian conversion to paired Western Pacific marginal types. Arrows show relative movement of ocean plates. Vertical ruling (older sediment and underlying continental crust) ; horizontal ruling (oceanic crust) ; fine stippling (basal transgressive quartzose clastic sediments) ; coarse stippling (conglomerate) ; LSG (lower St. George Group) ; UL (upper Laborador Group) ; LHA (lower Humber Arm Group) ; LFL (lower Fleur De Lys Group) ; LB (Lushs Bight Group) ; WB (Wild Bight Group) ; v (volcanic rocks).

plain sediments. The axis of the hypothetical Cambrian Protoatlantic coincides well with the boundary drawn to separate the North American (Pacific) trilobite faunal province from the European (Atlantic) province.

Two features distort the overall similarity between the Cambrian framework of sedimentation in Great Britain and Newfoundland. (1) An additional source area, the Irish Sea Geanticline, located in the area of northern Wales and the present Irish Sea had no counterpart in eastern Newfoundland. Coarse clastic sediments mark its margins and there can be no question of its existence. Yet the genesis of this geanticlinal source by plate tectonics mechanisms seems unlikely, and its rather unusual position at what would normally be a simple continental terrace-continental rise transition is puzzling. (2) Available evidence indicates that episodes of deformation, metamorphism, and volcanism (Gwna lavas of Wales, Tayvallich lavas of Scotland) which began in Late Cambrian time in Great Britain did not commence until Early Ordovician in Newfoundland. If such episodes are to be attributed to plate tectonics mechanisms, it is necessary to postulate the persistence of paired Atlantic-type margins on both sides of the "Newfoundland Protoatlantic" throughout Cambrian time, while Late Cambrian separation and underthrusting of ocean plates was converting both margins of the "British Protoatlantic" into Andean and/or Western Pacific marginal types.

ORDOVICIAN

Tectonics

Figure 5 relates changes in the lithology and thickness of Ordovician rocks across Great Britain and Newfoundland to features which plate tectonics associates with the underthrusting of ocean plates beneath continental crust: new sedimentary source areas (tectonic lands, volcanic island arcs), new sedimentary basins (ocean trenches, inland seas), and zones of volcanism, metamorphism, and orogeny.

The western margin of the Ordovician Protoatlantic in both Britain and Newfoundland is shown essentially as a Western Pacific continental margin. As previously discussed, actual conversion from Atlantic to Western Pacific margin type must have occurred earlier in Scotland (Late Cambrian) than in Newfoundland (Early Ordovician). The episodes of volcanism (Cape St. John and Rambler volcanics of Newfoundland; Ballantrae volcanics of Scotland), plutonism (Burlington Granodiorite of Newfoundland; "Older Granites" of Scotland),

metamorphism, and orogeny which consolidated the Orthotectonic Belts (Fleur de Lys-Dalradian terranes) can be attributed to subduction (consumption) of the descending oceanic plates.

The eastern (Welsh) margin of the Caledonian geosyncline can also be interpreted as a Western Pacific margin type. Substantial variations in sediment thickness and lithology, together with the existence of at least three volcanic belts (Borrowdale, Snowdon, and Cader Idris volcanics) suggest that any proposed trench, island arc, inland sea system must be complex. Dewey (1969) related the comparatively mild deformation, plutonism, and metamorphism there to several ancient zones of subduction. The eastern margin of the "Newfoundland Protoatlantic" is comparatively simple. It is shown as an Atlantic-type margin because Ordovician sediments are lithologically similar to the underlying Cambrian units and there is no evidence of Ordovician metamorphism, plutonism, or orogeny.

Sedimentary Facies and Provinces

Western Margins.—The Lower Ordovician rocks of western Newfoundland include carbonate bank (continental terrace?) deposits (upper part of St. George Group, Chimney Arm, Doucers, and Table Head Formations), bank-edge (continental slope?) breccias, and rhythmically alternating sequences of graywacke and shale (continental rise and/or inland sea deposits?) interfingered with thick volcanic rocks (an ancient volcanic island arc?). The Middle and Upper Ordovician flysch sequences of central Newfoundland (Badger Bay Series, Exploits Group, New World Island sequences) fill an ocean trench system developed above an ancient Benioff Zone. Underthrusting along this zone would account for the "Taconic" metamorphism, deformation, and uplift of the Fleur de Lys complex, terminate carbonate deposition and initiate erosion in the Western Platform, and eventually lead to the large-scale lateral displacement of terrigenous continental rise, inland sea sediments onto Lower Ordovician carbonates (Humber Arm and Hare Bay allochthons).

A similar tectonic framework is shown for Scotland. The upper Durness carbonates are interpreted as uplifted inland sea (or possibly continental terrace) deposits. The thick sequences of the "Moffat Geosyncline" fill a linear trench system developed above an ancient Benioff Zone. The postulated tectonic land-island arc complex of Cockburnland has an origin and position analogous to that inferred for the Fleur de Lys-Burlington Peninsula belt.

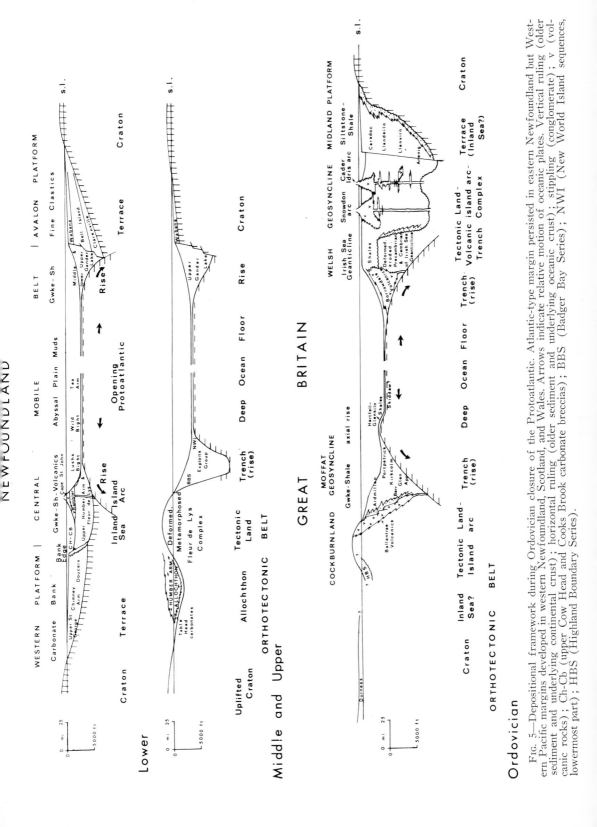

FIG. 5.—Depositional framework during Ordovician closure of the Protoatlantic. Atlantic-type margin persisted in eastern Newfoundland but Western Pacific margins developed in western Newfoundland, Scotland, and Wales. Arrows indicate relative motion of oceanic plates. Vertical ruling (older sediment and underlying continental crust); horizontal ruling (older sediment and underlying oceanic crust); stippling (conglomerate); v (volcanic rocks); Ch–Cb (upper Cow Head and Cooks Brook carbonate breccias); BBS (Badger Bay Series); NWI (New World Island sequences, lowermost part); HBS (Highland Boundary Series).

Eastern Margins.—The Ordovician sediments within the eastern part of the Central Mobile Belt of Newfoundland and in the Avalon Platform consist only of the thick graywacke-shale sequences of the upper Gander Lake Group (continental rise prism?) and the thinner subjacent sandstone, siltstone, and shale of the Clarenville, Bell Island, and Wabana Groups (continental terrace prism?)—a simple Atlantic-type marginal assemblage. However, Figure 5 infers a dramatically different and more complex tectonic framework for Wales where dominantly fine-grained clastic sediments of the Welsh-Midland Platform (continental terrace and/or inland sea deposits?) interfinger in Northern Wales and Angelsey with thicker graywacke-shale sequences of the "Welch Geosyncline" (a composite of ocean trenches and island arc)—a complex Western Pacific marginal assemblage.

Central Protoatlantic.—The thin, dominantly fine-grained Ordovician sediments of central England and central Newfoundland are interpreted as abyssal plain muds. Lithology and thickness vary locally, a feature common in deeper water marine deposits and attributed to variations in submarine topography (axial rises and troughs). The boundary drawn to separate American-Pacific from European-Atlantic faunal provinces roughly coincides with the center of the inferred Protoatlantic ocean basin.

Paleogeography and Provenance

Directional structures in many of the Ordovician sediments are perpendicular to the spreading axis of the inferred Protoatlantic. Regional variations in thickness and lithology suggest that material was derived from topographically high external source areas (the marginal continental segments) as well as tectonically active internal sources (orogenic belts of the "Cordilleran-type"). Additional directional structures imply the existence of a secondary dispersal system with transport parallel with the various trench and inland sea axes. Such dispersal is commonly observed in modern ocean trenches and inland sea areas.

SILURIAN

Tectonics

Regional variations in sediment thickness and lithology favor a Silurian Protoatlantic model in which both margins are Andean (i.e., simple ocean trench continent transitions). Zones of subduction along both sides of an ocean basin result in the gradual closure of the ocean and must eventually lead to the convergence (colli-

sion) of marginal continental blocks. Figure 6 schematically relates the eventual deformation of the Paratectonic Belts in the British Caledonides (Late Silurian-Early Devonian) and Newfoundland Appalachians (Middle and Late Devonian) to the progressive Silurian convergence of marginal continents. The "northern" continent consisted of the little deformed northwestern foreland and adjacent Orthotectonic Belts. The "southern" continent included the metastable southwestern foreland areas (Welsh-Midland and Avalon Platforms) as well as the deformed Cambrian-Ordovician trench, island arc, and inland sea complexes. Convergence of these marginal blocks might readily be expected also to produce the numerous Silurian "intra-geosynclinal" source areas documented across Newfoundland and Great Britain. The fact that different timing is assigned to the uplift of these source areas, to the structures in the Paratectonic Belts, and to the final episode of continental collision in the Newfoundland Appalachians and British Caledonides may mean that ocean "closings," like ocean "openings" are complex processes. Both may be more analogous to "zipping" and "unzipping" rather than being instantaneous episodes in which the timing of plate separation and/or plate collision does not vary along the entire length of a single plate boundary. In light of this possibility it is surprising that the axis of the inferred Silurian Protoatlantic coincides closely to the postulated boundary separating distinct faunal provinces.

Sedimentary Facies, Provinces, Paleogeography, and Provenance

The Silurian rocks of Britain and Newfoundland are now exposed in a series of widely separated fault basins located mainly within the Paratectonic Belts. However, Silurian rocks also occur in the Midland Valley of Scotland and in the Western Platform of Newfoundland (the White Bay area), regions which in Silurian time are inferred to have been within the "northern" continental landmass blocks. All these basins may have originally been contiguous, but their present separation and lithological heterogeneity make direct comparisons between Britain and Newfoundland meaningless. Consequently the Silurian sedimentary framework of the British Caledonides and Newfoundland Appalachians are discussed individually.

Newfoundland.—With the exception of the thin, fluvial-deltaic Clam Bank Formation exposed along the western coast, the contemporaneous but geographically isolated Silurian successions are lithologically almost identical. Each se-

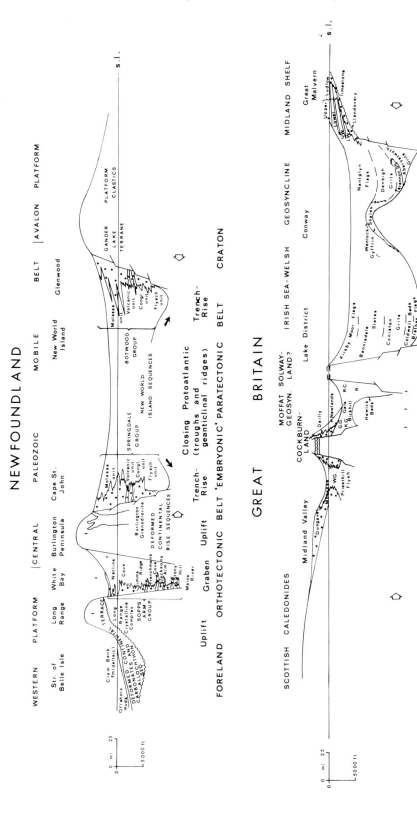

Fig. 6—Depositional framework during the continuing Silurian closure of the Protoatlantic. Convergence produces numerous "intrageosynclinal" source areas which separate a variety of intermontane basins and ocean trenches. Open arrows show relative motion of marginal continental blocks; small arrows show relative motion of oceanic plates. Stippling (conglomerate); GG (Garheugh Group); KG (Kilfallen Group); RC (Rasperry Castle Group); R (Ricarton Group); UW (upper Wenlock); LW (lower Wenlock).

Silurian

quence (Sopps Arm Group of the White Bay area, Springdale Group of the Cape St. John area, the Toogood, Cobbs Arm, and Dildo sequences of the New World Island area, and the Botwood sequence adjacent to the Avalon Platform) can be vertically subdivided into four units: (a) a basal sequence of graywacke, shale, and submarine volcanics (generally conformably deposited on Ordovician graywacke and shale); (b) an overlying unit of conglomerate interbedded with subordinate subgraywacke sandstone and shale; (c) a dominantly pyroclastic volcanic unit; and (d) an uppermost unit of (commonly red) molasse sandstone.

All these sequences, with the possible exception of the Sopps Arm Group, can be interpreted as having filled either paired trench areas which flanked the closing ocean basin or marginal basin areas developed locally along the flanks of uplifted source areas. Horne and Helwig (1969) have documented evidence for several varieties of Silurian source areas, many of which could have originated by the convergence of marginal continental blocks. Each sedimentary sequence shows the same gradual transition from deeper water flysch to continental molasse which progressive oceanic contraction might produce. The Sopps Arm Group may be a more local rift-block basin deposit produced as a result of tensional faulting within the "northern" continental block.

Great Britain.—The Silurian sequences of Britain include a variety of deposits which are remarkably similar to the Silurian sediments of Newfoundland. (1) Coarse terrigenous alluvial fan-floodplain-deltaic complexes (Dailly, Newlands, Garheugh, Kilfallen, Rasperry Castle, and Ricarton Groups) flank a number of postulated source areas (Cockburnland, Solwayland) whose growth could presumably be due to the closure of an ocean basin. (2) Thicker, generally finer-grained sandstone and shale sequences like the Kirkby Moor Flags and Stockdale Shale of the Lake District and the Aberystwyth and Denibigh Grits of northern Wales are presumably either continental rise and/or ocean trench deposits. (3) Thin pelitic sequences like the Wenlock and Gyffrin Shales ("Irish Sea Geosyncline") and the Gala-Birkhill Shales ("Moffat Geosyncline") conceivably represent abyssal plain muds deposited on fragmented remnants of the closing Protoatlantic ocean floor. (4) The deposits of the Welsh-Midland Platform are shown as a simple continental terrace prism. (5) The sedimentary sequences exposed as inliers within the Midland Valley of Scotland resemble the White Bay

deposits of Western Newfoundland (Sopps Arm Group) in lithology and overall tectonic setting (an intracontinental fault-block basin?) and exhibit a simple upward transition from deeper water flysch (Priesthill Flysch) to marginal, conglomeratic molasse (Dungavel and Waterhead Groups).

DEVONIAN

Tectonics

The final closure of an ocean basin necessarily culminates in the collision of the original laterally-rifted continental segments. Figure 7 infers that exactly such a collision in the British Caledonides and Newfoundland Appalachians generated the structures of the Paratectonic Belts in both regions and created a Devonian supercontinental landmass. As mentioned earlier variations in the timing and nature of these culminating events must imply complicated procedures by which lithospheric plates are separated and combined. In Great Britain, the final episodes of "Caledonian" folding, faulting, and intrusion ("Newer Granites") are confined to the central orogenic belt (mainly the Paratectonic Belt). These episodes postdate the deposition of the latest Silurian rocks and predate the Lower Old Red Sandstone (Lower Devonian). Conversely, the climactic "Acadian Orogeny" of Newfoundland includes episodes of folding, faulting, regional metamorphism, and granitic intrusion which affected the entire island, although effects outside the Paratectonic Belt were minimal. Acadian movements began in Early Devonian time, peaked in the Middle Devonian, and extended almost to the Mississippian Period.

A reunited supercontinental landmass might logically evolve further in any number of ways. In the British Caledonides and Newfoundland Appalachians only two processes, similarly timed and of identical origin, effectively determined the final framework of sedimentation. (1) Tensional rifting of the supercontinental landmass generated a series of linear intracontinental grabens which were rapidly filled with molasse-type clastic sediments (the Devonian Midland Valley and Orcadian Cuvettes of Scotland; the Carboniferous basins of western Newfoundland). (2) Normal isostatic subsidence of the southern (eastern) edge of the supercontinent initiated the filling along one margin of a new Hercynian ocean basin.

Sedimentary Facies and Provinces

The continental molasse deposits which constitute the Devonian Old Red Sandstone of Scotland consist of a series of alluvial fan,

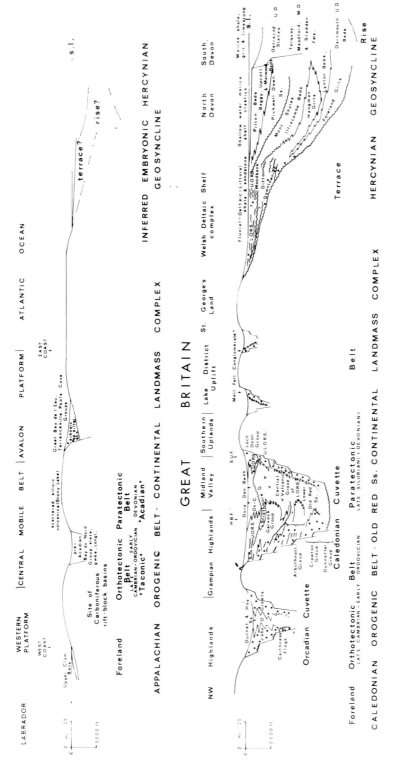

Fig. 7—Post-collision Devonian depositional framework showing interior molasse basins and the early Atlantic-type marginal deposits of the Hercynian system.

TABLE 1.—PLATE TECTONICS BASIN MODELS FOR THE NEWFOUNDLAND
APPALACHIANS AND BRITISH CALEDONIES

| Period | Continental margin type | | | |
| | Newfoundland | | Great Britain | |
	Western margin	Eastern margin	Northwestern margin	Southeastern margin
Late Precambrian	Distinctive continental margin types not clearly developed; new ocean basin evolves from a series of Red Sea-type grabens		Distinctive continental margin types not clearly developed; new ocean basin evolves from a series of Red Sea-type grabens	
Cambrian	Atlantic-type	Atlantic-type	Lower and Middle Cambrian: Atlantic-type; Upper Cambrian: Western Pacific-type	Lower and Middle Cambrian: Atlantic-type; Upper Cambrian: Western Pacific-type
Ordovician	Western Pacific-type	Atlantic-type	Western Pacific-type	Multiple Western Pacific-type
Silurian	Andean? (wider Protoatlantic)	Andean?	Andean? (narrower Protoatlantic)	Andean?
Devonian	Himalayan-Mediterranean-type collision		Himalayan-Mediterranean-type collision	
Postcollision	Development of interior rift-block basins and the initial Atlantic-type northwestern margin of the Hercynian Atlantic		Development of interior rift-block basins and the initial Atlantic-type northwestern margin of the Hercynian Atlantic	

channel, floodplain, delta, and nearshore marine clastic sediments. They are identical in lithology and overall setting to Carboniferous sequences exposed along a narrow belt of western Newfoundland which extends from Cape Anguille to White Bay (Anguille, Codroy, Barachois, and Deer Lake Groups). All these units typically coarsen and thicken towards bounding basin normal faults and their original extent may have originally been much greater. In Figure 7 they are all shown as classical post-orogenic "Newark-type" assemblages.

The early deposits of the inferred British Hercynian Geosyncline are shown as a composite of continental terrace and continental rise prisms developed along a Devonian analogue of the present Atlantic-type continental margin. Continental and nearshore shallow marine sandstone, shale, and carbonate interfinger with offshore deeper water grits and shales. A similar depositional framework shown extending along the southeastern coast of Newfoundland only generally can be inferred from the characteristics of the Devonian and Carboniferous rocks of Nova Scotia and New England.

Paleogeography and Provenance

Directional structures and lithology indicate that the fault-block basin deposits were derived from topographically high source areas which immediately bounded the depositional basins. However, the initial deposits of the inferred Hercynian Atlantic-type margin were apparently eroded from areas within the stable supercontinent and transported laterally across the continental terrace to the continental rise areas.

GEOSYNCLINAL THEORY: SOME PLATE
TECTONICS PERSPECTIVES

Table 1 summarizes the plate tectonics basin models which might explain the distribution and characteristics of late Precambrian to Carboniferous sedimentary rocks in the Newfoundland Appalachians and British Caledonides. How appropriate are these models? Does a clearer picture of how geosynclinal basins originate and evolve emerge by invoking the mechanisms of continental drift, sea-floor spreading, and plate tectonics in place of classical geosynclinal theory? What specific characteristics does such an approach imply generally for geosynclinal sedimentary provinces, paleogeography, and provenance? What apparent weaknesses, if any, are involved in applying plate tectonics to ancient orogenic belts? This final discussion attempts to answer these questions by outlining and evaluating the pertinent conclusions suggested by the preceding parts of this paper.

1. Geosynclinal sedimentary assemblages *are* actualistic, that is they *can be,* but not neces-

sarily *must be* interpreted as composites of discrete, but interrelated continental margin and ocean basin deposits. These deposits are superimposed upon one another laterally and vertically by the divergence and convergence of lithospheric plates.

2. Plate tectonics basin model reconstructions suggest that the sedimentary history of the Newfoundland Appalachians and British Caledonides is remarkably similar. Such similarity should not be surprising if in fact both regions are simply component parts of a single contiguous mobile belt which has been broken up by the post-Triassic growth of the present Atlantic Ocean.

3. Plate tectonics equates geosynclinal basins with several modern areas of regional subsidence: continental terrace and continental rise zones, inland sea areas, ocean trench systems, and ocean basins proper. Crustal subsidence is initially generated by simple isostatic downwarping of continental margins and later maintained by the underthrusting of ocean plates beneath adjacent continental blocks. Conventional geosynclinal theory instead subdivides geosynclinal troughs only into paired eugeosynclinal and miogeosynclinal basins and attributes regional subsidence to a number of unsatisfactory conceptual devices (i.e., the tectogene).

4. Sedimentologists generally agree that the composition and thickness of geosynclinal sediments require the almost continual erosion of large proximal masses of sial within the geosynclinal trough and along both its margins (a continental craton along one flank, a "borderland" block along the other). However conventional geosynclinal theory has not provided reasonable mechanisms to explain the origin of "intrageosynclinal" sialic sources. Furthermore there is little evidence that large borderlands lie submerged off the continental shelf areas of the present ocean basins. Plate tectonics theory readily generates new "intrabasinal" sialic source areas by subduction. "Borderlands" are simply equated with existing continental blocks which growing sea floor has laterally moved from earlier positions.

5. The overall framework of sedimentation across geosynclinal belts is more complicated when actualistic models are employed. The characteristics and arrangement of sedimentary provinces and paleogeography may be confusing and oversimplified. For example there is good evidence that some of the units designated in the basin models as abyssal plain sequences are in fact nearshore shallow marine sediments.

Similarly some of the composite sections collectively labelled as continental rise assemblages include a wide variety of probable depositional environments. Obviously until the characteristics which distinguish modern continental terrace, continental rise, inland sea, trench, and abyssal plain sediments are clarified, it will be impossible to accurately recognize ancient analogues of the three continental margin types or specifically locate remnant zones of plate generation, divergence, underthrusting, or convergence. Until a clearer picture of these modern features emerges, applying plate tectonics theory to ancient orogenic belts will often necessitate that sound geological data be obscured, manipulated, or even ignored.

6. If the plate tectonics models proposed for the Appalachian-Caledonian region apply generally, orogenic belts (and by implication, continental blocks) evolve through a systematic series of stages quite distinct from those expressed in the concept of "the geosynclinal cycle."

   a. Geosynclinal basins originate as linear rift-block grabens, for example, all geosynclinal basins are initially *intracontinental*.

   b. The spreading axis for any specific orogenic belt can be totally unrelated to either older or younger spreading axes. For example, the spreading axis of the Paleozoic Protoatlantic Ocean cuts directly across Precambrian orogenic trends, and the spreading axis of the present Atlantic Ocean is in turn discordant with Caledonian (and Hercynian) trends. This independent relationship between the location of plate boundaries of different ages reinforces earlier arguments against simple lateral continental accretion. The discordance between Precambrian orogenic belts visible in most shield areas becomes more understandable.

   c. Lateral accretion of new ocean floor soon separates segments of original supercontinents. Therefore, geosynclinal basins are essentially *intercontinental* (i.e., continental margin) features during most of their later development, despite their initial beginning as intracontinental basins.

   d. In the earliest stage of development as an intercontinental feature, the geosyncline consists mainly of coupled continental terrace-continental rise prisms (*Atlantic-type margin stage*). These prisms accumulate symmetrically at the aseismic continental-oceanic crustal boundary on both sides of the growing ocean basin. Little sediment accumulates on the abyssal plain areas whose growing breadth and depth may create a faunal province barrier.

e. To preserve a global balance between plate generation and destruction, ocean plates become detached from adjacent continental blocks. Newly generated ocean basins begin to close as ocean lithosphere underthrusts continental crust. These subsequent stages of geosynclinal basin evolution (*Andean and Western Pacific margin stages*) are marked by the development of new sedimentary basin components (inland seas, trenches, laterally accreted abyssal plains). Geosynclinal basins might be expected to lose their original symmetry and faunal province boundaries may be obscured.

f. The underthrusting of ocean plates produces new "intrageosynclinal" source areas and generates episodes of volcanism, plutonism, metamorphism, and orogeny. The rate of underthrusting can vary not only in time, but from place to place along a specific plate boundary.

g. Continued convergence of lithospheric plates *may* eventually result in the collision of island arcs and tectonic lands with marginal continental segments (generating new basins and further orogeny) and *must* ultimately lead to collisions between the rifted segments of the original continent. Such collisions finally consolidate geosynclinal basins into orogenic belts. Plate convergence might also juxtapose sedimentary sequences, source areas, and faunal provinces which originally developed in widely separated areas. Consequently orogenic belts ought to exhibit great variations in symmetry depending on their particular evolutionary history.

h. The final consolidation of geosynclinal basins into orogenic belts might be followed by short episodes of post-collision tension. Eventually new axes of rifting and spreading presumably might initiate new embryonic geosynclinal basins either within or along the margins of the consolidated supercontinental block.

7. The general evolutionary scheme proposed above yields logical explanations for many of the structural and lithological differences which exist along and across individual geosynclinal belts and between different segments of supposedly once-contiguous belts. Appreciable contrasts should be expected simply because the exact nature, location, and timing of initial rifting, subsequent spreading, conversion from one continental margin type to another, and final continental collision can all vary along single plate margins and between adjacent margins of expanding and contracting ocean basins. These variations should produce significant changes in the lithology and thickness of the sedimentary fill and strong local contrasts in structural symmetry. The orogenic history of individual belts might readily appear to be almost continuous regionally, despite being locally episodic.

8. If plate tectonics geosynclinal basin models are reasonable approximations of reality, the nature and extent to which continental accretion has occurred most be reassessed. According to these models, large areas of new ocean floor covered with sediment must eventually be incorporated into enlarged continental masses. In this sense plate tectonics supports the concept of continental accretion. However, most of the sediments that fill expanding and contracting ocean basins are eroded from pre-existing continents and are simply recycled, metamorphosed, and magmatized. Exactly how much of the material incorporated into reconsolidated supercontinental blocks represents newly generated sialic crust, rather than such laterally or vertically "re-accreted" pre-existing sial, remains a matter for considerable speculation.

Applying the mechanisms of continental drift, sea-floor spreading, and plate tectonics to explain ancient orogenic belts underlines the need for reassessing earlier notions about the nature and origin of geosynclinal basins and geosynclinal sedimentary provinces in terms of actualism. The classical concept of "the geosynclinal cycle" must also be revised. Palinospastic reconstructions of geosynclinal paleogeography must become the rule rather than the exception. The repeated recourse to geographically fixed and periodically active sites of sediment deposition and source uplift must be abandoned in favor of new basin models whose position in space and time is fundamentally controlled by the movement of rigid lithospheric plates.

ACKNOWLEDGMENTS

Preliminary research for this paper was done utilizing the library facilities generously provided by Harvard University. The study was completed while I held a National Science Foundation Science Faculty Fellowship at the University of Edinburgh, Scotland. I am grateful to the staff there at the Grant Institute of Geology for numerous helpful suggestions. I alone of course bear responsibility for the ideas expressed in this paper.

REFERENCES CITED: GENERAL

BIRD, J. M., AND J. F. DEWEY, 1970. Lithosphere plate-continental margin tectonics and the evolution of the Appalachian orogen. Bull. geol. Soc. Am. 81:1031–1060.

BOTT, M. H. P. 1971. The interior of the Earth. Edward Arnold, London. 316 p.

DALZIEL, I. W. D. 1969. Pre-Permian history of the British Isles, In KAY, G. M., North Atlantic-geology and continental drift. Mem. Am. Ass. Petrol. Geol. 12:5–31.

DEWEY, J. F. 1969. Evolution of the Appalachian/Caledonian Orogen. Nature. 222:124–129.

———, AND J. M. BIRD. 1970. Mountain belts and the new global tectonics. J. Geophys. Res. 75:2625–2647.

———, AND BRENDA HORSFIELD. 1970. Plate tectonics, orogeny, and continental growth. Nature. 225:521–525.

DIETZ, R. S. 1963. Collapsing continental rises: an actualistic concept of geosynclines and mountain building. J. Geol. 71:314–333.

———, AND J. C. HOLDEN. 1966. Miogeosynclines in space and time. Ibid. 74:566–583.

DRAKE, C. L., MAURICE EWING AND G. H. SUTTON. 1959. Continental margins and geosynclines: the east coast of North America north of Cape Hatteras, In Physics and chemistry of the Earth. Pergamon, London. 3:110–198.

ERNST, W. G. 1970. Tectonic contact between the Franciscan melange and the Great Valley sequence-crustal expression of a late Mesozoic Benioff Zone: J. Geophys. Res. 75:886–901.

GARRELS, R. M., AND F. T. MACKENZIE. 1971. Evolution of sedimentary rocks. W. W. Norton, New York. 397 p.

GILLULY, JAMES. 1971. Plate tectonics and magmatic evolution. Bull. geol. Soc. Am. 82:2383–2396.

———, J. C. REED, JR., AND W. M. CADY. 1970. Sedimentary volumes and their significance. Ibid. 81:353–376.

HAMILTON, W. R. 1969. Mesozoic California and the underflow of Pacific mantle. Ibid. 80:2409–2430.

HSU, K. J. 1971. Franciscan melanges as a model for eugeosynclinal sedimentation and underthrusting tectonics. J. geophys. Res. 76:1162–1170.

ISACKS, B. I., J. OLIVER, AND L. R. SYKES. 1968. Seismology and the new global tectonics. Ibid. 73:5855–5899.

LE PICHON, X. 1968. Sea-floor spreading and coninental drift. Ibid. 73:3661–3697.

MENARD, H. W. 1971. The Late Cenozoic history of the Pacific and Indian Ocean Basins, In TUREKIAN, K. K., Ed. Late Cenozoic glacial ages. Yale Univ. Press, New Haven, p. 1–14.

MITCHELL, A. H., AND H. G. READING. 1969. Continental margins and ocean floor spreading. J. Geol. 77:629–646.

———, AND ———. 1971. Evolution of island arcs. Ibid. 79:253–284.

RODGERS, JOHN. 1970. The Tectonics of the Appalachians. Wiley Interscience, New York. 271 p.

SEMENENKO, N. P. 1970. Geochronological aspects of stabilization of continental Precambrian platforms. Eclog. geol. Helv. 63:301–310.

VINE, F. J., AND P. M. MATTHEWS. 1963. Magnetic anomalies over ocean ridges. Nature. 199:947–949.

WILLIAMS, HAROLD. 1969. Pre-Carboniferous development of Newfoundland Appalachians. In, KAY, G. M., Ed. North Atlantic-geology and continental drift. Mem. Am. Ass. Petrol. Geol. 12:32–58.

WILSON, J. T. 1966. Did the Atlantic close and then reopen? Nature. 211:676–681.

WYLLIE, P. J. 1971. The dynamic Earth: textbook in Geosciences. John Wiley, New York. 416 p.

WYNNE-EDWARDS, H. R., AND Z. HASAN. 1970. Intersecting orogenic belts across the North Atlantic. Am. J. Sci. 268:289–308.

REFERENCES: SPECIFIC CROSS SECTIONS
Precambrian

CHURCH, W. R. 1969. Metamorphic rocks of Burlington Peninsula and adjoining areas of Newfoundland and their bearing on continental drift in North Atlantic. In, KAY, G. M., Ed. North Atlantic-geology and continental drift. Mem. Am. Ass. Petrol. Geol. 12:212–233.

JOHNSON, M. R. W. 1965. Dalradian. In, CRAIG, G. Y., Ed. Geology of Scotland. Archon, Hampden, Conn. p. 115–160.

———. 1965. Torridonian and Moinian. In, CRAIG, G. Y., Ed. Geology of Scotland. Archon, Hampden, Conn. p. 79–113.

———. 1969. Dalradian of Scotland. In, KAY, G. M., Ed. North Atlantic-Geology and continental drift. Mem. Am. Ass. Petrol. Geol. 12:151–158.

KENNEDY, M. J. 1971. Structure and stratigraphy of the Fleur de Lys Supergroup in the Fleur de Lys area, Burlington Peninsula, Newfoundland. Proc. Geol. Ass. Can. 24:59–71.

McCARTNEY, W. D. 1969. Geology of Avalon Peninsula, southeast Newfoundland. In, KAY, G. M., Ed. North Atlantic-geology and continental drift. Mem. Am. Ass. Petrol. Geol. 12:115–129.

POOLE, W. H. 1967. Tectonic evolution of Appalachian region of Canada. In, Spec. Pap. Geol. Ass. Can. 4:9–51.

SHACKLETON, R. M. 1969. Precambrian of North Wales. In, WOOD, A., Ed. The Precambrian and Lower Paleozoic rocks of Wales. Univ. Wales Press, Cardiff. p. 1–23.

STEWART, A. D. 1969. Torridonian rocks of Scotland revisited. In, KAY, G. M., Ed. North Atlantic-geology and continental drift. Mem. Am. Ass. Petrol. Geol 12:595–608.

WILLIAMS, G. E. 1969. Petrography and origin of pebbles from Torridonian strata (Late Precambrian), northwest Scotland. In, KAY, G. M., Ed. North Atlantic-geology and continental drift. Mem. Am. Ass. Petrol. Geol. 12:609–629.

WILLIAMS, HAROLD. 1964. The Appalachians in northeastern Newfoundland—a two-sided symmetrical system. Am. J. Sci. 262:1137–1158.

WRIGHT, A. E. 1969. Precambrian rocks of England, Wales, and southeast Ireland. In KAY, G. M., Ed. North Atlantic-geology and continental drifts. Mem. Am. Ass. Petrol. Geol. 12:93–109.

Cambrian

Allen, J. R. L. 1968. The Cambrian and Ordovician Systems. *In,* Sylvester-Bradley, P. C., and T. D. Ford, Eds. The Geology of the East Midlands. Leicester Univ. Press, Leicester. 400 p.

Bassett, D. A. 1963. The Welsh Paleozoic Geosyncline: a review of recent work on stratigraphy and sedimentation. *In,* Johnson, M. R. W., and Stewart, F. H., Eds. The British Caledonides. Oliver and Boyd, Edinburgh and London. p. 35–69.

Bennison, G. M., and A. E. Wright. 1969. The geological history of the British Isles. St. Martins Press, New York. 406 p.

Betz, Frederick, Jr. 1939. Geology and mineral deposits of the Canada Bay area, northern Newfoundland. Bull. Newfoundld. geol. Surv. 16:1–53.

——. 1948. Geology and mineral deposits of southern White Bay, Newfoundland. Bull. Newfoundld. geol. Surv. 24:1–23.

Bruckner, W. D. 1969. Geology of eastern part of Avalon Peninsula, Newfoundland. *In,* Kay, G. M., Ed. North Atlantic–geology and continental drift. Mem. Am. Ass. Petrol. Geol. 12:130–138.

Charlesworth, J. K. 1963. Historical geology of Ireland: Oliver and Boyd, Edinburgh and London. 565 p.

Church, W. R. 1969. *op. cit.* (Precambrian).

Crimes, T. P. 1970. A facies analysis of the Cambrian of Wales. Paleogeogr. Paleoclim., Paleoecol. 7:113–170.

Dewey, J. F., and J. M. Bird. 1970. *op. cit.* (General).

George, T. N., 1960. The stratigraphical evolution of the Midland Valley. Trans. geol. Soc. Glasg. 24:32–107.

——. 1963. Paleozoic growth of the British Caledonides. *In,* Johnson, M. R. W., and Stewart, F. H., Eds. The British Caledonides. Oliver and Boyd, Edinburgh and London. 280 p.

Harland, W. B. 1969. Fleur de Lys "Tilloid." *In,* Kay, G. M., Ed. North Atlantic–Geology and continental drift. Mem. Am. Ass. Petrol. Geol 12:234–235

Hutchinson, R. D. 1962. Cambrian stratigraphy and trilobite faunas of southeastern Newfoundland. Bull. geol. Surv. Can. 88:1–156.

Jenness, S. E. 1958. Geology of the Lower Gander River ultrabasic belt, Newfoundland: Rep. Newfoundld. geol. Surv. 14:1–58.

——. 1963. Terra Nova and Bonavista map areas, Newfoundland. Mem. Can. geol. Surv. 327:1–184.

Johnson, M. R. W. 1969. *op. cit.* (Precambrian).

Johnstone, G. S. 1966. British Regional Geology: The Grampian Highlands. Her Majesty's Stationary Office, Edinburgh. 103 p.

Kay, G. M. 1967. Stratigraphy and structure of northeastern Newfoundland and its bearing on drift in the North Atlantic: Bull. Am. Ass. Petrol. Geol. 51:579–600.

Kennedy, M. J. 1971. *op. cit.* (Precambrian).

Kennedy, W. Q. 1958. The tectonic evolution of the Midland Valley of Scotland. Trans. geol. Soc. Glasg. 23:106–133.

Knill, J. L. 1960. Paleocurrents and sedimentary facies of the Dalradian metasediments of the Craignish-Kimelfort district. Proc. Geol. Ass. Lond. 70:273–284.

——. 1963. A sedimentary history of the Dalradian Series. *In,* Johnson, M. R. W., and Stewart, F. H., Eds. The British Caledonides. Oliver and Boyd, Edinburgh and London. p. 99–121.

Lilly, H. D. 1967. Some notes on stratigraphy and structural style in central west Newfoundland. Spec. Pap. Geol. Ass. Can. 4:201–212.

McCartney, W. D. 1969. *op. cit.* (Precambrian).

North, F. K. 1971. The Cambrian of Canada and Alaska. *In,* Holland, C. H., Ed. Cambrian of the New World. Wiley Interscience, New York. p. 219–324.

Palmer, A. R. 1969. Cambrian trilobite distributions in North America and their bearing on Cambrian paleogeography of Newfoundland. *In,* Kay, G. M., Ed. North Atlantic–geology and continental drift. Mem. Am. Ass. Petrol. Geol. 12:194–211.

Phemister, J. 1960. British regional geology: Scotland: The Northern Highlands. His Majesty's Stationary Office, Edinburgh. 104 p.

Phillips, W. E. A., M. J. Kennedy, and G. M. Dunlop. 1969. Geologic comparison of western Ireland and northeastern Newfoundland. *In,* Kay, G. M., Ed. North Atlantic-geology and continental drift. Mem. Am. Ass. Petrol. Geol. 12:194–211.

Powell, D. W. 1956. Gravity and magnetic anomalies in North Wales; with an appendix on the magnetic anomalies of the Lleyn Peninsula by D. H. Griffiths and R. H. King. Q. Jl. geol. Soc. Lond. 111:375–393.

Pringle, J., and T. N. George. 1948. British Regional Geology: South Wales. Her Majesty's Stationary Office, London. 100 p.

Rast, N. 1963. Structure and metamorphism of the Dalradian rocks of Scotland. *In* Johnson, M. R. W., and Stewart, F. H., Eds. The British Caledonides. Oliver and Boyd, Edinburgh and London. p. 123–142.

Raynor, D. H. 1967. The stratigraphy of the British Isles. University Press, Cambridge. 453 p.

Rodgers, John. 1968. The eastern edge of the North American continent during the Cambrian and Early Ordovician. *In,* Zen, E., W. S. White, J. B. Hadley, and J. B. Thompson, Jr., Eds. Studies of Appalachian Geology: Northern and Maritime. Wiley Interscience, New York. p. 141–149.

——, and E. R. W. Neale. 1963. Possible "Taconic" klippen in western Newfoundland. Am. J. Sci. 261: 713–730.

Rose, E. R. 1948. Geology of the area between Bonavista, Trinity, and Placentia Bays, eastern Newfoundland, part 2. Bull. Newfoundld. geol. Surv. 32:39–49.

Smith, Bernard, and T. N. George. 1961. British regional geology: North Wales. Her Majesty's Stationary Office, London. 98 p.

Swett, Keene. 1969. Interpretation of depositional and diagenetic history of Cambrian-Ordovician succession of northwest Scotland. *In,* Kay, G. M., Ed. North Atlantic–geology and continental drift. Mem. Am. Ass. Petrol. Geol. 12:630–646.

WALTHIER, T. N. 1949. Geology and mineral deposits of the area between Corner Brook and Stephenville, western Newfoundland. Bull. Newfoundld geol. Surv. 35:1–62.

WILLIAMS, HAROLD. 1964. *op. cit.* (Precambrian).

WOOD, D. S. 1969. The base and correlation of the Cambrian rocks of North Wales. *In,* WOOD, A., Ed. The Precambrian and Lower Paleozoic Rocks of Wales. Univ. Wales Press, Cardiff. p. 47–66.

Ordovician

BRENCHLEY, P. J. 1969. The relationship between Caradocian volcanicity and sedimentation in North Wales. *In,* WOOD, A., Ed. The Precambrian and Lower Paleozoic Rocks of Wales. Univ. Wales Press, Cardiff. p. 181–202.

DEWEY, J. F. *op. cit.* (General).

EASTWOOD, T. 1953. British regional geology: Northern England. Her Majesty's Stationary Office, London. 71 p.

EDWARDS, W., AND F. M. TROTTER. 1954. Modified after Wray, D. A., British regional geology: The Pennines and adjacent areas. Her Majesty's Stationary Office, London. 86 p.

GEORGE, T. N. 1965. The Geological Growth of Scotland. *In,* CRAIG, G. Y., Ed. Geology of Scotland. Archon, Hampden, Conn. p. 1–48.

HELWIG, JAMES. 1969. Redefinition of Exploits Group, Lower Paleozoic, northeast Newfoundland. *In,* KAY, G. M., Ed. North Atlantic–geology and continental drift. Mem. Am. Ass. Petrol. Geol. 12:408–413.

———, AND ERNESTO SARPI. 1969. Plutonic-pebble conglomerates, New World Island, Newfoundland, and history of eugeosynclines. *In,* KAY, G. M., Ed. North Atlantic–geology and continental drift. Ibid. 12:443–466.

HORNE, G. S., AND JAMES HELWIG. 1969. Ordovician stratigraphy of Notre Dame Bay, Newfoundland. *In,* KAY, G. M., Ed. North Atlantic–geology and continental drift. Mem. Am. Ass. Petrol. Geol. 12:388–407.

HUBERT, J. F. 1969. Late Ordovician sedimentation in Caledonian geosyncline, southwestern Scotland. *In,* KAY, G. M., Ed. North Atlantic–geology and continental drift. Ibid. 12:267–283.

KAY, MARSHALL. 1969. Thrust sheets and gravity slides of western Newfoundland. *In,* KAY, G. M., Ed. North Atlantic–geology and continental drift. Ibid. 12:665–669.

———. 1969. Ordovician correlations between North America and Europe. *In,* KAY, G. M., Ed. North Atlantic–geology and continental drift. Ibid. 12:563–571.

LILLY, H. D. 1966. Late Precambrian and Appalachian tectonics in the light of submarine exploration of the Grand Bank of Newfoundland and in the Gulf of St. Lawrence, Preliminary views. Am. J. Sci. 264:569–574.

———. 1967. *op. cit.* (Cambrian).

NEALE, E. R. W., AND M. J. KENNEDY. 1967. Relationship of the Fleur de Lys Group to younger rocks of the Burlington Peninsula, Newfoundland. Spec. Pap. geol. Ass. Can. 4:139–170.

POCOCK, R. W., AND T. H. WHITEHEAD. 1948. British Regional Geology: The Welsh Borderland. Her Majesty's Stationary Office, London. 83 p.

RAST, NICHOLAS. 1969. The relationship between Ordovician structure and volcanicity in Wales. *In,* WOOD, A., Ed. The Precambrian and Lower Paleozoic Rocks of Wales. Univ. Wales Press, Cardiff. p. 305–335.

RAYNOR, D. H. 1967. *op. cit.* (Cambrian).

RODGERS, JOHN, AND E. R. W. NEALE. 1963. *op. cit.* (Cambrian).

SMITH, A. J., AND G. H. LONG. 1969. The Upper Llandovery sediments of Wales and the Welsh Borderland. *In,* WOOD, A., Ed. The Precambrian and Lower Paleozoic Rocks of Wales. Univ. Wales Press, Cardiff. p. 239–253.

SMYTH, W. R. 1971. Stratigraphy and structure of part of the Hare Bay Allochthon, Newfoundland. Proc. geol. Ass. Can. 24:47–57.

WALTON, E. K. 1965. Lower Paleozoic rocks–stratigraphy. *In,* CRAIG, G. Y., Ed. Geology of Scotland. Archon, Hampden, Conn. p. 161–200.

———. 1965. Lower Paleozoic rocks–paleogeography and structure. *In,* CRAIG, G. Y., Ed. Geology of Scotland. Archon, Hampden, Conn. p. 201–227.

———. 1969. Lower Paleozoic rocks in southern Scotland. *In,* KAY, G. M., Ed. North Atlantic–geology and continental drift. Mem. Am. Ass. Petrol. Geol. 12:265–266.

WILLIAMS, ALWYN. 1962. The Barr and Lower Ardmillian Series (Carodoc) of the Girvan district, southwest Ayrshire. Mem. geol. Soc. Lond. 3:1–265.

———. 1969. Ordovician of the British Isles. *In,* KAY, G. M., Ed. North Atlantic–geology and continental drift. Mem. Am. Ass. Petrol. Geol. 12:236–264.

———. 1969. Ordovician faunal provinces with reference to brachiopod distribution. *In,* WOOD, A., Ed. The Precambrian and Lower Paleozoic Rocks of Wales. Univ. Wales Press, Cardic. p. 117–154.

WHITTINGTON, H. B., AND C. H. KINDLE. 1969. Cambrian and Ordovician stratigraphy of Western Newfoundland. *In,* KAY, G. M., Ed. North Atlantic–geology and continental drift. Mem. Am. Ass. Petrol. Geol. 12:655–664.

Silurian

BAILEY, R. J. 1969. Ludlovian sedimentation in south central Wales. *In,* WOOD, A., Ed. The Precambrian and Lower Paleozoic Rocks of Wales. Univ. Wales Press, Cardiff. p. 283–304.

CUMMINS, W. A. 1957. The Denbigh Grits: Wenlock graywackes in Wales. Geol. Mag. 94:433–451.

———. 1969. Patterns of sedimentation in the Silurian rocks of Wales. *In,* WOOD, A., Ed. The Precambrian and Lower Paleozoic Rocks of Wales. Univ. Wales Press, Cardiff. p. 219–237.

EASTLER, T. E. 1969. Silurian geology of Change Islands and eastern Notre Dame Bay, Newfoundland. *In,* KAY, G. M., Ed. North Atlantic–geology and continental drift. Mem. Am. Ass. Petrol. Geol. 12:425–432.

HELWIG, JAMES, AND ERNESTO SARPI. 1969. *op. cit.* (Ordovician).

HOLLAND, C. H. 1958. The Ludlovian and Downtownian rocks of the Kinighton district, Radnorshire. Q. Jl. geol. Soc. Lond. 114:449.

———. 1969. The Welsh Silurian geosyncline in its regional context. *In,* WOOD, A., Ed. The Precambrian and Lower Paleozoic Rocks of Wales. Univ. Wales Press, Cardiff. p. 203–217.

———. 1969. Irish counterpart of Silurian of Newfoundland. *In,* KAY, G. M., Ed. North Atlantic–geology and continental drift. Mem. Am. Ass. Petrol. Geol 12:298–308.

KAY, G. M. 1969. Silurian of northeast Newfoundland. *In,* KAY, G. M., Ed. North Atlantic–geology and continental drift. Ibid. 12:414–424.

LOCK, B. E. 1969. Silurian rocks of west White Bay area, Newfoundland. *In,* KAY, G. M., Ed. North Atlantic–Geology and Continental Drift. Ibid. 12:433–442.

McKERROW, W. S. 1969. Silurian rocks of Ireland and a comparison with those of Newfoundland. *In,* KAY, G. M., Ed. North Atlantic–geology and continental drift. Ibid. 12:284–288.

PIPER, D. J. W. 1969. Geosyncline-margin sedimentary rocks in Silurian of west Connacht, Ireland. *In,* KAY, G. M., Ed. North Atlantic–geology and continental drift. Ibid. 12:289–297.

RODGERS, JOHN. 1965. Long Point and Clam Bank Formations, western Newfoundland. Proc. geol. Ass. Can. 16:83–94.

WILLIAMS, HAROLD. 1967. Silurian rocks of Newfoundland. Spec. Pap. geol. Ass. Can. 41:93–138.

Devonian

ALLEN, J. R. L. 1962. Petrology, origin and deposition of the highest Lower Old Red Sandstone of Shropshire, England. J. Sedim. Petrol. 32:657–697.

———. 1965. Upper Old Red Sandstone (Farlovian) paleogeography in South Wales and the Welsh Borderland. Ibid. 35:167–195.

———, DINELEY, D. L., AND P. F. FRIEND. 1967. Old Red Sandstone basins of North America and northwest Europe. *In,* OSWALD, D. H., Ed. Int. Symp. Devonian Syst. Calgary. Alberta Soc. Petrol. Geol. 1:69–98

ANDERSON, J. G. C., AND T. R. OWEN. 1968. The structure of the British Isles. Pergamon Press, New York. 162 p.

BELT, E. S. 1968. Post-Acadian rifts and related facies, eastern Canada. *In,* ZEN, E., W. S. WHITE, J. B. HADLEY, AND J. B. THOMPSON, JR., Eds. Studies of Appalachian Geology: Northern and Maritime. Wiley Interscience, New York. p. 95–113.

———. 1969. Newfoundland Carboniferous stratigraphy and its relation to the Maritimes and Ireland. *In,* KAY, G. M., Ed. North Atlantic–geology and continental drift. Mem: Am. Ass. Petrol. Geol. 12: 734–753.

BLUCK, B. J. 1969. Old Red Sandstone and other Paleozoic conglomerates of Scotland. *In,* KAY, G. M., Ed. North Atlantic–geology and continental drift. Ibid. 12:711–723.

BRADLEY, D. A. 1962. Gisbourne Lake and Terrenceville Map areas, Newfoundland. Mem. geol. Surv. Can. 321:1–56.

CHARLESWORTH, J. J. 1953. The Geology of Ireland. Oliver and Boyd, Edinburgh and London. 276 p.

COOPER, J. R. 1954. La Poile-Cinq Cerf map area, Newfoundland. Mem. geol. Surv. Can. 276:1–62.

CRAMPTON, C. B., AND G. CARRUTHERS. 1914. The Geology of Caithness. Mem. geol. Surv. (Gt Br.) 1:1–194.

FRANCIS, E. H. 1965. Carboniferous. *In,* CRAIG, G. Y., Ed. Geology of Scotland. Archon, Hampden, Conn. p. 309–357.

———. 1965. Carboniferous-Permian Igneous rocks. *In,* CRAIG, G. Y., Ed. Geology of Scotland. Archon, Hampden, Conn. p. 359–382.

FRIEND, P. F. 1967. Tectonic implications of sedimentation in Spitzbergen and Midland Scotland. *In,* OSWALD, D. H., Ed. Int. Symp. Devonian Syst. Calgary. Alberta Soc. Petrol. Geol. 2:1141–1147.

———. 1969. Tectonic features of Old Red sedimentation in North Atlantic borders. *In,* KAY, G. M., Ed. North Atlantic–geology and continental drift. Mem. Am. Ass. Petrol. Geol. 12:703–710.

———, HARLAND, W. B., AND J. D. HUDSON. 1963. The Old Red Sandstone and the Highland Boundary in Arran, Scotland. Trans. Edinb. geol. Soc. 19:363–425.

LILLY, H. D. 1966. *op. cit.* (Ordovician).

MACGREGOR, M., AND A. G. MACGREGOR. 1948. British regional geology: The Midland Valley of Scotland. Her Majesty's Stationary Office, Edinburgh. 95 p.

RICHEY, J. E. with revision by A. G. MACGREGOR, AND F. W. ANDERSON. 1961. British regional geology: The Tertiary Volcanic districts. Her Majesty's Stationary Office, Edinburgh. 120 p.

RODGERS, JOHN. 1965. *op. cit.* (Silurian).

———. 1970. *op. cit.* (General).

WATERSON, C. D. 1965. Old Red Sandstone. *In,* CRAIG, G. Y., Ed. Geology of Scotland. Archon, Hampden, Conn. p. 269–303

WILLS, L. J. 1959. A paleogeographic atlas of the British Isles and adjacent parts of Europe. Blackie and Son, London. 64 p.

SEDIMENTARY PETROGRAPHIC PROVINCES: AN EVALUATION

LEE J. SUTTNER

Department of Geology, Indiana University, Bloomington, IN 47401

ABSTRACT—Mineralogic provinces are compositionally distinctive three-dimensional bodies of rock constituting natural units in terms of age, origin and distribution. More than one province likely will be present within the same sedimentary basin. Unconformities and not necessarily group, formation or member boundaries are the sharpest stratigraphic boundaries of provinces. Lateral boundaries are frequently gradational; depending on the scale of the basin analysis these areas of gradation can be separately defined as hybrid provinces.

Over-generalization and over-simplification of interpretation of mineralogic provinces has resulted from inadequate appreciation and evaluation of the relative influence of the four principal factors controlling composition of a province: provenance, transportation, depositional environment and diagenesis. Each of these factors is in turn a dependent variable. A total of 13 immediate processes controlling province composition are identified.

Improved ability to interpret ancient mineralogic provinces will develop from i) better documentation of starting or parent detritus, ii) quantitative estimation of the effects of transportation and environment on sediment composition through study of Holocene sediment, iii) more precise characterization of mineralogic provinces and iv) refinement of current techniques used in interpreting the origin of detrital quartz, feldspar, and accessory minerals.

MEANING AND SIGNIFICANCE OF A MINERALOGIC PROVINCE

A *mineralogic* or *sedimentary petrologic province* was first defined by Edelman (1933, p. 6) as a group of distinctive, homogeneous sediments which constitute a natural unit by age, origin and distribution . . . a three-dimensional body *characterized by a distinctive suite of light and heavy minerals*. Sedimentary provinces are broadly defined by unique *mineral associations*. Four principal characteristics of mineralogic or sedimentary provinces are illustrated in figure 1:

(1) Several different provinces of approximately the same age can occur in the same sedimentary basin, depending on the number of distinct source areas contributing sediment to the basin. In figure 1 source areas A and B have given rise to their own unique petrologic provinces within the same sedimentary basin by generating distinct mineral associations. The Gulf of Mexico is a well-documented actual example of a basin containing at least four petrologic provinces or sub-provinces (Goldstein, 1942, Van Andel, 1960, and Davies and Moore, 1970). Unique mineral associations in the Gulf have been derived from the southern Appalachians, the cratonic interior drained by the Mississippi River and its tributaries, the Texas coastal plain, and the Rio Grande drainage basin.

(2) Hybrid provinces can be formed by the mixing of detritus from two or more distinct, but adjacent source areas. In figure 1 province A and B is a product of derivation in part from area A and in part from area B. Baak (1936, p. 13–14) referred to hybrid provinces as areas of "chaotic sedimentation" or "abnormal variations" in provinces and suggested that they seldom are of regional importance.

Hybrid provinces undoubtedly characterize orogenic source areas where a wide variety of rock types occur in adjacent drainages. Füchtbauer (1964) for example has recognized mixed mineral assemblages in the Tertiary molasse of southern Germany. The mixed assemblages are the result of coalescence of alluvial fans derived from the Alps.

(3) Major unconformities are normally the best stratigraphic boundaries for provinces be-

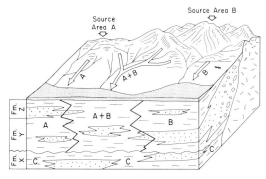

FIG. 1—Schematic block diagram illustrating multiple and hybrid mineralogic provinces within a single sedimentary basin. Province A was derived from source area A; province B from source area B; province A + B is a hybrid derived in part from both source areas; province C is an older province derived from a now extinct source area.

cause they typically reflect major changes in tectonic conditions that control sediment composition. In figure 1 province C is bounded at the top by an unconformity of basinal extent. Differences in composition between province C and the younger provinces should be sharp if the unconformity in any way reflects tectonic events within the source area, assuming that the effects of reworking are relatively minimal.

(4) Boundaries of mineral provinces need not coincide with stratigraphic boundaries (i.e., group, formation, or member boundaries) defined either paleontologically or lithologically. Time, environmental change, and new organisms yield stratigraphic boundaries, but if the sediment source area is not changing simultaneously, stratigraphic boundaries of provinces will not exist. For example, in figure 1 province A spans formation Y and Z stratigraphic boundaries, because source area A persisted in a relatively unchanged manner throughout the time environments were changing during deposition of formations Y and Z.

Conversely, environments can remain unchanged in time and space at the same time unroofing of new source rocks or changes in drainage in the source can produce new mineral associations. In such cases mineral assemblages may be useful in correlation. Numerous case histories of the use of heavy mineral assemblages in stratigraphic correlation and zonation are found in Milner (1962, v. 2, p. 413–424). Furer (1970) successfully used light minerals and rock fragment associations in correlation of the nonmarine Upper Jurassic and Lower Cretaceous from central Wyoming to western Wyoming.

PROBLEM OF INTERPRETATION OF PETROLOGIC PROVINCES

The mineralogy of a petrologic province is a function of four variables: i) provenance, ii) modification of detritus during transportation, iii) modification during deposition, and iv) modification during lithification or diagenesis. Each of these four principal variables is dependent on variables given in table 1. From table 1 it is apparent that the composition of a basin fill is controlled by a minimum of 13 immediate processes. Therefore the interpretation of a petrologic province is exceedingly complex, unless certain of the variables play insignificant roles. Currently sedimentary petrologists have insufficient empirical basis for evaluating the relative influence of each of the process variables on the compositional response—mineral associations.

Clearly tectonism exerts a dominating and overriding influence on sedimentation. Without tectonism there would be no continuous sedimentation and production of new mineral associations because tectonism triggers erosion, and unroofing of new source rocks. Also it can be argued that tectonism controls topography which in turn modifies climate in source areas. Obviously tectonism also directly affects rates of sedimentation and indirectly controls the evolution of environments. The assumption of the fundamental tectonic control of sedimetation is the basis for definition and recognition of lithologic associations—groups or suites of sedimentary rocks formed under essentially similar tectonic conditions (Krumbein and Sloss, 1963, p. 424). Within a given lithologic association however, numerous petrologic provinces can occur because of the varying influence of other variables (table 1). Failure to recognize this has resulted in a gross oversimplification and generalization of interpretation of terrigenous rock composition. An obvious tendency exists to simply relate sandstone mineralogy directly to source rock mineralogy. The role of intermediate processes in modifying detritus is assumed to be relatively unimportant. Exceptions include interpretations of quartz arenites or interpre-

TABLE 1.—FACTORS CONTROLLING THE COMPOSITION OF A MINERALOGIC PROVINCE

$DM = f(P, T, D, L)$
 DM = Detrital mineralogy of basin fill
 P = Provenance
 T = Modification during transportation
 D = Modification during deposition
 L = Modification during lithification or diagensis

Where:
$P = f(srk, w_{ch}/w_m, r)$ and
 srk = source rock
w_{ch}/w_m = relative amounts of chemical and mechanical weathering in the source areas
 r = relief in the source area

$T = f(a, d, v, t_t/t_{sa}/t_{su})$ and
 a = agent of transportation
 d = distance of transportation
 v = velocity of transporting agent
$t_t/t_{sa}/t_{su}$ = relative amount of sediment transported by traction, saltation and in suspension

$D = f(e, rdb, c)$ and
 e = environment
 rdb = rate of deposition and burial
 c = climate at depositional site

$L = f(po, pe, gw)$ and
 po = porosity
 pe = permeability
 gw = groundwater chemistry

tations where appeal to the effects of the other processes is the last-resort explanation of anomolous observation. Thus we encounter statements such as the following in the literature:

". . . subquartzose sandstones derived exclusively from plutonic provenances . . . have less than 25 percent, and commonly less than 10 percent unstable lithic fragments . . . a quartz content commonly close to 50 percent and a high mica content, commonly 5 to 10 percent" (Dickinson, 1970, p. 705).

The following illustration shows that perhaps the assumption that source rock is the foremost factor in controlling sandstone composition is not always valid. Figure 2 is a photomicrograph of Holocene sand collected from a stream draining a high-relief area underlain by granodiorite in southwestern Montana. Figure 3 is a photomicrograph of sand from a stream draining a high-relief area underlain by quartz-feldspathic gneiss in southwestern Montana. The sands are representative of approximately 60 samples collected from a number of streams in the northern Rocky Mountains. They are compositionally immature. The sand in figure 2 contains 68 percent rock fragments—aggregates of two or more crystal units; the sand in figure 3 contains 78 percent polymineralic rock fragments and polycrystalline quartz. Including the feldspar bound up in the rock fragments between 30 percent and 35 percent feldspar is found in the two samples. Rarely do ancient sandstones contain this high a content of liable constituents. Obviously modification of detritus between the time it is derived from the source rock and the time it is lithified is quite significant. But insufficient empirical data currently is available to determine how much of the modification can be related to each of the processes of derivation, transportation, deposition and lithification.

Modification of Detrital Mineralogy During Soil Formation

Changes in detritus that take place between the time the detritus is released from a source rock and the time it is first moved by a transporting agent can be significant. The critical controlling factor presumably is climate, especially annual amount and distribution of precipitation, and to a lesser extent relief. In the case of the sands in figures 2 and 3 changes in the nature of the sand as it passed through the

Fig. 2—Photomicrograph of Holocene sand collected from Willow Creek in the Tobacco Root Mountains of southwestern Montana. Willow Creek's drainage basin is exclusively underlain by granite and grandiorite. Most of the grains are rock fragments consisting of quartz and feldspar (qf).

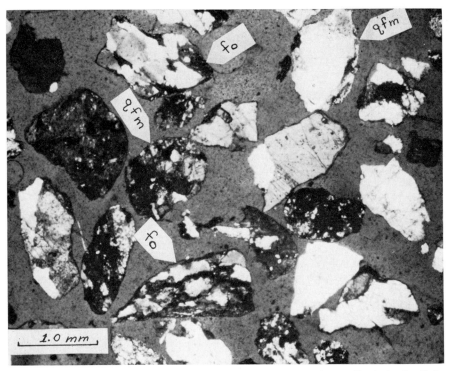

Fig. 3—Photomicrograph of Holocene sand collected from Quaking Aspen Creek in the Tobacco Root Mountains of southwestern Montana. Quaking Aspen Creek's drainage basin is exclusively underlain by Precambrian crystalline metamorphic rock, largely quartz-feldspathic gneiss. Virtually all grains shown are rock fragments. Two possess foliated texture (fo). Several are aggregates of quartz, feldspar and a mafic mineral, usually hornblende (qfm).

soil profile were obviously slight. Feldspar is fresh and abundant and most of the mineral aggregates appear to have been derived through simple disintegration of the source rocks. However, the effects of climatic modification of

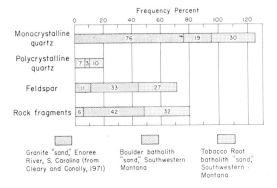

Fig. 4—Bar graphs summarizing the differences in composition of Holocene sand from streams draining the Tobacco Root and Boulder Batholiths of southwestern Montana and streams draining grainite in South Carolina, (Enoree River; after Cleary and Conolly, 1971).

composition during soil formation became apparent with modal analyses of sand such as that shown in figure 2 (derived from granite and granodiorite in an area of semi-arid climate) are compared with the modal analyses of sand derived from areas underlain by granite in the more humid climate of South Carolina (fig. 4). Marked differences exist. Approximately two to three times as much feldspar and six to seven times as many rock fragments are found in the first-cycle sand from southwestern Montana versus that from South Carolina. In contrast approximately two to four times as much chemically and mechanically stable monocrystalline quartz is found in the Holocene sand from the more humid climate.

Figure 5 further illustrates the interaction of climate and fluvial sand composition. Feldspar content in Holocene sand shows a near linear inverse relation with mean annual precipitation. Because most of the sands in figure 5 were sampled less than 200 miles from the stream's headwater, and several from less than 50 miles, it can be assumed that feldspar destruction during transport was probably minimal relative to destruction which occurred in the source rock weathering process.

Table 2 is an attempt to more directly evaluate the influence of precipitation in destruction of feldspar during soil formation. Although a faint inverse correlation of precipitation and frequency percent feldspar in soil is suggested by the data, it is readily apparent that a wide range of feldspar content is found within areas possessing a narrow range of mean annual precipitation. In large part this reflects the large number of variables such as soil grain size, age, parent rock type, relief, and sample depth that cannot be established or held constant in view of the limited number of publications providing the light mineral data given in the table. The shortage of such data in existing literature points to the need for carefully controlled studies of the non-clay mineral fraction of soils by sedimentary petrologists.

It is especially interesting to note that figure 5 and table 2 both suggest that only in the most exreme humid climates (annual precipitation at least 100 inches) is there near total destruction of feldspar in the weathering profile. Conse-

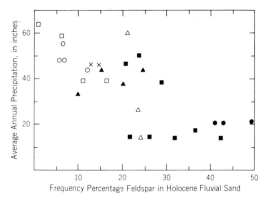

FIG. 5—Frequency percentage of feldspar in Holocene sand as a function of average annual precipitation. □ samples from Hsu, 1960; ○ samples from Giles and Pilkey, 1965; × samples from Cleary and Connolly, 1971; ▲ samples from Willman, 1942; △ samples from Whetten, 1966; ● samples from Hayes, 1962, ■ samples from this study.

quently it is necessary to reconsider the prevailing notion that quartz arenites can readily form in humid to sub-humid climates.

TABLE 2.—FREQUENCY PERCENTAGES OF FELDSPAR IN SOILS

Parent Material	Locality	Mean annual precipitation in inches	Depth below surface in inches	Grain size	Number of samples	Range in frequency in percent	Average frequency in percent	Reference
Granite	British Guiana	100	8–32	Sand	2	2–7	4.5	Harrison (1934)
Gneiss	Malabar Coast, India	100	Not given	Sand	2	2–3	2.5	Harrassowitz (1926)
Granite gneiss	Ibadan, Nigeria	55–65	12–18	Medium sand	1		1	Nye (1955)
Granite gneiss	Ibadan, Nigeria	55–65	12–18	Fine sand	1		20	Nye (1955)
Quartz diorite and granite	Ituri, Belgian Congo	40–60	0–16	Fine sand	1		10	Ruhe (1956)
Granite	Ituri, Belgian Congo	40–60	0–28	Fine sand	3	2–40	21	Ruhe (1956)
Outwash derived from granite gneiss and schist	Connecticut Valley	45–50	0–3	Medium sand	1		15	Bourbeau and Swanson (1954)
Outwash derived from granite gneiss and schist	Connecticut Valley	45–50	0–3	Very fine sand	1		22	Bourbeau and Swanson (1954)
Granite	Piedmont, S E United States	45–50	0–12	Sand	4	12–40	28	Cleary and Conolly (1971)
Gneiss	Piedmont, S E United States	45–50	0–12	Sand	1		20	Cleary and Conolly (1971)
Granite	Ozark Mtns., Missouri	42–46	1–6	Sand	1		47	Short, 1961
Granite	Malvern Hills, England	25–35	0–10	Fine sand	2	45–58	52	Stephen (1952)
Biotitite	Malvern Hills, England	25–35	2–12	Fine sand	2	20–28	24	Stephen (1952)
Granite	Balos, Sudan	26	0–6	Sand	8	22–40	34	Ruxton (1958)
Granite	Transbaikalia, Russia	12–16	0–3	Fine sand	2	59–67	63	Sokolova and Smirnova (1965)
Granodiorite	Bighorn Mtns., Wyoming	15	1–4	Sand	1		43	Short (1961)

Modification of Detrital Mineralogy during Transportation

Most studies on the survivability of detritus during transportation have focused on feldspars in low gradient streams. The classic work of Russell (1937) on the Mississippi River sand showed less than 20 percent destruction of feldspar in 1100 miles of transport. Abrasionary destruction of feldspar in the Mississippi is minimal; most of the destruction apparently is related to soil formative processes when the sand is temporarily caught up on bars or floodplains. Pollock (1961) reported little or no compositional change in channel sands along 650 miles of the South Canadian River in New Mexico, Texas and Oklahoma. He noted that a decrease in feldspar content of coarse sand is compensated by increase in feldspar content of the fine sand due to breakage along cleavage or twin planes. Pittman (1969) found a similar significant mechanical reduction in size, but not ultimate destruction, of feldspar along 20 to 25 miles of the Merced River.

On the other hand, Plumley (1948) found a 50-percent decrease in feldspar in 40 to 45 miles of transport in Battle Creek in the Black Hills of South Dakota. Hayes (1962) found erratic variations in feldspar content downstream in the high gradient South Platte River between Fairplay and Denver, Colorado. Cameron and Blatt (1971, p. 571, p. 575) observed a reduction of feldspar from four percent to two percent in 20 miles of transport in Elk Creek in the Black Hills. More significantly they noted a 75-percent reduction in schist fragments in 20 miles of transport.

The above apparent inconsistencies in studies of grain survivability were first pointed out by Pettijohn (1957, p. 125). As Pettijohn concluded the differences probably reflect differences in the gradient of the streams studied; mechanical destruction taking place faster in higher gradient streams. Bradley (1970) has concluded that possibly a major factor affecting the survivability of grains in transport is the length of time they are not in transport, but instead subject to chemical weathering on point-bars or floodplains.

More controlled studies of sand content of both high and low gradient streams in a variety of climates are needed. Special effort in these studies must be directed to documentation of the survivability of rock fragments.

Modification of Detrital Mineralogy during Deposition

Evaluating the control of depositional environment on sandstone composition is dependent on understanding the significance of grain destruction through abrasion. It has generally been assumed in provenance determinations that the environmental processes which bring about grain destruction are minimal or obscured by more important effects (Pettijohn, Potter, Siever, 1972). In large part this assumption probably reflects the impact of a number of empirical studies of abrasion (Wentworth, 1919; Marshall, 1929; Krumbein, 1941; Rayleigh, 1944; Kuenen, 1955, 1956, 1959, 1964, and others). Kuenen (1959) for example extrapolated his experimental data to show that 20,000 km. of fluvial transport would cause no more than one percent reduction in volume of medium sand size quartz through abrasion. Similar low orders of magnitude of destruction of feldspar and limestone fragments were reported. Although destruction of quartz during aeolian transport was estimated by Kuenen to be 100 to 1000 times greater than destruction during equal distances of fluvial transport, net reduction in quartz volume through mechanical abrasion was not assumed to be important. However, Swett and others (1971, p. 411–412) have calculated that sand deposited in a tide-dominated environment can conceivably travel an average of 36.5 km/year. During a million years of reworking before burial a conservative estimate of travel for grains in this environment would be in the order of 36.5×10^6 km— a distance approximately 10^4 times greater than the distance of Kuenen's experimental studies. Sand in the tidal environment is alternately wet and dry, thereby catalyzing the chemical weathering processes. Presumably, therefore, in such rigorous near-shore environments significant mineralogic maturation could occur.

Destruction of feldspar through abrasion in beach and dune environments is indicated by the average feldspar content of over 400 samples of Holocene and Pleistocene sand from North America tabulated by Pettijohn, Potter and Siever (1972, table 2-1). River sands average twice as much feldspar as either beach or dune sand. It is interesting to note however, that the beach and dune sands contain an average of 10 percent feldspar. This is well above the average content of quartz arenites, the compositions of which have sometimes been related to abrasionary destruction in high energy environments.

APPROACHES TO IMPROVED INTERPRETATION OF MINERALOGIC PROVINCES

Three of the four principal factors controlling sandstone composition have been briefly considered. The fourth, diagenesis or intrastratal solution is the most complex factor to evaluate and perhaps the least understood. In view of our overall inability to evaluate the four factors it is imperative that we re-examine the hypotheses on which interpretation of mineral provinces are based. Four avenues of approach to re-examination deserve immediate consideration.

1. Documentation of Differences in Starting or Parent Materials.—Currently little is known about how detritus derived from a granite differs from that derived from a gneiss; or for that matter even how detritus derived from a sedimentary terrane differs from that derived from an igneous terrane. Sedimentary petrologists and soil mineralogists have too long overlooked the nature of first-cycle non-clay mineral fractions of soils developed on different bedrock, in different climates and in areas of contrasting relief. Until the differences imparted on sediment composition by the provenance variables such as source rock, climate, and relief are determined, our interpretations of the provenance of ancient rocks will be hazardous generalizations.

2. Estimation of Compositional Modification during Transportation and Deposition through Study of Holocene Sand.—Major advances in igneous and metamorphic petrology were made when microscope observation was supplemented with laboratory experimentation. The same will be true in sedimentary petrology. However, the sedimentary petrologist need not simulate in the laboratory; he has natural access to sediment-forming processes. It is up to him to establish how these processes modify sediment composition within the framework of Uniformitarianism—*by looking at the Holocene,* before attempting to make provenance interpretations about the ancient.

3. More Exact Characterization of Mineralogic Provinces through Precise Definition of Mineral Species and Rock Fragments.—Problems of compositional interpretation are too complex to be solved with the generalized data that appear on traditional quartz-feldspar-rock fragment triangular portrayals of sandstone composition. We must begin to identify quartz and feldspar varieties in the same, if not in greater detail, than attempted for detrital tourmaline and zircon, for instance. The classic attempts by Krynine (1940, 1946) and Folk (1968) to utilize character of extinction and nature of inclusions to define sub-species of quartz are well-known examples of a means of precise definition of a single mineral species. An analogous example

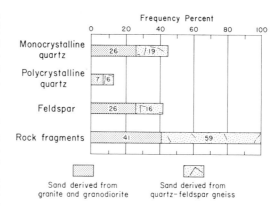

FIG. 6—Bar graphs of the average composition of 9 samples of Holocene sand derived from plutonic source rocks and 10 samples of Holocene sand derived from Precambrian metamorphic rock.

involving feldspar is illustrated in figure 6 and table 3. The bar graphs in figure 6 summarize the gross differences in a sand derived from a plutonic source and sand derived from a metamorphic source, using the compositional end members of standard sandstone classifications. Figures 2 and 3 are photomicrographs of representative samples from these same two populations. It is apparent from figure 6 that discrimination between the populations would be impossible on the basis of the four standard end member ingredients chosen. Moreover, several of the rock fragments in both populations lack distinctive textural identifying characteristics, thereby precluding use of this criterion in distinguishing between the two groups of samples. However, precise description of feldspar enables distinction between the two populations with a high degree of confidence. Using the feldspar data in table 3, a X^2 test of distinctness of the population of "igneous sand" and population of "metamorphic sand" indicated a probability of .98 that the two sets of samples are indeed different. Furthermore, the probability of individual samples of "plutonic sand" coming from a population different from the compound metamorphic sample is greater than .70 in 8 of the 10 samples examined. Although the provenance significance of twinning in detrital feldspar is still inadequately understood (Pittman, 1970), this sample strongly suggests that precise characterization of mineralogic provinces and standard petrographic analyses should include more than a simple tabulation of percent feldspar, quartz, and rock fragments in addition to the normal heavy mineral data.

TABLE 3.—VARIATIONS IN THE KIND AND AMOUNT OF FELDSPAR[1]

Number of samples	Number of grains	Percent K-spar	Percent plagioclase	Percent untwinned plagioclase	Percent A-twins	Percent C-twins
			Plutonic derived sand			
10	2291	45	55	18	48	34
	Std. dev.	8.1	8.1	4.4	6.1	6.1
			Metamorphic derived sand			
9	1482	28	72	22	43	35
	Std. dev.	7.7	7.4	4.1	7.1	7.6

[1] Data taken from the samples of Holocene sand of plutonic and metamorphic origin portrayed in figure 6. Twin determinations were made with standard flat stage microscope. A-twins include the albite and pericline types and C-twins the more complex Carlsbad and Baveno types.

4. Improve Capabilities for Reading Genetic "Tags" or "labels" on Ubiquitous Minerals Such as Quartz and Feldspar.—Given a mineralogic province, presumably the major concern will always be determination of the source rock type or types for the province. If the grains that ultimately make it through the various destructive process filters do indeed retain some form of identity tag which in effect says "I am metamorphic" or "I was derived from a granite" we must learn how to read the tag. Obviously we must then also use those physical-property tags or labels that we best understand to more precisely define mineralogic provinces as discussed in number 3 above.

What might be the nature of such "tags" or "labels"? In the case of quartz several modern examples exist. Taylor and Epstein (1962) have shown that the ratio of the stable isotope of oxygen (O^{18}) to the less stable isotope O^{16} is a direct function of temperature of crystallization of quartz. Consequently this O^{18}/O^{16} ratio should be a key to the origin of detrital quartz. Dennen (1967) indicated that the trace element content of quartz is provenance significant. Dennen's technique was used by this author to discriminate between quartz from the populations of plutonic and metamorphic sand referred to earlier in this report. Differences in

the trace-element signature of the quartz populations are tabulated in table 4. Using both mean and standard deviation values for individual trace elements a distinction between the metamorphic quartz and quartz from the Boulder and Tobacco Root Batholiths is readily possible. Probable genetic explanations for the distribution of trace elements in the quartz in Table 3 are given in Suttner and Leininger (1972).

Quartz thermoluminescence and density are other physical properties potentially useful in determining the origin of detrital quartz. Charlet (1971) proposed that the thermoluminescence of individual quartz grains uniquely fingerprints crystallization conditions. Charlet satisfactorily tested the technique through studies of the Carboniferous of the Pyrenean mountains and Alpine sediments from Sicily and North Africa. His results were in agreement with earlier interpretations of the provenance of these rocks based on more traditional techniques. Hayase (1960) has shown that the smokiness of quartz as revealed by gamma irradiation of individual grains, is indicative of the crystallization temperature of the quartz. Katz (1970) and Katz and Muravyov (1970) have developed a thermally controlled, gravitation gradient tube enabling precision measurement ($\pm$ .01) of the density distribution of

TABLE 4.—PARTIAL TRACE-ELEMENT CONTENT OF QUARTZ FROM THE TOBACCO ROOT AND BOULDER BATHOLITHS OF SOUTHWESTERN MONTANA AND FROM AN AREA OF PRECAMBRIAN METAMORPHIC ROCK IN SOUTHWESTERN MONTANA

Item	Ti ppm		Mg ppm		Fe ppm		Al ppm	
	$\bar{x}$	σ	$\bar{x}$	σ	$\bar{x}$	σ	$\bar{x}$	σ
Nine samples of Boulder Batholith quartz	72	9	6	4	17	16	468	447
Six samples of Tobacco Root Batholith quartz	31	7	3	2	20	11	158	124
Ten samples of metamorphic quartz	30	15	19	17	112	82	298	283

quartz grain populations. Subtle variations in the density of quartz reflect variations in the kind and amount of submicroscopic to microscopic inclusions in the quartz. Density histograms of quartz populations may form the basis for additional statistical means of better defining mineralogic provinces and determining the origin of detrital quartz.

SUMMARY

The current status of studies of the detrital mineralogy of sand and sandstone is perhaps most succinctly summarized by a quote sometimes attributed to P. D. Krynine, "The problem appears to be hopelessly complex, but given a will and a proper approach it does not need to be so."

REFERENCES CITED

BAAK, J. A. 1936. Regional petrology of the southern North Sea. H. Veenman and Sons, Wageningen, Netherlands. 127 p.

BLATT, H. 1967. Provenance determination and the recycling of sediments. J. sedim. Petrol. 37:1031–1044.

BOURBEAU, G. A., AND C. L. W. SWANSON. 1954. Morphology, mineralogy and genesis of two southern New England soils. Bull. Conn. agric. Exp. Stn. 584:1–59.

BRADLEY, W. D. 1970. Effect of weathering on abrasion of granitic gravel, Colorado River, Texas. Bull. geol. Soc. Am. 81:61–80.

CAMERON, K. L., AND H. BLATT. 1971. Durabilities of sand size schist and "volcanic" rock fragments during fluvial transport, Elk Creek, Black Hills, South Dakota. J. sedim. Petrol. 41:565–576.

CHARLET, J. M. 1971. Thermoluminescence of detrital rocks used in paleogeographical problems. Mod. Geol. 2:265–274.

CLEARY, W. J., AND J. R. CONOLLY. 1971. Distribution and genesis of quartz in a Piedmont coastal plain environment. Bull. geol. Soc. Am. 82:2755–2766.

DAVIES, D. K., AND W. R. MOORE. 1970. Dispersal of Mississippi sediment in the Gulf of Mexico. J. sedim. Petrol. 37:1031–1044.

DENNEN, W. H. 1967. Trace elements in quartz as indicators of provenance. Bull. geol. Soc. Am. 78:125–130.

DICKINSON, W. R. 1970. Interpreting detrital modes of graywacke and arkose. J. sedim. Petrol. 39:1243–1247.

EDELMAN, C. H. 1933. Petrologische provinces in let Nederland se Kwartair. Centen Publishing Company, Amsterdam. 104 p.

FOLK, R. L. 1968. Petrology of Sedimentary Rocks. Hemphill's, Austin, Texas. 159 p.

FÜCHTBAUER, H. 1964. Sedimentpetrographische untersuchungen in der älteren molasse nördlich der Alpen. Eclog. geol. Helv. 57:158–298.

FURER, L. C. 1970. Petrology and stratigraphy of nonmarine Upper Jurassic-Lower Cretaceous rocks of western Wyoming and southeastern Idaho. Bull. Am. Ass. Petrol. Geol. 54:2282–2302.

GILES, R. T., AND O. H. PILKEY. 1965. Atlantic beach and dunes sediments of the southern United States. J. sedim. Petrol. 35:900–910.

GOLDSTEIN, AUGUST, JR. 1942. Sedimentary petrologic provinces of the northern Gulf of Mexico. Ibid. 12:77–84.

GREEN, PATRICIA. 1966. Mineralogical and weathering study of a red-brown earth formed on granodiorite. Aust. J. Soil Res. 4:181–197.

HARRASSOWITZ, H. 1926. Laterites. Fortschr. Geol. Palaeont. 4:253–566.

HARRISON, J. B. 1934. The katamorphism of igneous rocks under humid tropical conditions. Imp. Bur. Soil Sci. Harpenden. 79 p.

HARRISS, R. C., AND A. S. ADAMS. 1966. Geochemical and mineralogical studies on the weathering of granitic rocks. Am. J. Sci. 264:146–173

HAYASE, I. 1961. Gamma irradiation effect on quartz: (I) A mineralogical and geological application. Kyoto Univ. Inst. Chem. Res. 39:133–137.

HAYES, J. R. 1962. Quartz and feldspar content in South Platte, Platte, and Missouri River sands. J. sedim. Petrol. 32:793–800.

HSU, K. J. 1960. Texture and mineralogy of the recent sands of the Gulf Coast. Ibid. 30:380–403.

KATZ, M. YA. 1970. Mineral studies in the gravitational gradient field. Sedimentology. 15:147–159.

———, AND V. I. MURAVYOV. 1970. Density and optical data of low temperature feldspars and mica. Ibid. 15:123–127.

KRUMBEIN, W. C. 1941. The effects of abrasion on the size, shape, and roundness of rock particles. J. Geol. 49:482–520.

KRUMBEIN, W. C., AND L. L. SLOSS. 1963. Stratigraphy and sedimentation. W. H. Freeman, San Francisco. 660 p.

KRYNINE, P. D. 1940. Petrology and genesis of the Third Bradford Sand. Bull. Miner. Ind. Exp. Stn. Penn. St. Coll. 29:1–134

———. 1946. Microscopic morphology of quartz types. Pan-Am. Congr. Min. geol. Eng. Ann. 2nd Commn. p. 36–49

KUENEN, P. H. 1955. Experimental abrasion of pebbles: (I) wet sand blasting. Leid. geol. Meded. 20:142–147.

———. 1956. Rolling by current. J. Geol. 64:336–368.

———. 1959. Experimental abrasion: (3) fluvialtile action on sand. Am. J. Sci. 257:172–190.

———. 1964. Eolian action. J. Geol. 68:427–449.

MARSHALL, PATRICK. 1927. The wearing of beach gravels. Trans. N. Z. Inst. 58:507–532.

MILNER, H. B. 1962. Sedimentary petrography. MacMillan, New York. v. II, 715 p.

NYE, P. H. 1955. Some soil forming processes in the humid tropics, II. the development of the upper-slope members of the Catena. J. Soil Sci. 6:51–62.

PETTIJOHN, F. J. 1957. Sedimentary rocks. Harper, New York. 718 p.

PETTIJOHN, F. J., P. E. POTTER, AND R. SIEVER. 1972. Sand and sandstone. Springer-Verlag, New York. 618 p.

PITTMAN, E. D. 1970. Plagioclase feldspars as an indicator of provenance in sedimentary rocks. J. sedim. Petrol. 40:591–598.

PLASTER, R. W., AND W. C. SHERWOOD. 1971. Bedrock weathering and residual soil formation in central Virginia. Bull. geol. Soc. Am. 82:2813–2826

PLUMLEY, W J. 1948. Black Hills terrace gravels. A study in sediment transport. J. Geol. 48:527–577.

POLLACK, J. M. 1961. Significance of compositional and textural properties of South Canadian River channel sands, New Mexico, Texas and Oklahoma. J. sedim. Petrol. 31:15–37.

RADWANSKI, S. A., AND C. D. OLLIER. 1959. A study of an East African Catena. J. Soil Sci. 10:149–168.

RAYLEIGH, LORD. 1944. Pebbles, natural and artificial. Their shapes under various conditions of abrasion. Proc. R. Soc. Ser. A. 182:321–335.

RUHE, R. V. 1956. Landscape evolution in the high Ituri, Belgian Congo. Inst. Natn. Agron. Congo Belge, Ser. Sci. 66:1–108.

RUSSELL, R. D. 1937. Mineral composition of Mississippi River sands. Bull. geol. Soc. Am. 48:1307–1348.

RUXTON, B. P. 1958. Weathering and subsurface erosion in granite at the Piedmont angle, Balos, Spain. Geol. Mag. 95:353–377.

SHORT, N. M. 1961. Geochemical variations in four residual soils. J. Geol. 69:534–571.

SMITH, W. W. 1962. Weathering of some Scottish basic igneous rocks with reference to soil formation. J. Soil Sci. 13:202–215.

SOKOLOVA, T. A., AND V. V. SMIRNOVA. 1965. Development of podzolic soils on granite. Soviet Soil Sci. 6:642–649 (Engl. trans. 1966)

STEPHEN, I. 1952. A study of rock weathering with reference to the soils of the Malvern Hills, pt. I. Weathering of biotitite and granite. J. Soil Sci. 3:219–237.

SUTTNER, L. J., AND R. K. LEININGER. 1972. Comparison of the trace element content of plutonic, volcanic, and metamorphic quartz from southwestern Montana. Bull. geol. Soc. Am. 83:1855–1862.

SWETT, K., G. DEV. KLEIN, AND D. E. SMITH. 1971. A Cambrian tidal sand body—the Eriboll sandstone of northwest Scotland: An ancient-recent analog. J. Geol. 79:400–415.

TAYLOR, H. P., JR., AND S. EPSTEIN. 1962. Relationship between O^{18}/O^{16} ratios in coexisting minerals in igneous and metamorphic rocks, Pt. 2. Application to petrologic problems. Bull. geol. Soc. Am. 73:675–694.

VAN ANDEL, TJ. H., AND D. H. POALE. 1960. Sources of Holocene sediments in the northern Gulf of Mexico. J. sedim. Petrol. 30:91–122.

WENTWORTH, C. K. 1919. A laboratory and field study of cobble abrasion. J. Geol. 27:507–521.

WHETTEN, J. T. 1966. Sediments from the lower Columbia River and origin of graywacke. Science. 152:1057–1058.

WILLMAN, H. B. 1942. Feldspar in Illinois sands; a study in resources. Rept. Invest. Ill. St. geol. Surv. 79:1–87.

OLIGOCENE CALCAREOUS NANNOFOSSIL PROVINCES

THOMAS R. WORSLEY and MAURICE L. JORGENS
Department of Oceanography, University of Washington, Seattle, WA 98195

ABSTRACT—Investigations of modern calcareous nannoplankton and their fossil record have shown that the distribution of coccoliths in marine sediments is influenced by latitudinal provinciality, neritic or oceanic habitat selection, selective solution, and diagenesis. These factors have operated in the past, although not always at the same intensity. Because they may cause a species to be absent from parts of the sediment volume deposited within its biochron, significant improvements in biostratigraphic zonations depend upon evaluating their influence. Methods developed for objectively comparing the distributions of fossil species discriminate the relative effects of some of these factors upon the distributions. This study applies these methods to the Oligocene based on published equatorial and northern hemisphere data.

INTRODUCTION

Investigation of the distribution of fossil coccoliths (nannofossils) in the stratigraphic record has met with remarkable success with respect to their biostratigraphic utility. They are ideally suited for this purpose because of their ease of identification, relatively widespread geographic occurrence, rapid evolutionary rate, and high resistance to destruction. Intensive study of land-based section by several investigators (for a complete bibliography see Loeblich and Tappan, 1966, 1968, 1969, 1970a, 1970b) resulted in a world-wide subdivision (Hay and others, 1967; Bramlette and Wilcoxon, 1967) of about 35 units for the 65-million-year Cenozoic Era, approximating the resolution attained for planktonic Foraminifera, a group that has received intensive study since the early 1950's. Hopes were high that nannofossil biostratigraphic resolution for the Cenozoic would rapidly surpass that of any other group, especially in light of the long continuous cores being recovered by the Deep Sea Drilling Project. However, initial study of many Deep Sea Drilling Project cores has only resulted in further refinement to about one and one-half million years (Gartner, 1969; Martini and Worsley, 1970; Martini, 1970, 1971). This increased refinement has been matched in Foraminifera (Blow, 1969) and is being rivalled by Radiolaria (Riedel and Sanfillipo, 1970). Considering the rapid early success of nannofossil biostratigraphy, this refinement is surprisingly small relative to the man-hours expended in studying the long stratigraphic sections now available. It appears that "global" resolution, attainable by current techniques, is being approached.

Significant improvement in biostratigraphic subdivision using nannofossils no longer depends solely upon the description of more new species from more sections, but also upon concurrent development of methods for objectively comparing the area-time distributions of fossil species and ascertaining the relative influence of the physical factors that control their distributions.

Causes of Provincialism.—This study is directed toward examining in detail the dimensions of species-enclosing area-time volumes and investigating some of the factors controlling nannofossil distribution as far as they can be determined exclusively from the stratigraphic record. This requires that 1) all species studied be unambiguously defined and 2) their vertical and lateral ranges are accurately known.

Progress with respect to the first has been slow because of widespread use of loosely defined species and lack of coordination between users of light, transmission and scanning electron microscopy. Progress toward the second has also been slow, partly because of taxonomic and microscopic problems, but also because lateral irregularities of nannofossil ranges were originally ignored on the assumption that they were quite small. This led to the belief that the volumes they described were bounded by parallel time-planes and so could be accurately determined by studying a few sections. This is not the case (McIntyre and others, 1970; McIntyre and McIntyre, 1971; Worsley and Martini, 1970; Bukry, 1970; Bukry and others, 1971).

The dimensions of any species-enclosing area-time volume are obtained through the summation of all known local stratigraphic ranges. Two main factors influence the local time-range of a taxon: 1) paleogeographic restriction, and 2) post-mortem destruction. Paleogeographic restriction is manifest in two ways: A) the total absence of a taxon from a selected area throughout its evolutionary (vertical) range [e.g., the exclusion of discoasters from cold water (Roth, 1970)]; or B) absence from an area for a part of its evolutionary range [e.g., the diachronous lowest occurrence surfaces of *Tetralithus murus* and *Nephrolithus frequens* (Worsley and Martini, 1970)]. Type A is relatively easy to demonstrate but B, although probably the more common of the two, is more subtle and is often overlooked with respect to nannofossils in Tertiary and older sediments, although it has been amply demonstrated for Quaternary nannofloras (McIntyre, and others, 1972). This omission is responsible, along with taxonomic confusion, for limiting biostratigraphic resolution by current methods (i.e., world-wide datum surfaces and zones based on them) to about one or two million years (Martini, 1971). Postmortem destruction simulates the effects of provincialism in that it too locally alters fossil ranges. In the case of nannofossils, several processes may operate: a) selective chemical solution in the oceanic water column, b) selective removal by winnowing (probably rare), c) postdepositional diagenetic alteration in the upper few meters of unconsolidated sediment still exchanging ions with sea water, and d) postburial alteration (i.e., groundwater leaching or recrystallization during lithification or metamorphism).

SCOPE AND APPROACH

This study focuses on describing the areal and stratigraphic distribution of northern hemisphere calcareous nannofossils from the Oligocene Epoch. Several considerations make the Oligocene particularly attractive.

1. World-wide biostratigraphic resolution for this epoch is presently 2.5 million years per zone whereas the average nannofossil zone for the rest of the Cenozoic spans 1.3 million years (Gartner, 1969; Martini and Worsley, 1970; Martini, 1970, 1971); Better resolution is needed for the Oligocene.

2. The relatively low species diversity as compared to other parts of the stratigraphic record (Tappan and Loeblich, 1971) makes the project logistically manageable.

3. The relatively slow rate of nannofossil evolution for the epoch (Haq, 1971) coupled with strongly shifting climatic belts (Wolfe and Hopkins, 1966; Emiliani, 1966) enables tracing of climatically induced species migrations.

4. Large vertical migrations in the carbonate compensation depth (Hay, 1970; Ramsay, in press) have probably superimposed a pattern of variable selective solution on the paleoclimatic record of sections in the ocean basins. The effects of these should be distinguishable.

5. A large number of sections are available for study from each of these diverse environments.

6. The relatively small translatitudinal migrations of crustal plates since Oligocene time makes palinspastic reconstruction unnecessary.

The objectives of this research are to: 1) examine the stratigraphic distribution of as many Oligocene fossils from as many sections as possible, mainly from literature analysis augmented by personal examination of samples; 2) use information thereby obtained to determine a most likely sequence for the Oligocene— a) on a global scale, b) above 35 degrees north latitude, and c) between 35 degrees north latitude and 12 degrees south latitude; 3) compare differences among these sequences to determine and map the areal distribution of selected nannofossil species for given time periods; and 4) use the paleobiogeographic information thus obtained to separate the effects of the possible processes or factors accounting for these differences.

Methods.—These four objectives entail the solving of two problems: 1) quantifying existing data and 2) collecting new data in a manner amenable to statistical analysis. Because the amount of raw data to be gathered and reduced was so large, it was decided to computer-reduce it.

Quantification of data and the application of probability and statistical methods to biostratigraphic problems in paleontology were discussed by Shaw (1964). Dennison and Hay (1967) have developed a graph, based in large part on Shaw's principles and binomial sampling theory, which can be used to establish reliable criteria for determining the absence or presence of a species in a sample. This is an important advance because most biostratigraphic subdivision schemes or paleoecological studies rely on accurately determining the sequence of stratigraphically highest and lowest occurrences (or geographic limits) of fossil species at precisely those places where those species are exceedingly scarce in samples (i.e., near the limits of their stratigraphic or geographic ranges). Therefore the accuracy with which boundaries between biostratigraphic or environmental units can be determined is a function of the precision with which the range limits of species are determined, or in other words, how long one should look before he is willing to believe that a species is absent in a sample.

The computer analysis system, MASS, was developed to handle the reduction of the raw fossil data as taken directly from published information or from microscope slide check lists.

The four major components of the MASS system are the programs ALPHA, SWITCH, MATRIX, and POSNEG. The MASS system was specifically designed for use on the CDC 6400 at the University of Washington, but is written in the FORTRAN IV language and is adaptable to most computer installations with a storage capacity of seven million bytes or greater.

Program ALPHA allows for synonymy assignments, permits an investigator to reduce the number of fossils on the data cards, and alphabetizes the remaining species. It can also combine occurrences of any number of species under one name in case one wants to use an entire genus or related group of species as a single taxonomic unit.

Program SWITCH converts the raw occurrence data into range charts for easier graphical viewing, and better keypunch error checking. SWITCH also prints and punches as a fractional value the number of samples in which a taxon occurs over the number of samples available for that section. This permits a crude estimate of its abundance in that section.

Program POSNEG plots the position of localities where: (1) any 2 datum surfaces occur in sequence; (2) any 2 data both occur at the same level; (3) only one of 2 selected data occurs; (4) neither of 2 selected data occur. It can be used to: A) map the areal distribution of significant fossil species; B) map the areal distribution of localities where any 2 datum surfaces occur in sequence; and C) show the places where they reverse.

Program MATRIX reduces raw data indicating vertical positions of the limits of fossil ranges within sections compiled by ALPHA and SWITCH, and synthesizes them into a most probable sequence for all sections studied. Initially, the input data is broken into occurrences within samples from levels within each section. An occurrence matrix is then generated and filled one section at a time. An entry is made in the matrix each time one datum point (highest or lowest occurrence of a species) occurs at a distinctly separate level from another in a section. When the occurrence matrix is completed, the probability (expectation) of each pair being in sequence is calculated using Hay's (1972) bionomial expansion formula. The information is then used to construct the most probable sequence.

In its present state, MASS can analyze as many as 170 species (340 datum surfaces) simultaneously. Insofar as the number of datum surfaces compared is approximately the square of twice the number of species analyzed, costs rapidly increase as additional species are added. For example, if 170 species were actually used, computer storage requirements would approach 1.8 million bytes. In this project, however, the number of fossil species actually used is only 25 because published stratigraphic information for others is still too limited to be profitably analyzed by MASS.

Of the 50 datum surfaces (25 species) and 51 sections analyzed here, the highest number of times any pair was found to occur in sequence is about 35, the average only being about five or six. Essentially this means that from present published data one can expect any given pair of Oligocene datum surfaces to be found in sequence in only about one in ten sections. Several factors can account for this somewhat surprising finding:

1. All of the species within each section were not detected.

2. Sampling interval was insufficiently close to separate all the datum surfaces within each section.

3. Unconformities within sections prevent separation of datum surfaces within the intervals missing.

4. Many of the sections are short and therefore contain few datum surfaces.

5. One or both of the species in the pair whose datum surfaces are being compared do not occur in all of the sections.

The first two factors may be remedied by more detailed sample collection or more detailed analysis of samples on hand, but little can be done to improve situations three and four. Factor five is a function of paleobiogeography. This is the factor which must be separated from the others if a detailed knowledge of the lateral ranges of species is to be obtained.

Before progressing to the preliminary analysis of Oligocene biostratigraphy and provinciality of nannofossils, one additional factor affecting results requires examination; namely, the difference in reliability between published stratigraphic information and personally examined samples. In relying on published data for the results obtained below, two main assumptions had to be made in order to adapt it to MASS analysis: 1) that sampling densities and analysis are uniform and free of bias; and 2) that sample collection and analysis are free of operator error.

The main effect of bias is to introduce systematic distortions into collected data without altering its internal consistency. Therefore, it distorts results in such a way that they may not closely approximate truth but are consistent and reproducible. For example, the stratigraphic

ROTH·REDUCED TO MARTINI GUIDE FOSSILS
NUMBER OF CORES   7 NUMBER OF FOSSILS   5

EV.=1	EXT.=2	SPHENOLITHUS CIPEROENSIS
EV.=3	EXT.=4	SPHENOLITHUS DISTENTUS
EV.=5	EXT.=6	CYCLOCOCCOLITHUS FORMOSUS
EV.=7	EXT.=8	DISCOASTER SAIPANENSIS
EV.=9	EXT.=10	RETICULOFENESTRA UMBILICA

FIG. 1—Species analyzed from Roth (1970).

range of a species within a section may be found to be different among several investigators because of their slightly different species concepts.

Operator error (or "noise level") reduces the internal consistency of data but is generally random and introduces no bias. Although operator error can never be eliminated, its effects can be minimized by increased data collection.

Historically, the effects of bias and operator error have been standardized because many investigators personally collected, examined, and reduced their own data, only using the results of others when those results could reasonably be correlated with that investigator's own data. This personal approach was necessary when automated data processing was not available for mass comparisons and is still a highly regarded technique. Its disadvantage is that it does not make efficient use of all available data.

Automated data processing allows easy use of the results of many authors simultaneously and effectively randomizes the effects of bias in proportion to the number of authors used. Unfortunately, randomizing bias converts it to noise so that a large volume of data must be analyzed before the internally consistent results of a single author can be surpassed.

To introduce the analysis, MASS is used to compare results obtained by using a small amount of internally consistent data collected by a single author (Roth, 1970, and Roth and others, 1971) with results based on a synthesis of published information of many authors. At the same time, treatment of the Roth data will provide a simple illustration of the mechanics of MASS. This will in turn make the results of the larger-scale analysis more comprehensible.

Figure 1 shows the five species (therefore 10 datum surfaces) considered for evaluation using the Roth data. The asterisks in the appendix indicate the seven sections from which they were recorded. With the exception of the extinction of *Sphenolithus ciperoensis*, which is used in place of the extinction of *Helicopontosphaera recta* as the top of NP25, all the datum surfaces used by Martini (1971) appear in this analysis. Roth did not record *Helicopontosphaera recta* in his range charts.

Figure 2 indicates the most probable sequence of these 10 datum surfaces and the expectation that adjacent pairs are in correct sequence after MASS has ordered them. The highest expectation available in this case is 0.98, which would occur if two datum surfaces occur in the same sequence for all seven sections. With Roth's data applied to Martini's zonation, the highest number of times adjacent surfaces actually occur in sequence without reversal is four times ($\approx .875$).

Figure 3 is the unordered X-array and contains all the information necessary to solve for the most probable sequence shown in figure 2. The number of sections in which a species occurs is found by comparing the number of times its evolution occurs below its extinction, for example, *Sphenolithus ciperoensis* occurs in four sections (circled in fig. 3).

Figure 4 is a reorganization of figure 3 so that all zeros appear below the main diagonal (the line connecting the black squares). The correct sequence of events is listed in the left-hand column with the highest datum surface on the top. This table represents the heart of the MASS system. From it may be read:

1. The most probable sequence;

POSITION NUMBER	DATUM NUMBER			FOSSIL NAME	LINK EXPECTATION
1		2	EXT.	SPHENOLITHUS CIPEROENSIS	.75000
2	NP25*	4	EXT.	SPHENOLITHUS DISTENTUS	.87500
3	NP24*	1	EV.	SPHENOLITHUS CIPEROENSIS	.75000
4		3	EV.	SPHENOLITHUS DISTENTUS	.87500
5	NP23*	10	EXT.	RETICULOFENESTRA UMBILICA	.87500
6	NP22*	6	EXT.	CYCLOCOCCOLITHUS FORMOSUS	.75000
7	NP21*	8	EXT.	DISCOASTER SAIPANENSIS	.75000
8		5	EV.	CYCLOCOCCOLITHUS FORMOSUS	0.00000
9		7	EV.	DISCOASTER SAIPANENSIS	0.00000
10		9	EV.	RETICULOFENESTRA UMBILICA	.87500

FIG. 2—Most probable sequence of datum surfaces of Figure 1 (*Martini, 1971).

2. The number of times any pair of datum surfaces occurs in sequence; and;

3. The number of times, if any, that sequence is reversed.

For example, datum 10 (the extinction of *Reticulofenestra umbilica*) occurs above datum 8 (the extinction of *Discoaster saipanensis*) three times (circled) but datum 8 never occurs above datum 10 (circled).

Figure 5 displays the expectations shown on the previous figure. For the above example, this table shows that based on the data given, the probability of finding datum 10 above 8 (or 8 below 10) is 0.75.

Two more aspects of this simple example of MASS need elucidation. First, the evolution of *Sphenolithus distentus* (figs. 2, 4, and 5) occurs within NP23 and is below the evolution of *Sphenolithus ciperoensis* and above the extinction of *Reticulofenestra umbilica* with corresponding expectations of 0.75 and 0.875 respectively. This indicates that NP23 (bounded above at 0.875 and below at 0.875) can be subdivided into two zones at almost no cost in reliability. Similar situations are equally evident for the larger data volumes to be shown below.

Second, no mention has been made of the three evolutionary datum surfaces 5, 7, and 9. They have been ordered by MASS and so are in proper sequence, but this sequence is apparent and does not represent a real stratigraphic situation. Datum 8, the extinction of *Discoaster saipanensis*, was chosen to represent the base of the Oligocene and stratigraphic data were not recorded below the highest appearance of *Discoaster saipanensis*. Therefore only the sequence above this datum should be considered

X ARRAY, ORDERED

I/J	2	4	1	3	10	6	8	5	7	9
2	■	3	4	4	4	4	2	4	2	4
4	0	■	4	4	4	4	2	4	2	4
1	0	0	■	3	4	4	2	4	2	4
3	0	0	0	■	4	4	2	4	2	4
10	0	0	0	0	■	4	3	7	4	7
6	0	0	0	0	0	■	3	7	4	7
8	0	0	0	0	0	0	■	3	3	3
5	0	0	0	0	0	0	0	■	0	0
7	0	0	0	0	0	0	0	0	■	0
9	0	0	0	0	0	0	0	0	0	■

FIG. 4—Ordered X-array of the Roth data.

EXPECTATION ARRAY, ORDERED

I/J	2	4	1	3	10	6	8	5	7	9
2	■	.75	.88	.88	.88	.88	.50	.88	.50	.88
4	.75	■	.88	.88	.88	.88	.50	.88	.50	.88
1	.88	.88	■	.75	.88	.88	.50	.88	.50	.88
3	.88	.88	.75	■	.88	.88	.50	.88	.50	.88
10	.88	.88	.88	.88	■	.88	.75	.98	.88	.98
6	.88	.88	.88	.88	.88	■	.75	.98	.88	.98
8	.50	.50	.50	.50	.75	.75	■	.75	.75	.75
5	.88	.88	.88	.88	.98	.98	.75	■	0.00	0.00
7	.50	.50	.50	.50	.88	.88	.75	0.00	■	0.00
9	.88	.88	.88	.88	.98	.98	.75	0.00	0.00	■

FIG. 5—Ordered expectation array of the Roth data.

significant. This is intuitively apparent because *Cyclococcolithus formosus, Discoaster saipanensis* and *Reticulofenestra umbilica* evolve in the lower to middle Eocene and only their extinctions are important in the Oligocene. A similar situation holds for datum surfaces which may occur above the highest *S. ciperoensis* (i.e., above the top of the Oligocene).

Finally, two pecularities of MASS not illustrated above deserve explanation before we proceed to an evaluation of Oligocene provincialism. First, if a species is programmed for MASS evaluation and is found never to occur in the sections studied, it will remain in its initial input position on the list, appear to be within a sequence, and to become extinct before it evolves. This is because an evolution datum

X ARRAY, UNORDERED

I/J	1	2	3	4	5	6	7	8	9	10
1	■	0	3	0	4	4	2	2	4	4
2	4	■	4	3	4	4	2	2	4	4
3	0	0	■	0	4	4	2	2	4	4
4	4	0	4	■	4	4	2	2	4	4
5	0	0	0	0	■	0	0	0	0	0
6	0	0	0	0	7	■	4	3	7	0
7	0	0	0	0	0	0	■	0	0	0
8	0	0	0	0	3	0	3	■	3	0
9	0	0	0	0	0	0	0	0	■	0
10	0	0	0	0	7	4	4	3	7	■

FIG. 3—Unordered X-array of the Roth data.

Evolution	Extinction	
1	2	Discoaster barbadiensis (TAN SIN HOK)
3	4	Sphenolithus belemnos BRAMLETTE and WILCOXON
5	6	Zygrhablithus bijugatus (DEFLANDRE)
7	8	Reticulofenestra bisecta (HAY, MOHLER and WADE)
9	10	Triquetrorhabdulus carinatus MARTINI
11	12	Sphenolithus ciperoensis BRAMLETTE and WILCOXON
13	14	Helicopontosphaera compacta (BRAMLETTE and WILCOXON)
15	16	Sphenolithus distentus (MARTINI)
17	18	Cyclococcolithus formosus KAMPTNER
19	20	Markalius inversus (BRAMLETTE and MARTINI)
21	22	Lanthernithus minutus STRADNER
23	24	Pontosphaera multipora (KAMPTNER)
25	26	Chiasmolithus oamaruensis (DEFLANDRE)
27	28	Transversopontis obliquipons (DEFLANDRE)
29	30	Sphenolithus predistentus BRAMLETTE and WILCOXON
31	32	Sphenolithus pseudoradians BRAMLETTE and WILCOXON
33	34	Isthmolithus recurvus DEFLANDRE
35	36	Helicopontosphaera reticulata BRAMLETTE and WILCOXON
37	38	Discoaster saipanensis BRAMLETTE and RIEDEL
39	40	Helicopontosphaera seminulum (BRAMLETTE and SULLIVAN)
41	42	Ericsonia subdisticha et. aff. (ROTH and HAY)
43	44	Discoaster Tani BRAMLETTE and RIEDEL
45	46	Rhabdosphaera tenuis BRAMLETTE and SULLIVAN
47	48	Helicopontosphaera truncata (BRAMLETTE and WILCOXON)
49	50	Reticulofenestra umbilica (LEVIN)

Fig. 6—Twenty-five species whose 50 datum surfaces have been considered in this paper.

is assigned a specific number code and the extinction of that fossil is assigned the next higher number reading down the column of species names. If the species never occurs, its datum positions will remain unchanged in the list. This has not happened with any of the 25 species studied here but occurred commonly in earlier runs using less well-known species.

Second, although obviously a species must evolve before it becomes extinct, the MASS results for the evolution of a species occurring below its extinction will indicate an expectation below 1.00 unless it occurs in over eight sections. This is because MASS treats each datum surface individually and assigns no particular significance to either evolution or extinction, even of the same species.

ANALYSIS OF THE LATITUDINAL DISTRIBUTION OF OLIGOCENE NANNOFOSSILS

Having demonstrated how MASS works for a simplified situation, the remainder of this paper outlines the results of a literature study of the Oligocene conducted to: 1) suggest the present levels of nannofossil biostratigraphic resolution available from published data, 2) illustrate some of the differences between high-to-middle latitude sequences and low latitude ones, and 3) map the areal distributions through time of some of the more diachronous surfaces. As the MASS system became operative only recently, the following must be regarded as preliminary.

Latitudinal Gradients.—Figure 6 lists the 25 species whose datum surfaces have been considered for this project. Therefore 50 datum surfaces have been analyzed. As previously, the base of the Oligocene is arbitrarily chosen as the extinction surface of *Discoaster saipanensis,* and the top of the Oligocene as the extinction surface of *Sphenolithus ciperoensis.* Figure 7 shows the most probable stratigraphic order of the 29 datum surfaces within the Oligocene based on the 51 published sections shown. Figures 8 and 9 present results for 32 sections below 35° latitude and 19 sections above 35° north latitude respectively.

The unordered X-array, ordered X-array, and expectation array for these three sequences are not reproduced here because of space considerations. Each takes four pages of computer printout (total = 12 pages) and when assembled, is a two by two-foot matrix containing 2,500

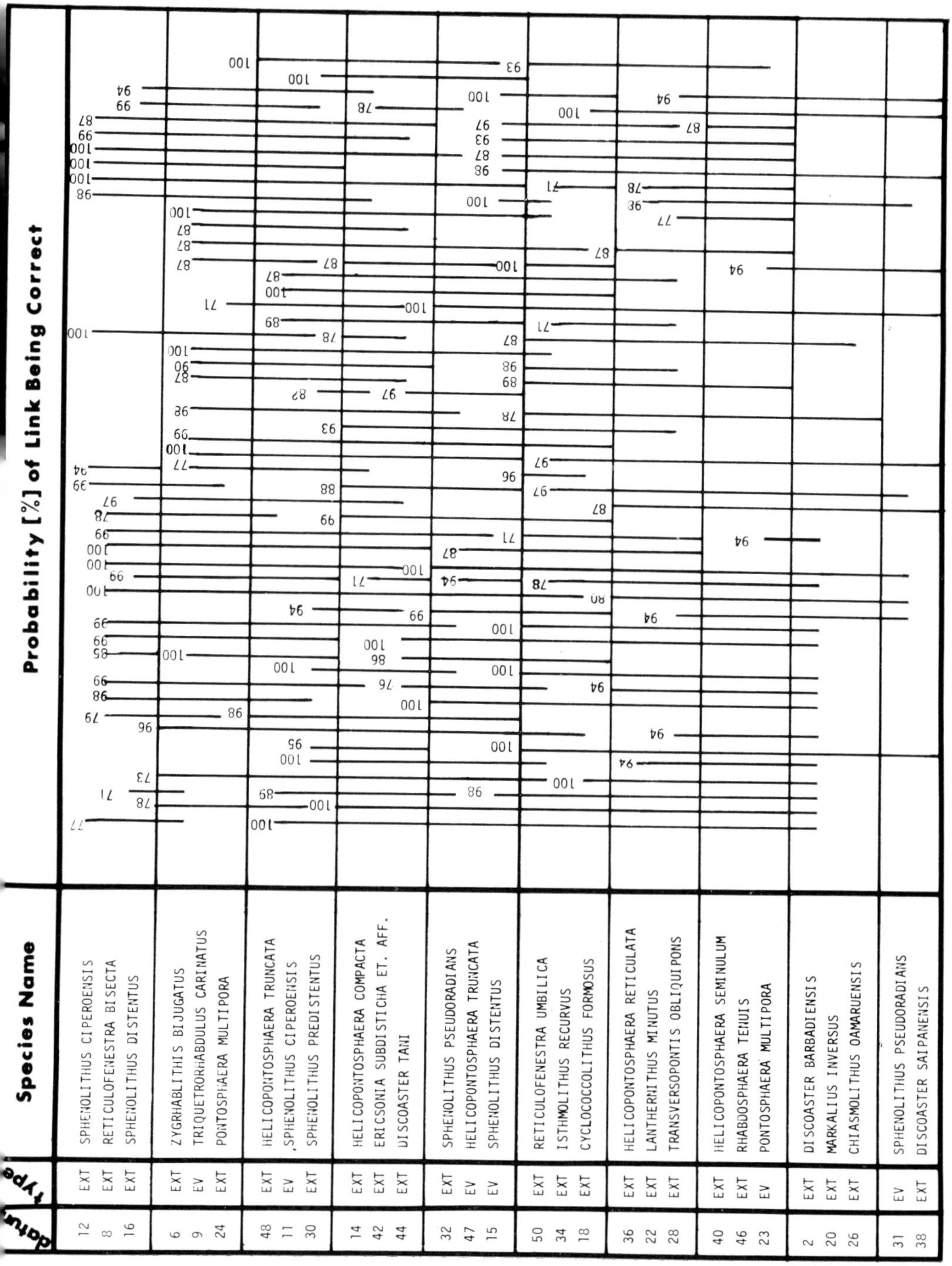

Fig. 7—The most probable sequence of 29 datum surfaces from 51 sections. The bars show some of the probabilities (times 100) that the order between two datum surfaces is correct.

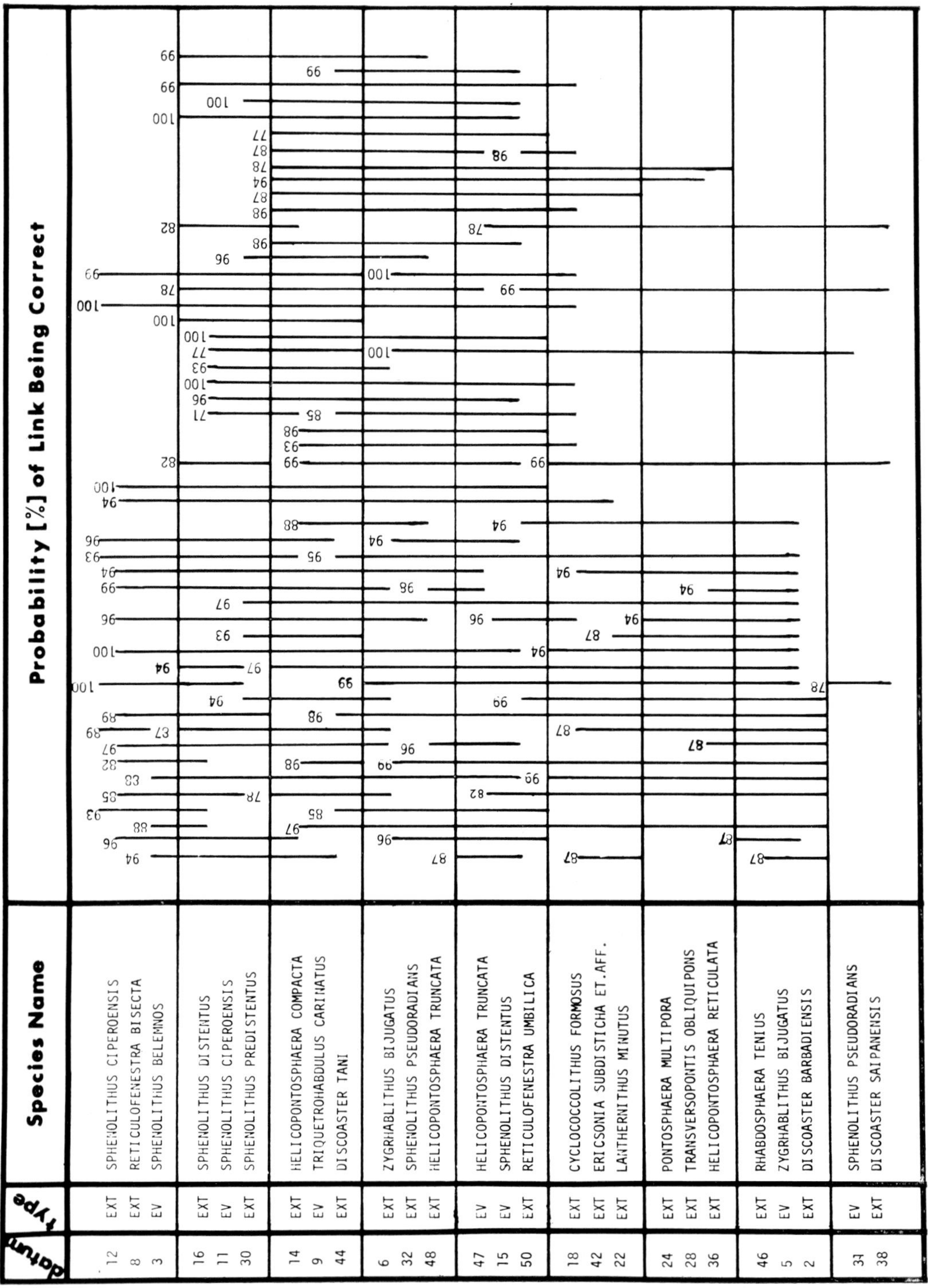

Fig. 8—The most probable sequence of 26 datum surfaces from 32 sections below 35 degrees latitude. The bars show some of the probabilities that the order between two datum surfaces is correct.

points. Instead, some of the probability links for better studied datum surfaces are plotted on figures 7–9 and may be read directly.

Figures 7–9 may also be used to estimate the degree of biostratigraphic resolution available in the published data. For instance, in figure 7 (a composite of all 51 sections used), 29 datum surfaces can be placed in sequence and seven of them (12, 9, 44, 15, 50, 34, 31) form a chain with a minimum link of .96 between adjacent intervals. If one is willing to accept a 0.80 minimum link, nine surfaces (12, 16, 11, 14, 47, 15, 50, 34, 31) are available for subdivision. This increases to 12 at 0.70 (12, 16, 6, 11, 14, 42, 44, 15, 50, 23, 18 2) and 17 at 0.50 (12, 8, 16, 6, 9, 11, 14, 42, 44, 32, 15, 50, 34, 18, 23, 2, 38). Other chains are available and the reader may wish to construct different subdivisions of his own using figures 7–9.

The results of the study also indicate that sequences change as a function of latitude. Comparison of the most probable sequence in figures 8 and 9 indicates weaker probability chains for higher latitude assemblages. The low-latitude sequence contains 26 surfaces. Six of them (12, 11, 15, 50, 18, 2) form a chain with a minimum link of 0.96, and chains of ten (12, 8, 16, 11, 32, 15, 50, 18, 5, 2), and eleven (12, 8, 16, 11, 14, 47, 15, 50, 18, 5, 2) are available at the 0.80 and 0.70 levels respectively. There is no increase at the 0.50 level for this case. In the higher latitudes, only 16 datum surfaces

can be placed in sequence (fig. 9) and no chains can be formed above 0.95. Only five surfaces can be ordered (12, 30, 50, 22, 27) at the 0.80 level, six (12, 30, 15, 50, 34, 18) at the 0.70 level, and seven (12, 30, 15, 50, 34, 18, 27) at 0.50.

This lower stratigraphic resolution is reasonable because fewer sections containing fewer fossils are available for study from higher latitudes (19 sections, 16 surfaces) than from latitudes below 35° (32 sections, 26 surfaces).

Figure 10 depicts the relative positions across latitude of 17 Oligocene datum surfaces and shows the adjacent probability link of each for latitudes below 35 degrees, latitudes above 35 degrees, and a composite. Some probability links for non-adjacent surfaces may be obtained from figures 7–9. The bracketed intervals show the link probabilities of the datum surfaces bounding Martini's (1971) Oligocene zones. This figure demonstrates that:

1. The longest chains result for the composite of 51 sections, followed by the low-latitude ones and then high-latitude ones;

2. Many datum surfaces reverse positions as they transect latitude, but that this effect is much more pronounced for the lower Oligocene;

3. None of the datum surfaces bounding the standard Oligocene Zones of Martini (1971) cross, but diminish in reliability at higher latitudes.

datum	type	Species Name	Probability [%] of Link Being Correct
12	EXT	SPHENOLITHUS CIPEROENSIS	
30	EXT	SPHENOLITHUS PREDISTENTUS	
15	EV	SPHENOLITHUS DISTENTUS	
44	EXT	DISCOASTER TANI	
50	EXT	RETICULOFENESTRA UMBILICA	
2	EXT	DISCOASTER BARBADIENSIS	
34	EXT	ISTHMOLITHUS RECURVUS	
18	EXT	CYCLOCOCCOLITHUS FORMOSUS	
22	EXT	LANTHERNITHUS MINUTUS	
11	EV	SPHENOLITHUS CIPEROENSIS	
14	EXT	HELICOPONTOSPHAERA COMPACTA	
26	EXT	CHIASMOLITHUS OAMARUENSIS	
28	EXT	TRANSVERSOPONTIS OBLIQUIPONS	
27	EV	TRANSVERSOPONTIS OBLIQUIPONS	
32	EXT	SPHENOLITHUS PSEUDORADIANS	
38	EXT	DISCOASTER SAIPANENSIS	

FIG. 9—The most probable sequence of 16 datum surfaces from 19 sections above 35 degrees latitude. The bars show some of the probabilities that the order between two datum surfaces is correct.

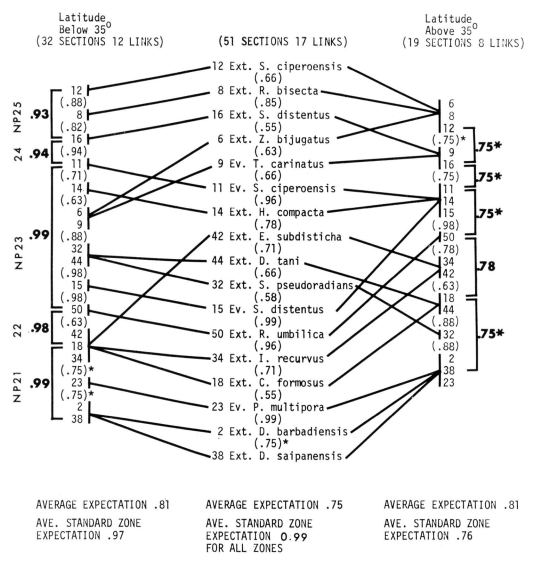

FIG. 10—The relative positions across latitude of 17 Oligocene datum surfaces. The decimals in parentheses indicate the probabilities of the adjacent links being correct and in order. The bracketed intervals show the link probabilities of Martini's (1971) Standard NP Zones.

One of the major surprises of these results is the sharply diachronous nature of some datum surfaces across latitude. It is reasonable that calcareous nannofossil biostratigraphic subdivision should be lower at high latitude because of the generally tropical-subtropical habitat of most nannofossil species and fewer species are available for subdivision at high latitudes. However, this cannot account for the reversals seen in figure 10 which are especially pronounced for the lower Oligocene (NP21–22) and become less evident higher in the Oligocene. It appears that reversals are in part caused by species

having migrated across latitude through time as climate changed to keep within the climatic tolerances in which they evolved. For example, *Zygrhablithus bijugatus, Ericsonia subdisticha,* and *Isthmolithus recurvis* all persist higher into the Oligocene at high latitudes than at low latitudes. This would indicate that although they may have been cosmopolitan in the Eocene, these species preferred cooler waters in the early Oligocene and first disappeared near the equator, existing only at higher latitudes thereafter until their ultimate extinctions. The reverse seems to happen with *Discoaster tani* which disappears within NP21 above latitude 35 degrees, but persists into NP23 below 35 degrees. With respect to lowest occurrence surfaces, *Sphenolithus pseudoradians* first appears in NP21 at high latitude, but not until NP23 at low latitude.

In middle and upper Oligocene strata (above NP22), nannofossil distribution seems more cosmopolitan with datum surface diachroneity becoming much less pronounced possibly because of climatic amelioration during which latitudinal temperature gradients became less pronounced. This is in agreement with the results of Devereux (1967), Wolfe and Hopkins (1966), and Emiliani (1966).

Although the above discussion concerns only 17 of the better-studied Oligocene nannofossil datum surfaces, similar effects have been observed for others. Unfortunately, these have received far less study and are recorded from far fewer sections, however, they will surely show similar patterns as more information is gained about their distribution.

Distribution Mapping.—The sharp latitudinal differences among nannoflora for the Oligocene suggest the feasibility of mapping world wide distribution of several species for the entire Oligocene or selected parts of it. Several types of distribution should be observable on such maps. They are:

1. Oceanic versus shelf habitat;
2. High (35 degrees or greater) versus low (35 degrees or lower) latitude habitat;

and combinations of the above.

However, present data on abundance are still too crude and translatitudinal correlation is still too imprecise to yield results for any but the most obvious patterns. Furthermore, data are still totally lacking for large parts of the world and will never be obtained for Precambrian shield areas or other places where rocks of the required age are not preserved. Currently only the Atlantic and Pacific Oceans, North America, and Europe have had sufficient sampling to warrant mapping Oligocene nannofossil distribution. Even for these areas, data are so sparse that several assumptions had to be made in order to obtain distribution maps.

First, abundance data are lacking or are non-uniform for many of the 51 Oligocene sections used here and only absence-presence relationships have been used in constructing the following maps. This process is biased, especially when only a small number of samples are available for a section. This drawback would be correctable if sampling intervals were made uniform with respect to time, however, this would

depend on knowing which datum surfaces most closely approximate time-planes, a difficult procedure when the only calibration tools are other datum surfaces. Fortunately, this situation will improve as more uniform search criteria and relative abundance standards are adopted, and calibration among investigators is attained (see Hay, 1972, Worsley, in press).

Despite present drawbacks, distribution maps for certain species show obvious patterns. Generally two basic types of maps can be drawn using POSNEG. The first is the relatively straight forward mapping of the distribution of a single species by plotting all the sections in which it occurs versus those where it does not. In the second type, one plots the stratigraphic relationship between any two datum surfaces. The following describes examples of both.

Figures 11 to 24 show the areal distributions of some Oligocene nannofossil species commonly used for biostratigraphic subdivision. These figures illustrate several types of restriction common to many Oligocene groups. The "X" signs represent localities where the specified species occurs and the zeros those where it doesn't. Because of the close proximity of many of the 51 sections studied, 11 of them overlap on the computer printed maps. Therefore, the maps show 51 sections plotted at 39 locations.

Figures 11 and 12 plot the known areal distribution of *Reticulofenestra bisecta* and *R. umbilica* which are among the most cosmopolitan of the species we have studied. They are apparently free of most facies control and are shown here mainly for comparison with the more restricted species to follow. To a lesser extent, *Triquetrorhabdulus carinatus, Cyclococcolithus formosus,* and the sphenoliths, including *Sphenolithus distentus, S. predistentus,* and *S. pseudoradians* are also cosmopolitan. However, they appear to have been less tolerant of cold water than *R. bisecta* and *R. umbilica.* Two other sphenolith species, *S. ciperoensis* and *S. belemnos* are widely dispersed but occur in few sections. Insofar as all these latter species have distributions similar to *R. bisecta* and *R. umbilica,* they are not mapped here.

Figures 13 and 14 represent the distributions of *Chiasmolithus oamaruensis* and *Isthmolithus recurvus* which were apparently restricted to temperate regions in the lower Oligocene. *C. oamaruensis* enjoyed wide dispersal in the upper Eocene but persisted into the Oligocene only in higher latitudes. This cool water preference was probably shared by many other Paleogene chiasmoliths. In similar fashion, *I. recurvus,* a descendant (A. R. Edwards, personal communication) of the widespread *Zygolithus dubius*

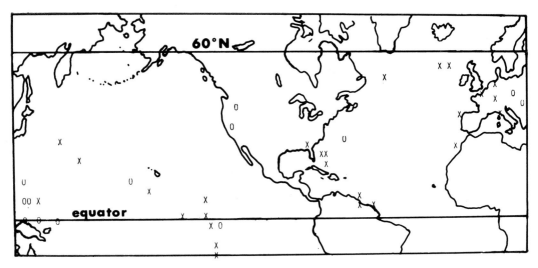

FIG. 11—The Oligocene areal distribution of *Reticulofenestra bisecta.*

complex of upper Eocene age, also preferred temperate waters. However, *I. recurvus* was far more provincial than *C. oamaruensis,* being restricted from the tropics throughout its stratigraphic range. Interestingly, *I. recurvus* became extinct in NP 21 in subtropical regions but persisted into NP 22 in higher latitudes.

Other temperate nannofossil species might include *Zygrhablithus bijugatus* (fig. 15) and *Cyclococcolithus inversus* (fig. 16). However, these are further restricted to only neritic deposits. This is reasonable for *Z. bijugatus* because it is a holococcolith (a type of coccolith in which each structural element is identical)

and all known Recent and fossil holococcoliths have been recovered only from neritic deposits (Gartner and Bukry, 1969). *C. inversus,* on the other hand, is a placolith which are among the most widely distributed and structurally resistant of all nannofossils so that the absence of *C. inversus* from oceanic sediments is peculiar. Its scarcity in neritic sediments of Oligocene age suggests that perhaps its presence may not have been detected in oceanic sections.

Lanternithus minutus, Pontosphaera multipora, Transversopontis obliquipons, Rhabdosphaera tenuis, and *Ericsonia subdisticha* (figs. 17, 18, 19, 20, 21) possessed climatic tolerance

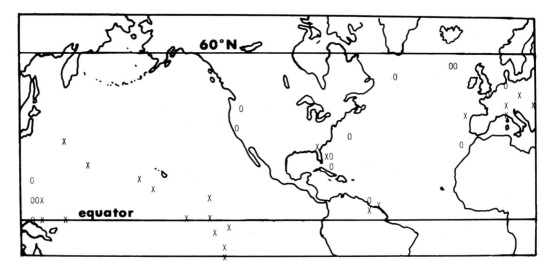

FIG. 12—The Oligocene areal distribution of *Reticulofenestra umbilica.*

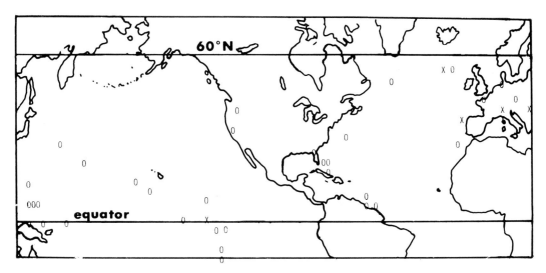

FIG. 13—The Oligocene areal distribution of *Chiasmolithus oamaruensis*.

but were restricted to neritic environments. *L. minutus* (fig. 17) is a holococcolith so its distribution is in agreement with the results of Gartner and Bukry (1969). *P. multipora* and *T. obliquipons* (figs. 18, 19) are both members of the pontosphaerids, a group known to favor neritic environments; a trait they share with the lower Cenozoic rhabdosphaerids as illustrated by the distribution of *R. tenuis* (fig. 20). *E. subdisticha* (fig. 21) is a placolith so that its distribution, like that of *C. inversus,* is somewhat anomalous. *E. subdisticha* was originally used as a zonal marker but, because of its restricted water depth, it was a poor choice.

The last group of nannofossils considered is the helicopontosphaerids which have received considerable attention regarding zonation because of their recognizability even in poorly preserved deposits. Unfortunately they are virtually absent in both higher latitudes and oceanic deposits and appear to be one of the most laterally restricted of all the major nannofossil groups in the Oligocene. Figures 22, 23 and 24 illustrate the distributions of *Helicopontosphaera reticulata, H. seminulum* and *H. compacta,* three species commonly used in Oligocene subdivision. With the exception of *H. compacta,* which is found in palenspastic positions

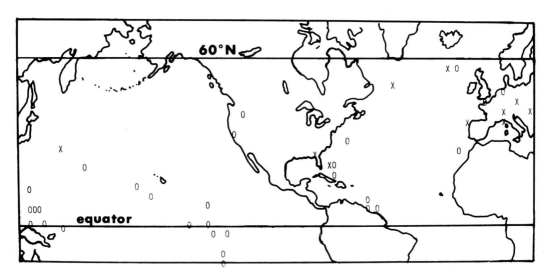

FIG. 14—The Oligocene areal distribution of *Isthmolithus recurvus*.

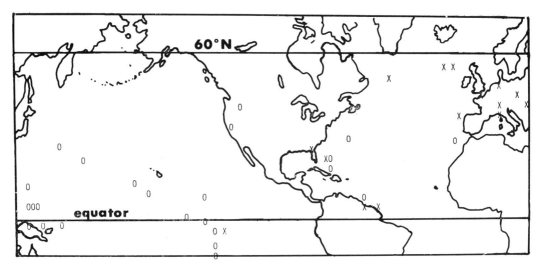

FIG. 15—The Oligocene areal distribution of *Zygrhablithus bijugatus.*

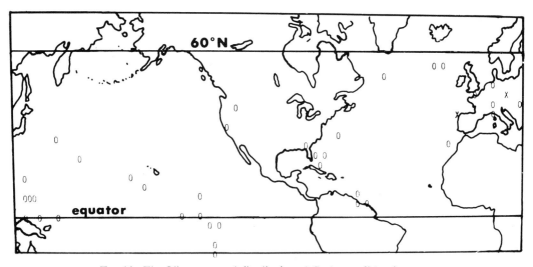

FIG. 16—The Oligocene areal distribution of *Cyclococcolithus inversus.*

of the East Pacific Rise and which therefore can be considered shallow oceanic deposits, these species are found exclusively on the continents and at low to intermediate latitudes.

Proceeding from the areal distribution of single species to the more complex and interesting problem of mapping the stratigraphic relationships between any two fairly closely appressed datum surfaces, several configurations are possible including: 1) a similar sequence for several or many sections, 2) stratigraphic reversal in sections as a function of paleoecological conditions, usually paleoclimatic, 3) randomly distributed reversal patterns among sec-

tions, and 4) non co-occurrence of the two species in sections. In the following maps the symbols used to illustrate these situations are:

0, non-occurrence of both species
1, species 1 occurs without 2
2, species 2 occurs without 1
—, both occur, surface 1 below 2
+, both occur, surface 1 above surface 2
=, both datum surfaces occur at the same
   level.

As before the extreme proximity of some of the sections does not allow for the plotting of all 51 used, so that again, only 39 are shown.

Figure 25 illustrates an example in which the sequence is similar for most sections in which it occurs. This is common if the two surfaces have fairly wide stratigraphic separation. The extinction of *Sphenolithus pseudoradians* is just below the top of NP 23 whereas that of *S. predistentus* occurs high in NP 24. Those localities where both occur, but are not stratigraphically separated, probably indicate sections which either contain unconformaties or are insufficiently closely sampled to separate the two surfaces. In general, such a datum surface pair will show a high probability of being in sequence in figures 7, 8, and 9. In future studies,

these pairs will have little chance of showing reversals in the province in which they occur.

Figures 26–31 are maps of surfaces that reverse stratigraphic position across latitude, probably as a result of changes in their maximum areal dispersion through time. When a species evolves, it is usually adapted to the climatic conditions under which it evolved and will migrate to remain within those conditions should climates change. Clearly an evolution or extinction can only occur at a specific point in space-time. However, the terms "evolution" and "extinction" are used loosely here because of the awkwardness of "lowest stratigraphic occur-

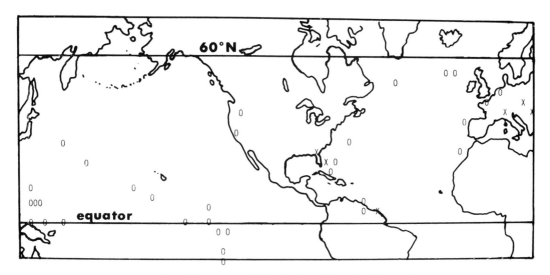

Fig. 17—The Oligocene areal distribution of *Lanthernithus minutus*.

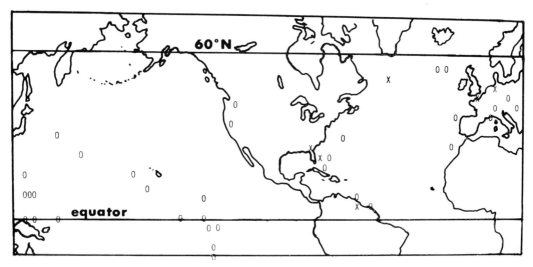

Fig. 18—The Oligocene areal distribution of *Pontosphaera multipora*.

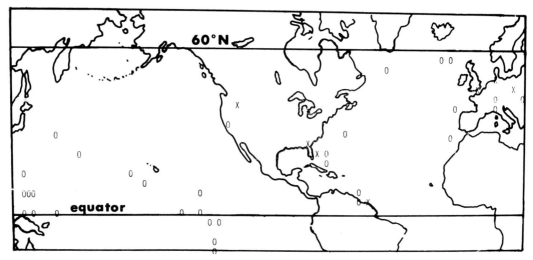

Fig. 19—The Oligocene areal distribution of *Transversopontis obliquipons*.

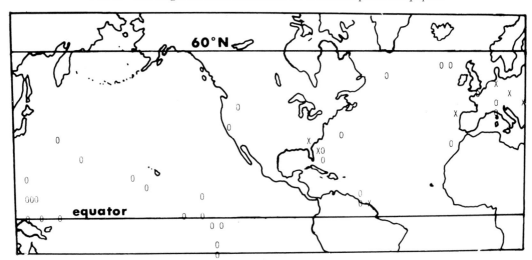

Fig. 20—The Oligocene areal distribution of *Rhabdosphaera tenuis*.

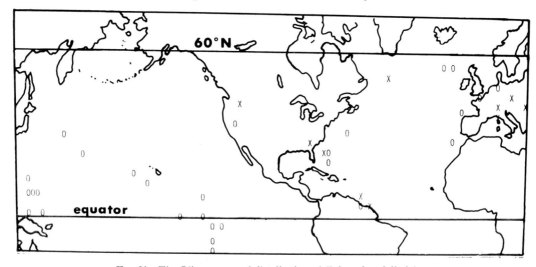

Fig. 21—The Oligocene areal distribution of *Ericsonia subdisticha*.

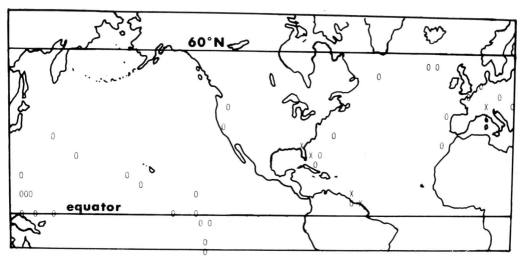

Fig. 22—The Oligocene areal distribution of *Helicopontosphaera reticulata.*

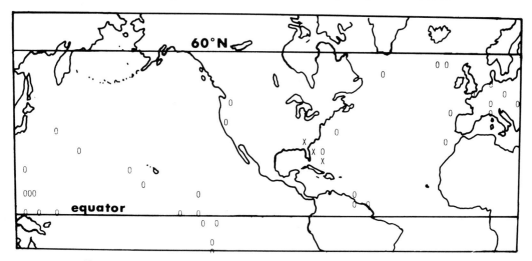

Fig. 23—The Oligocene areal distribution of *Helicopontosphaera seminulum.*

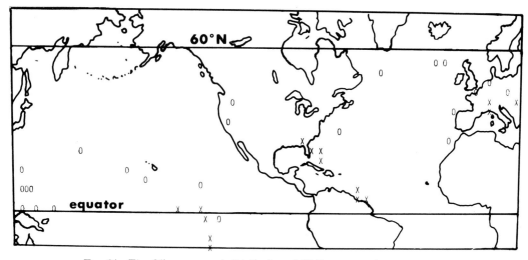

Fig. 24—The Oligocene areal distribution of *Heliconpontosphaera compacta.*

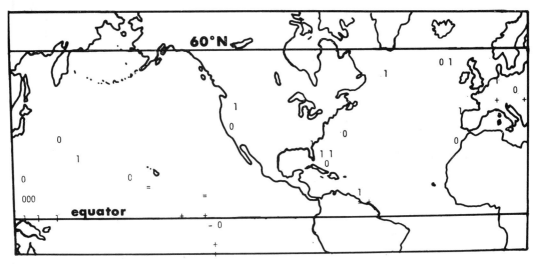

FIG. 25—The areal relationship between the extinction of *Sphenolithus predistentus* and extinction of *Sphenolithus pseudoradians.*

rence" and "highest stratigraphic occurrence." In figure 26, *Spenolithus predistentus* evolves below the extinction of *Discoaster saipanensis* in higher latitudes but above its extinction in lower latitudes. This suggests that either the highest occurrence surface of *D. saipanensis,* the lowest occurrence surface of *S. predistentus,* or both are time-transgressive across latitude. A similar situation exists for the evolution of *S. pseudoradians* and *D. saipanensis* (fig. 27) suggesting that these two sphenolith species shared a common habitat.

Figure 28 demonstrates that *Isthmolithus recurvus,* previously shown to be restricted from the tropics throughout its stratigraphic range, becomes extinct below *Cyclococcolithus formosus* in the subtropical Gulf Coast region, but above *C. formosus* in Europe. In this instance, the top of *I. recurvus* is almost certainly more diachronous than that of *C. formosus* because of the comparatively universal latitudinal distribution of *C. formosus. I. recurvus* also shows added restriction in being virtually absent from oceanic areas.

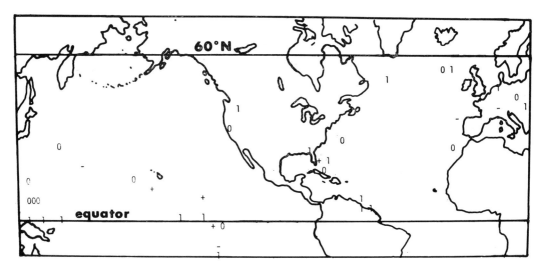

FIG. 26—The areal relationship between the evolution of *Sphenolithus predistentus* and extinction of *Discoaster saipanensis.*

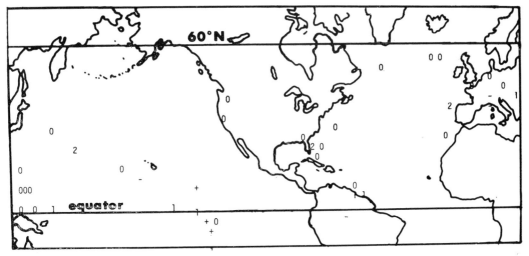

FIG. 27—The areal relationship between the evolution of *Sphenolithus pseudoradians* and extinction of *Discoaster saipanensis*.

Figure 29 illustrates an example somewhat similar to that shown in figure 28 except that *Helicopontosphaera compacta* is restricted to tropical shelf environments rather than temperate ones (as in the example of *I. recurvus*). *Sphenolithus distentus* is cosmopolitan. The occurrences of *H. compacta* in the east Pacific are actually on palenspastic positions of the East Pacific Rise, a fairly shallow oceanic area.

Figures 30 and 31 are more subtle. In figure 30, the extinction of the holococcolith *Lanternithus minutus* occurs below that of *C. formosus*

in the Caribbean and Gulf Coast regions but is at or slightly above it in Europe. Other comparisons are not presently available because like other holococcoliths, *L. minutus* is restricted from oceanic areas. Figure 31 maps the known relationship between the extinctions of *Discoaster saipanensis* and *D. barbadiensis*. These extinctions are thought to approximate the Eocene–Oligocene boundary, however, this is probably true only in the tropics. At higher latitudes *D. barbadiensis* tends to become extinct below *D. saipanensis,* a contention borne out

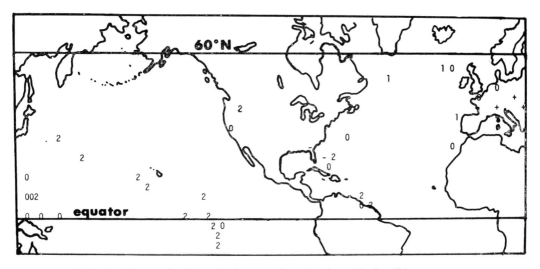

FIG. 28—The areal relationship between the extinction of *Isthmolithus recurvus* and extinction of *Cyclococcolithus formosus*.

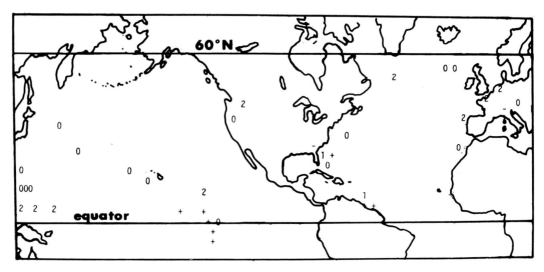

FIG. 29—The areal relationship between the extinction of *Helicopontosphaera compacta* and evolution of *Sphenolithus distentus.*

for both the Northern Hemisphere data presented here and limited results for higher latitudes of the Southern Hemisphere also (A. R. Edwards, personal communication).

As more sections are studied, such pairs as illustrated in figures 26–31 should show a fairly low probability of being in sequence in low latitudes but high probabilities, but of opposite sense, for tropical and temperate provinces. Other datum surface pairs show many reversals but, unlike those shown in figures 26–31, reveal no obvious patterns. These represent closely ap-

pressed surfaces which, while perhaps not synchronous, at least have similar diachroneity patterns (figs. 32, 33, and 34). In figure 32 both *Spenolithus ciperoensis* and *S. predistentus* are cosmopolitan and show an essentially random reversal pattern to their mapped datum surfaces. Figures 33 and 34 show the relationship of the extinction of *Heliconpontosphaera compacta*, a neritic-restricted species, with those of the extinction of *S. predistentus* and *S. pseudoradians*, which are both cosmopolitan. No patterns can be discerned for the neritic sections in which

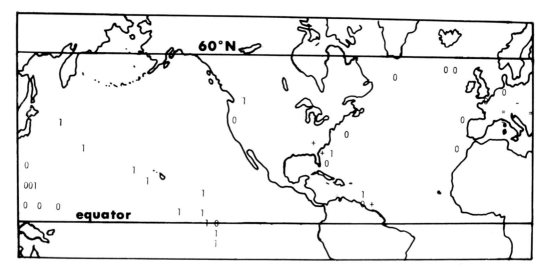

FIG. 30—The areal relationship between the extinction of *Cyclococcolithus formosus* and extinction of *Lanthernithus minutus.*

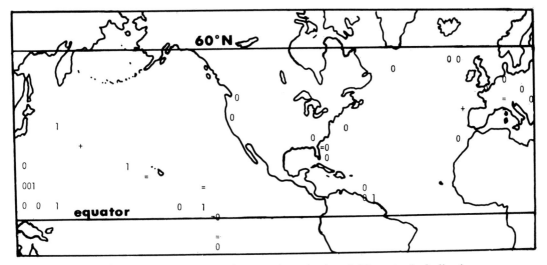

F IG. 31—The areal relationship between the extinction of *Discoaster barbadiensis* and extinction of *Discoaster saipanensis*.

both pairs occur. These surfaces have a reasonable chance of showing stratigraphic separation as more sections are studied and, therefore, offer the chance for increased biostratigraphic resolution.

ACKNOWLEDGMENTS

We wish to thank W. W. Hay, the originator of probabilistic biostratigraphy for his valuable advice and criticism during the early stages of this project. We also are indebted to Bill Snow who wrote, developed, and operated the computer program system used here with the help of Dick and Craig Suchland. Don Stevens and Connie Aitkin provided valuable technical assistance, and Gretchen Blechschmidt assisted in many of the geological and paleontological aspects.

Funding was supplied by National Science Foundation Grants GU-2655, GA-36628X, and by the Department of Oceanography. This is contribution number 766 of the Department of Oceanography, University of Washington.

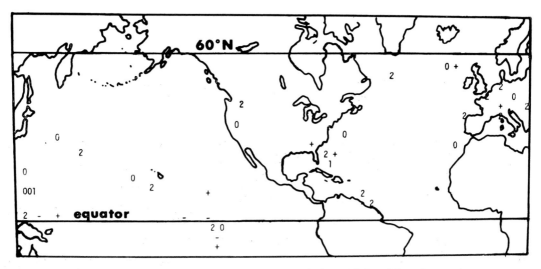

F IG. 32—The areal relationship between the evolution of *Sphenolithus ciperoensis* and extinction of *Sphenolithus predistentus*.

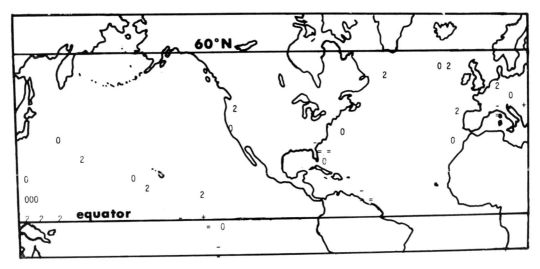

Fig. 33—The areal relationship between the extinction of *Helicopontosphaera compacta* and extinction of *Sphenolithus predistentus.*

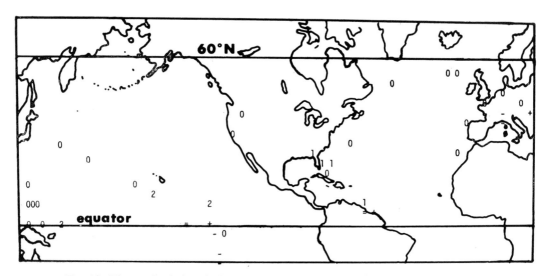

Fig. 34—The areal relationship between the extinction of *Helicopontosphaera compacta* and extinction of *Sphenolithus pseudoradians.*

REFERENCES CITED

Blow, W. H. 1969. Late Middle Eocene to Recent planktonic foraminiferal biostratigraphy. *In,* Brönni-
    mann, P., and H. H. Renz, Eds. Proc. First Int. Conf. Plankt. Microfossils. 1:199–422.
Bramlette, M. N., and J. A. Wilcoxon. 1967. Middle Tertiary calcareous nannoplankton of the Cipero
    section, Trinidad, W.I. Tulane Stud. Geol. 5(3):93–131.
Bukry, D. 1970. Coccolith age determinations Leg 2, deep sea drilling project. *In,* Peterson, M. N. A.,
    and others. Initial reports deep sea drilling project. 2:349–356.
———, R. G. Douglas, S. A. Kling, and V. Krasheninnikov. 1971. Planktonic microfossil biostratigraphy
    of the northwestern Pacific Ocean. *In,* Fischer, A. G. and others. Initial reports deep sea drilling
    project. 6:1253–1300.
Dennison, J. M., and W. W. Hay. 1967. Estimating the needed sampling area for subaquatic ecologic studies.
    J. Paleont. 41:706–708.
Devereux, I. 1967. Oxygen isotope paleotemperature measurements on New Zealand Tertiary fossils: N. Z.
    Jl. Sci. 10(4):988–1011.
Emiliani, C. 1966. Isotopic paleotemperatures. Science. 154:851–857.

GARTNER, S., JR. 1969. Correlation of Neogene planktonic foraminifer and calcareous nannofossil zones. Trans. Gulf Cst Ass. geol. Socs. 19:585–599.

——. 1972. Site Reports. *In*, HAY, J. D., AND OTHERS. Initial reports deep sea drilling project. 9:833–840.

——, AND D. BUKRY. 1969. Tertiary holococcoliths: J. Paleont. 43:1213–1221.

HAQ, BILAL UL. 1971. Paleogene calcareous nannoflora, part IV: Paleogene nannoplankton biostratigraphy and evolutionary rates in Cenozoic calcareous nannoplankton. Stockholm Conf. Geol. XXV(4):129–158.

——, AND J. H. LIPPS. 1971. Site Reports. *In*, TRACEY, J. I., JR., AND OTHERS. Initial reports deep sea drilling project. 8:70, 146, 298, 545, 627, 681.

HAY, W. W. 1970. Calcium carbonate compensation. *In*, BADER, R. G., AND OTHERS. Initial reports deep sea drilling project. 4:659–673.

——. 1971. Preliminary Dating by Fossil Calcareous Nannoplankton Deep Sea Drilling Project, Leg 6. *In*, FISCHER, A. C., AND OTHERS. Initial reports deep sea drilling project. 6:1005–1012.

——. 1972. Probabilistic stratigraphy: Eclog. geol. Helv. 65(2):255–266.

——, H. P. MOHLER, P. H. ROTH, R. R. SCHMIDT, AND J. E. BOUDREAUX. 1967. Calcareous nannoplankton zonation of the Cenozoic of the Gulf Coast and Caribbean-Antillean area, and transoceanic correlation. Trans. Gulf-Cst Ass. geol. Socs. 17:428–480.

LOEBLICH, A. R., AND H. TAPPAN. 1966. Annotated index and bibliography of the calcareous nannoplankton: Phycologia. 5:81–126.

——, AND ——. 1968. Annotated index and bibliography of the calcareous nannoplankton II: J. Paleont. 42:584–598.

——, AND ——. 1969. Annotated index and bibliography of the calcareous nannoplankton III. Ibid. 43:568–588.

——, AND ——. 1970a. Annotated index and bibliography of the calcareous nannoplankton IV. Ibid. 44:558–574.

——, AND ——. 1970b. Annotated index and bibliography of the calcareous nannoplankton V. Phycologia. 9:157–174.

MARTINI, E. 1970. Standard Paleogene calcareous nannoplankton zonation. Nature. 226:560–561.

——. 1971. Standard Tertiary and Quaternary calcareous nannoplankton zonation. *In*, FARINACCI, A., Ed. Proc. II Planktonic Conf. 2:739–786.

——, AND C. LEBENZON. 1971. Nannoplankton-Untersuchungen im oberen Tal des Tarcau (Ostkarpaten, Rumänien) und stratigraphische Ergebnisse. Neuis Jb. Geol. Paläont. Mh. 9:552–565.

——, AND T. WORSLEY. 1970. Standard Neogene calcareous nannoplankton zonation. Nature. 225:289–290.

MCINTYRE, A., A. W. H. BÉ, AND M. B. ROCHE. 1970. Modern Pacific coccolithophorida: a paleontological thermometer: Trans. N. Y. Acad. Sci, Ser. II. 32(6):720–731.

——, AND R. McINTYRE. 1971. Coccolith concentrations and differential solution in oceanic sediments. *In*, RIEDEL, W. R., AND B. M. FUNNEL, Eds. The Micropaleontology of the Oceans. p. 253–262.

——, AND W. F. RUDDIMANN, AND R. JANTZEN. 1972. Southward penetrations of the North Atlantic polar front: faunal and floral evidence of large-scale surface water mass movements over the last 225,000 years. Deep Sea Res. 19:61–77.

RAMSAY, A. T. S. 1971. The investigation of Lower Tertiary sediments from the North Atlantic. *In*, FARINACCI, A., Ed. Proc. II Planktonic Conf. 2:1039–1055.

——, in press. History of Cenozoic carbonate compensation depth changes in the Atlantic Ocean. *In*, HAY, W. W., Ed. Symposium on the history of the ocean basins. Spec. Publ. Soc. Econ. Paleont. Mineol.

RIEDEL, W. R., AND A. SANFILLIPO. 1970. Cenozoic Radiolaria from the Western Tropical Pacific, Leg 7. *In*, WINTERER, E. L. AND OTHERS. Initial reports deep sea drilling project. 7:1529–1672.

ROTH, P. H. 1970. Oligocene Calcareous nannoplankton biostratigraphy. Eclog. geol. Helv. 63(3):799–881.

——, P. BAUMANN, AND V. BERTOLINO. 1971. Late Eocene-Oligocene calcareous nannoplankton from central and northern Italy. *In*, FARINACCI, A., Ed. Proc. II Planktonic Conf. 2:1069–1097.

SHAW, A. B. 1964. Time in stratigraphy. McGraw Hill, New York. 365 p.

SCHNEIDERMANN, N. 1971. Selective dissolution of recent coccoliths in the Atlantic Ocean: geol. Soc. Am. Abstr. 3(7):695.

TAPPAN, H., AND A. R. LOEBLICH, JR. 1971. Geobiologic implications of fossil phytoplankton evolution and time-space distribution. *In*, KOSANKE, R., AND CROSS, A. T., Eds. Symposium on palynology of the Late Cretaceous and Early Tertiary. Spec. Pap. geol. Soc. Am. 127:247–340.

WOLFE, J. A., AND D. M. HOPKINS. 1966. Climatic changes recorded in northwestern North America. *In*, Tertiary correlations and climatic changes in the Pacific. Symp. 25. 11th Pacif. Sci. Congr. p. 67–76.

WORSLEY, T. R., AND E. CRECELIUS. 1972. Paleogene calcareous nannofossils from the Olympic Peninsula, Washington. Bull. geol. Soc. Amer. 83:2859–2862.

——, AND E. MARTINI. 1970. Late Maastrichtian nannoplankton provinces. Nature. 225:1242–1243.

WORSLEY, T. R., in press. The Cretaceous Tertiary boundary event in the ocean. *In*, HAY, W. W., Ed. Symposium on the history of the ocean basins. Spec. Publ. Soc. Econ. Paleont. Mineral.

(Appendix follows on next page)

APPENDIX

PART A—Oceanic Sections Listed in Order of Increasing Latitude

Latitude	Longitude	Locality
N00.26	W138.52	JOIDES Hole 72, Haq, B., and J. Lipps, Initial Reports, Leg 8
N00.28	W133.14	JOIDES Hole 78, Gartner, S., Jr., Initial Reports, Leg 9
N00.29	W133.14	JOIDES Hole 77B, Gartner, S., Jr., Initial Reports, Leg 9
N00.50	E147.53	JOIDES Hole 63, Worsley, T., and E. Martini, Initial Reports, Leg 7
N01.52	E141.56	JOIDES Hole 62, Worsley, T., and E. Martini, Initial Reports, Leg 7
N01.45	E158.37	JOIDES Hole 64, Worsley, T., and E. Martini, Initial Reports, Leg 7
N04.28	W140.19	JOIDES Hole 71, Haq, B., and J. Lipps, Initial Reports, Leg 8
N06.00	W152.52	JOIDES Hole 69, Haq, B., and J. Lipps, Initial Reports, Leg 8
N06.20	W140.22	JOIDES Hole 70, Haq, B., and J. Lipps, Initial Reports, Leg 8
N08.22	E143.34	JOIDES Hole 56, Hay, W., Initial Reports, Leg 6
N08.41	E143.32	JOIDES Hole 57, Hay, W., Initial Reports, Leg 6
N09.14	E144.25	JOIDES Hole 58, Hay, W., Initial Reports, Leg 6
N09.18	E142.33	JOIDES Hole 55, Hay, W., Initial Reports, Leg 6
N09.27	W054.21	JOIDES Site 144A, Roth, Peter, Hans Thierstein, Calc. Nanno. Ranges, DSDP, Leg 14
N09.27	W054.20	JOIDES Site 144B, Roth, Peter, Hans Thierstein, Calc. Nanno. Ranges, DSDP, Leg 14
N11.47	E147.35	JOIDES Hole 59, Hay, W., Initial Reports, Leg 6
N13.15	W059.30	Bath Cliff, Barbados, West Indies, Roth, Peter
N18.02	E141.12	JOIDES Hole 53, Hay, W., Initial Reports, Leg 6
N24.16	W178.31	JOIDES Hole 45, Hay, W., Initial Reports, Leg 6
N25.22	W077.18	JOIDES Site 98, Wilcoxon, James, Calc. Nanno. Ranges, DSDP, Leg 11
N27.54	E171.26	JOIDES Hole 46, Hay, W., Initial Reports, Leg 6
N30.05	W079.15	JOIDES Hole 6, Blake Plateau, Western Atlantic, Roth, Peter
N32.27	E157.43	JOIDES Hole 47, Hay, W., Initial Reports, Leg 6
N35.20	W010.25	JOIDES Site 135, Roth, Peter, Hans Thierstein, Calc. Nanno. Ranges, DSDP, Leg 14
N36.25	W069.25	JOIDES Site 106B, Wilcoxon, James, Calc. Nanno. Ranges, DSDP, Leg 11
N39.28	W127.17	JOIDES Hole 34, Bukry, D. and M. N. Bramlette, Coccolith Age Det., Leg 5
N45.01	W007.58	JOIDES Site 119, Perch-Nielsen, Site Summary, Leg 12
N54.01	W046.36	JOIDES Site 112, Perch-Nielsen, K., Site Summary, Leg 12
S01.55	W137.28	JOIDES Hole 73, Haq, B., and J. Lipps, Initial Reports, Leg 8
S06.14	W136.06	JOIDES Hole 74, Haq, B., and J. Lipps, Initial Reports, Leg 8
S12.31	W134.16	JOIDES Hole 75, Haq, B., and J. Lipps, Initial Reports, Leg 8

Part B—Neritic Sections in Order of Increasing Latitude

Latitude	Longitude	Locality
N10.50	W061.25 ⎫Com-	Zone of Bolli, Trinidad, West Indies, Bramlette, M. N., and J. Wilcoxon
N10.50	W061.25 ⎭posite	Zones of Bolli, Trinidad, West Indies, Roth, Peter
N13.51	W140.11	JOIDES Hole 42, Bukry, David, and Bramlette, M. N., Coccolith Age Det., Leg 5
N19.19	W169.00	JOIDES Hole 44, Hay, W., Initial Reports, Leg 6
N28.30	W077.31	*JOIDES Hole 3, Blake Plateau, western Atlantic, Roth, Peter
N30.23	W080.18	*JOIDES Hole 5, Blake Plateau, western Atlantic, Roth, Peter
N34.00	W086.00	*St. Stephens Quarry, Clark County, Alabama, Roth, Peter
N43.00	E012.00	*Monte Cagnero, Central Apennines, Italy, Roth, Peter
N43.04	E012.37	*Assisi, Roth, Peter, et al.
N45.10	E010.15	*Possagno Marl Formation, Possagno, Italy, Roth, Peter, et al.
N46.00	E013.00	*Scalette, Roth, et al., paper, northern Italy, Roth, et al., Oligocene and Eocene of northern and central Italy
N46.30	E026.00	Miercurea Ciuc, Rumania, Martini, E., and Carol Lebenzon
N48.10	W123.58	Twin River, Olympic Penninsula, Worsley, T. R.
N51.05	E004.22	De Roeck and Verstrpen Boom, Belgium, Roth, Peter
N51.50	E019.00	Hankenbuttel Sud 32, Martini, E., and Carol Lebenzon
N52.13	E011.01	Alversdorf Helmstedt, north Germany, Roth, Peter
N52.14	E011.01	Treue IV, Helmstedt, north Germany, Roth, Peter
N53.00	E011.00	Hollkopf, Glimmerode, north Germany, Roth, Peter
N57.20	W015.24	JOIDES Site 117, Perch-Nielsen, Site Summary, Leg 12
N57.29	W015.55	JOIDES Site 116, Perch-Nielsen, Site Summary, Leg 12

* Used for demonstration of MASS system

MARSUPIALS AND THE NEW PALEOGEOGRAPHY

RICHARD H. TEDFORD

The American Museum of Natural History, New York, NY 10024

ABSTRACT—The dynamic model of the world postulated by plate tectonic theory provides a new basis for speculation about the biogeography of living organisms. Previous interpretations of the history of the marsupial mammals have constituted important arguments for both the stabilist and mobilist (or land bridge) concepts of zoogeography. However, the geological record of the marsupials has never permitted an adequate test of the views of these divergent schools of thought. Now, however, plate tectonics places geographic constraints on biogeographic hypotheses and helps to establish levels of probability among the various hypotheses proposed on biological grounds. In this paper consideration of relevant geological and biological evidence has led to ideas regarding the origin, evolution, and dispersal of the marsupials that are consistent with the new paleogeography. They are offered as logical alternatives to those currently held. Further fossil evidence, especially from the Cretaceous, will be necessary to test the various hypotheses developed from the information presently available.

Plate tectonic models of the Late Jurassic and Early Cretaceous world show the Gondwana continents in an intermediate dispersal stage. Lingering contacts between South America and Africa and archipelagic links of South America with Laurasia and to the united Australoantarctic continent are corroborated by the wide distribution of similar terrestrial biota. Pantothere stocks (possibly peramurids) ancestral to the higher theria apparent were widely distributed, although among the southern continents they are so far known only in Africa. Therians with fully tribosphenic molars of metatherian-eutherian grade are known from the mid-Cretaceous of North America and Asia; their absence elsewhere in the world at that time is regarded as an artifact. Metatherians of didelphid-grade, ancestral to all later marsupials, apparently arose in the environmentally varied South American continent in Late Cretaceous (post-Albian) time. Adaptive radiation through a wide range of environments extending from latitude 0°–70°S produced species which dispersed northward through the tropical middle American archipelago and southward following an archipelagic path to temperate Australoantarctica. Increasing geographic and climatic isolation in Late Cretaceous time led to endemic continental faunas, although the close proximity of North and South America still allowed limited exchange of marsupicarnivorans. Marsupial evolution was drastically reduced in Tertiary time in North America, probably due to competition with the adaptively similar placental insectivores of Holarctica. Only in the isolated southern continents did marsupials form important elements in the terrestrial fauna. Their importance is directly correlated with their degree of isolation from Holarctica. Australia remained a part of East Antarctica and at high latitudes until Eocene time. Dispersal of mammals to the region involved island-hopping along the volcanic archipelago bordering the Pacific side of Antarctica. Although this temperate region seems to have acted as a strong filter to the dispersal of mammals (no placentals were able to reach Australia), other terrestrial organisms found their way across it readily, giving the flora and other elements of the fauna of these temperate southern continents a remarkable similarity. Little is known of the early adaptive radiation that presumably resulted after the arrival of marsupials in Australia. A second major period of diversification may have followed the rifting and drift of Australia north into warmer latitudes. Marsupials shared the South American continent with placental edentates and protungulates, and their interaction probably shaped to some degree the adaptive radiation of each.

INTRODUCTION

Marsupial mammals have greatly interested students of natural history since their discovery by the early Spanish travelers in South America in the 16th Century. Their unique mode of reproduction was early recognized, although not used for the taxonomic separation from other mammals until the 19th Century. Strong structural resemblances and some striking cases of convergence in morphology contributed to the long submergence of the marsupials among the other mammals in early classifications. Continued study has reinforced the conclusion that marsupials and placentals, because they share so many morphological and physiological similarities, must share a common origin. Paleontological and biochemical evidence (Lillegraven, 1969; Air and others, 1971) indicate that the divergence of these major groups of mammals took place no later than medial Cretaceous time (Albian, 100–106 m.y. ago).

Marsupials show a distinctive geographic distribution. Today they are most abundant and diverse in the southern hemisphere, most strikingly in Australia where they form the dominant element in the native terrestrial mammal fauna. In South America they occur from the temperate forests of Chile to the tropical lowlands of the Amazon Basin and north through the Central American isthmus with dwindling diversity into temperate North America. In the Cenozoic they reached Europe, but they have not been important elements of the Holarctic fauna since the Late Cretaceous. Previous explanations of this geographical distribution have taken two opposing views, the stabilist concept, on the one hand, and the mobilist or land bridge concept, on the other.

The fundamental assumption of the stabilist view is that the present arrangement of ocean basins and continents has been maintained from Mesozoic through Cenozoic time, or at least over the span of time covered by the origin, evolution, and dispersal of the mammals. Matthew (1915), in his classic "Climate and Evolution," interpreted the considerable evidence then available as support for the view that the continents of the northern hemisphere ("Holarctica" of biogeographers) were the sites of origin of all the major mammalian groups. Primitive forms, such as marsupials, were thought to have been displaced to the continents of the southern hemisphere by the adaptive radiation of placentals in the north. The routes traveled were believed to be a Middle American isthmus or archipelagic chain to South America and an island-hopping route to Australia through the Indonesian Archipelago. The curious marsupial dominated fauna of Australia was viewed as an expression of the geographic isolation of that continent from Asia and the fortuitous dispersal of the early marsupials on rafts of tangled vegetation torn from swollen river banks and drifted on ocean currents to successively colonize the islands of eastern Indonesia and finally Australia. South America was also an island during the Late Cretaceous and through most of the Cenozoic, although it was more intimately associated with lands to the north. Africa was a partially isolated southern continent during the late Mesozoic and early Cenozoic time. These views, elaborately and eloquently expressed in a series of papers by Simpson (see Simpson, 1965, for summary), seem to explain much about the composition and history of the faunas of the southern continents and especially some difficult consequences of the opposing landbridge view of biogeography.

With respect to the southern continents, the land-bridge theory envisioned closer geographical relationships, or land-bridge connections, between these lands now widely separated by the oceans. Some of the remarkable relationships among the biota of the widely separated southern continents were noted as early as the voyages of scientific exploration in the 19th Century (see recent summaries of Darlington, 1965; Raven and Axelrod, 1972).

Early in this century, comparisons of members of the carnivorous marsupial family Borhyaenidae from the South American Miocene with the living Tasmanian "wolf," *Thylacinus* Temminck 1827, led Sinclair (1906) and Gregory (1910) to place these forms in the same family. These comparisons suggested a former link between South America and Australia. Wood (1924) later reviewed and concurred in the thylacine-borhyaenid relationship. Osborn (1910), and for a time Matthew (1906), believed the evidence from this and several other groups of vertebrates indicated an Antarctic link between South America and Australia. Such biological relationships were accepted as welcome independent evidence of former continental connections by the leading exponents of continental drift, Wegener (1967) and Du Toit (1937).

Matthew's (1915) persuasive arguments led to a critical reexamination of opposing evidence in the ensuing years. Simpson, in a long series of carefully presented papers (see Simpson, 1965, for collected essays), reviewed mammalian zoogeography and reinforced Matthew's conclusions. The affinity between the borhyaenids and thylacines was reexamined by Simpson (1941) and considered to be the result of parallel evolution from a common stock and not conclusive evidence for a connection between South America and Australia. Matthew's (1915) and Simpson's (1941) views, which have come to dominate the field of vertebrate zoogeography, envision a Holarctic source for all mammals. Secondary centers of diversification, such as those in the southern continents, are attributed to adaptive radiation of primitive, formerly northern forms in isolation after sweepstakes dispersal from Holarctica. Darlington (1957) modified this concept slightly by suggesting that the major center of origin was the Old World tropical portion of Holarctica rather than temperate Holarctica, as Matthew thought. Later, Darlington (1965) in his stimulating analysis admitted that certain circumantarctic distributions implied a closer connection between the southern continents in late Paleozoic or early Mesozoic time. Since then ocean gaps have separated the southern continents; their contacts with the northern continents, particularly in the tropics, have accounted for most of the biota of southern lands.

By itself the known history of the marsupials offers little choice between opposing biogeographic concepts. Landbridge builders or mobile continent advocates have had to explain the lack of an ancient placental component in the Australian fauna while maintaining that close geographic links existed between land masses; stabilists have had to contend with the lack of marsupials in Asia, where they should be in order to have found their way south to Australia. Such negative evidence is never satisfactory and so the issues remained deadlocked.

New evidence is now at hand, coming from a

multi-disciplinary effort within the geological sciences. Evidence from geophysics, oceanography, seismology, paleomagnetism, structural geology, and stratigraphy indicates a world composed of interacting lithospheric plates moving away from the sites of crustal generation, the midoceanic ridges, toward zones of subduction, the great ocean trenches, where plate interaction returns simatic (oceanic) crust to the mantle or molds sialic (continental) crust into mountain ranges. The concepts of plate tectonic theory are having an impact on the geological sciences in much the same way that Charles Darwin's and Alfred Wallace's concept of evolution had on the biological sciences over a century ago. In the process, a new geographic framework based primarily on the data of physical science is gradually becoming available to biogeographers. The biological evidence needs to be interpreted within the concept of a mobile world of shifting continents and expanding and contracting oceans. The following pages represent an attempt to fit the known record of the marsupials to the new paleogeography.

THE NEW PALEOGEOGRAPHY

The geographic framework (figs. 1–4) for the following discussion is taken from many sources, as indicated by the figure legends, but is based mainly on Dietz and Holden's (1970) reconstruction of continental relationships prepared by computer fitting the 1,000-meter isobath as the best approximation of the continental margin and charting the rafting and drift of the lithospheric plates from sea-floor spreading and paleomagnetic data. Some modifications and details have been added from more recently published interpretations, particularly

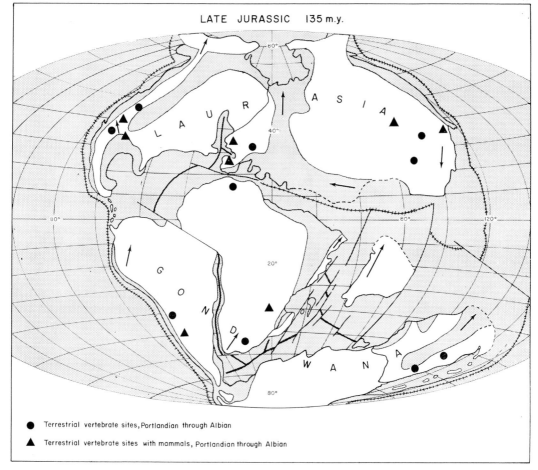

FIG. 1—Late Jurassic and Early Cretaceous terrestrial vertebrate sites plotted on a reconstruction of the latest Jurassic world. The continental shelves (miogeoclines) and epicontinental seas show the distribution of land and sea in Late Jurassic time following the compilations of Kummel (1961).

on the biogeographically critical Caribbean (primarily following Malfait and Dinkelman, 1972) and Scotia Sea (Dalziel and Elliot, 1971) and on the history of the Pacific border of the Australian plate (Griffiths and Varne, 1972; Chase, 1971; and Davies and Smith, 1971). The Oligocene map (fig. 3) was prepared on the base map used by Dietz and Holden (1970) by removing all sea floor formed after 35 m.y.a., following the reconstruction given by Jardine and McKenzie (1972, fig. 2). Additional pertinent data was added to bring this map into conformity with published interpretations as indicated below.

In the Late Jurassic and Early Cretaceous map (fig. 1) the position of the continental parts of the various Gondwana and Laurasian plates is based on Dietz and Holden (1970), somewhat modified: a circum-Pacific subduction zone must have bordered the developing Pacific Ocean to consume crust formed along the Pacific Rise (position not shown). Behind this trench, the western edge of the Americas plate formed an orogenic zone interrupted only in the Middle American area where differentiating continental crust of the proto-Antilles formed a volcanic island arc linking North and South America. The American orogenic zone extended south through West Antarctica (Halpern, 1968) and then north along the Australian peninsula to include proto-New Zealand and continental crust at the mobile edge of the Australoantarctic continent (Griffiths, 1971). Madagascar is shown adjacent to Mozambique, rather than to Tanzania, in accordance with recent interpretations (Green, 1972).

In the map of the Late Cretaceous world (fig. 2) the following modifications and details have been added to the map of Dietz and Holden (1970) based on recent contributions: Relationships between the East Pacific Rise and trench along the Pacific border of North America follows the interpretations of Atwater (1970). The Caribbean Sea is shown as an extension of the East Pacific plate into the westward drifting Americas plate (Malfait and Dinkelman, 1972), considerably lengthening the proto-Antillean volcanic arc and dispersal route between North and South America. The Caribbean and Tethyan Seas formed part of a globe-girdling east-west belt of westward flowing surface water (North Equatorial Current) that may have facilitated south-to-north waif dispersal along the Antillean chain. Northward and westward drift of South America has separated it from Africa and extended the area of narrow continental crust in the Antarctic Peninsula (Dalziel and Elliot, 1971). The Pacific Rise extended west-

ward to separate the Campbell Plateau and proto-New Zealand from West Antarctica (Griffiths, 1971), thus initiating the separation of Australia from Antarctica. Details around Madagascar attempt to follow Green (1972). Laurasia was still intact, but cut by two epicontinental seas, the Western Interior Seaway across North America and the Turgai Strait crossing Eurasia east of the Urals. These barriers isolated western North America-eastern Asia from eastern North America-Europe.

On the early Oligocene map (fig. 3) continental positions follow those given by Jardine and McKenzie (1972). Relationship between the East Pacific Rise and west American trench off North America follows Atwater (1970). The Caribbean area is reconstructed according to Malfait and Dinkelman (1972). The position of the East Pacific Rise and relationship between the Chile Rise and the trench and the developing Scotia Arc are conjectural and are based on the idea that the Chile Rise may be a remnant of a Mesozoic Pacific Rise (Herron, 1972) which was subducted in early Cenozoic time and that subduction terminated the trench south of 50°S latitude (including the former trench bordering West Antarctica). Reorientation of spreading in the South Pacific about 50 m.y. ago (Griffiths and Varne, 1972) may have accompanied rifting of the Australoantarctic continent and establisment of a continuous rise from the central part of the Indian Ocean to the eastern border of the Pacific. Sea-floor spreading in marginal basins (Tasman and Coral seas) along the eastern edge of the Australian continent rafted segments of continental crust (Lord Howe and Norfolk ridges) eastward, isolating these portions of the Australian continent from the mainland (Griffiths and Varne, 1972). New Zealand was further isolated from the Australian mainland in the process. Bending and attenuation of the narrow band of continental crust to form the Scotia Arc (Dalziel and Elliot, 1971) was underway, possibly in response to the reordering and continuing annihilation of the old Pacific Rise crest.

In figure 4 the present world is shown for comparison to depict the result of changes taking place since the Jurassic. The northern and southern portions of the Americas plate have been reunited through orogeny and development of continental crust along Middle America, allowing the mingling of terrestrial biota, including marsupials, which again spread into North America. Northward drift of South America and the further penetration of oceanic crust into Drakes Passage has bent the Scotia Arc into its present form, further isolating

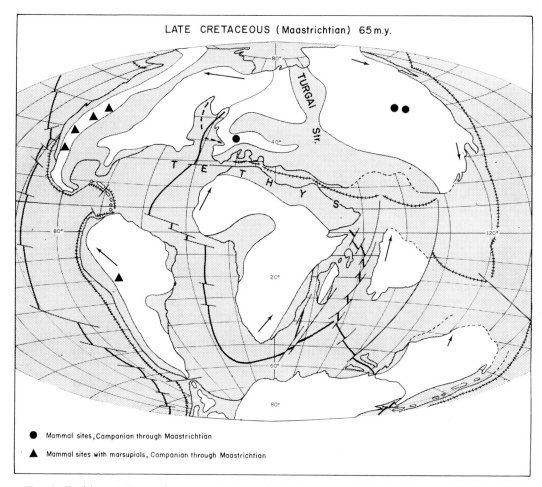

FIG. 2—Position of the continents at the close of the Cretaceous, following Dietz and Holden (1970), with continental shelves and epicontinental seas superposed to show the distribution of land and sea (Kummel, 1961).

South America and West Antarctica. India completed its spectacular northward journey by late Cenozoic time and, along with the northward drift of Africa and opening of the Red Sea, destroyed the Tethyan Seaway. Australia, on a plate partly decoupled from India along the Ninety-East Fracture Zone, has drifted north into the complex subduction zone which forms part of its boundary with the Pacific plate. The formation of New Guinea is related to this late Cenozoic event (Davies and Smith, 1971). Marsupials spread north to this large tropical highland, which also served as a dispersal route that allowed placentals to reach the long isolated Australian continent from the Indonesian Archipelago. Continued spreading in marginal basins on the eastern edge of the Australian plate further isolated fragments of its continental border.

As the distribution of land and sea is a critical factor in the dispersal of terrestrial vertebrates, the epicontinental seas and continental shelves have been superimposed on the maps. In this way the pattern of dispersal can be more realistically deduced from the available evidence, and error in equating the outline of the continents with emergent land is avoided. From the standpoint of terrestrial biogeography, the important features shown by these maps are: the separation of Africa following the Triassic to mid-Jurassic opening of the Indian Ocean (Smith and Hallam, 1970) and subsequent opening of the South Atlantic; the full separation of the Americas plate from Africa by the middle Cretaceous (Funnell and Smith, 1968); the continued juxtaposition of North America and Europe until the final opening of the North Atlantic in early Tertiary time (Pitman and Tal-

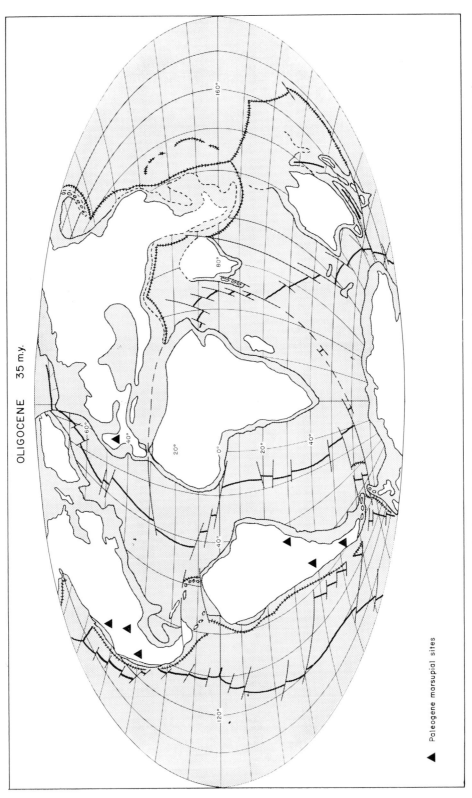

Fig. 3—Reconstruction of the distribution of land and sea in early Oligocene time, compiled from many sources (see text).

wani, 1972); the persistent isolation of eastern Asia from Europe in the Paleogene by the epicontinental seaway (Turgai Strait) east of the Ural fold belt; geographic continuity of eastern Asia with North America across Beringia throughout much of the Cenozoic (Pitman and Talwani, 1972; Churkin, 1972; Szalay and McKenna, 1971); the presence of a volcanic archipelago along the east Pacific subduction zone linking the North and South American portions of the Americas plate during the Mesozoic and Cenozoic; and the presence of similar archipelagic chains in the South Pacific linking the Andean orogenic belt with West Antarctica (Dalziel and Elliot, 1971) and with the orogenic belt bordering the Antartic plate (together with its Australian peninsula) in the late Mesozoic and early Cenozoic (Griffiths and Varne, 1972). The volcanic island chain linking the continents bordering the southern and eastern Pacific was extended by the northward drift of the Americas plate and the separation of the Australian plate. This began in Late Cretaceous with the extension of the East Pacific Rise between Maire Byrd Land and the Campbell Plateau of New Zealand and later completed by the extension of the East Indian Ocean Rise between Australia and East Antarctica in the middle to late Eocene. This led to the final isolation of the Antarctic plate (including its orogenic borderland, West Antarctica) and the partial decoupling of the North and South American portions of the Americas plate. The Caribbean and Scotia Seas resulted as complex transform fault bounded zones of direct interaction between oceanic or quasi-oceanic portions of the Americas and Pacific plates.

Thus the geographic entity of Gondwana of the Triassic slowly fragmented in Mesozoic and early Cenozoic time. Close north-south archipelagic links in the Early Cretaceous were gradually extended and finally broken by early Cenozoic time, but close geographic proximity and the persistence of the South America-Antarctica-Australia linkage into Late Cretaceous time is of great biogeographic importance.

THE MARSUPIAL–PLACENTAL DIVERGENCE

Among Late Jurassic mammals the Pantotheria (=Eupantotheria) appear to be the only adequate morphological antecedents of the marsupials and placentals. Their geographic distribution in Late Jurassic and Early Cretaceous time is thus of importance in determining the area of origin of the higher therian mammals. Pantotheres occur in the Upper Jurassic Morrison Formation of the Rocky Mountains of the United States, in the Upper Jurassic Purbeck beds and Lower Cretaceous Wealden deposits of England, and in the Upper Jurassic or Lower Cretaceous Tendaguru Formation of Tanzania, East Africa. These scattered records imply even wider occurrences in both the Gondwana and Laurasian land masses, in agreement with the seemingly cosmopolitan nature of the Late Jurassic-Early Cretaceous dinosaur faunas with which they are associated (Charig, 1969; Colbert, 1971). Similar dinosaur faunas occur in eastern Asia, South America, and Australia, although no mammals are known there except for some mammalian trackways in the Jurassic of Argentina (Casamiquela, 1961). These vertebrate faunas were associated with the equally widespread pre-angiosperm forests or gymnosperms and cycads, which gave a rather uniform aspect to the terrestrial biomes of the Late Jurassic and Early Cretaceous world.

None of the known Late Jurassic pantotheres acquired the tribosphenic cheek teeth characteristic of marsupials and placentals, although some groups, notably the peramurids (Clemens and Mills, 1971), seem to have acquired the dental morphology that could represent a proto-tribosphenic stage. The Late Jurassic Morrison and Purbeck faunas resemble one another except that peramurids, known from the English Purbeck beds, are not found in the large Morrison mammal fauna of western North America.

Forms with tribosphenic lower molars (*Aegialodon* Kermack, Lees, and Mussett, 1967) are known from the Early Cretaceous (Neocomian) in England. By mid-Cretaceous time mammals with fully tribosphenic molars had appeared. The earliest fossil remains recognized as marsupial are cheek teeth (*Holoclemensia* Slaughter, 1969) from the medial Cretaceous (Albian) Paluxy Formation, Trinity Group, of southeastern Texas, recently described by Slaughter (1968, 1971). The presence in these Texas deposits of teeth resembling in some features those of placental or eutherian mammals (*Pappotherium* Slaughter, 1965) and morphologically similar remains (*Endotherium* Shikama, 1947) in Lower Cretaceous deposits of Manchuria and Mongolia (Barsbold and others, 1971) suggests an Early Cretaceous divergence of these major groups.

Despite these specific dental resemblances to one or the other group of higher therians, the mid-Cretaceous therians retain considerable overall similarity, implying that differentiation of dentition more typical of later marsupials and placentals was only in an incipient stage at that point in time. Until other osteological evidence is available, it seems best to acknowledge the structural position of the mid-Cretaceous the-

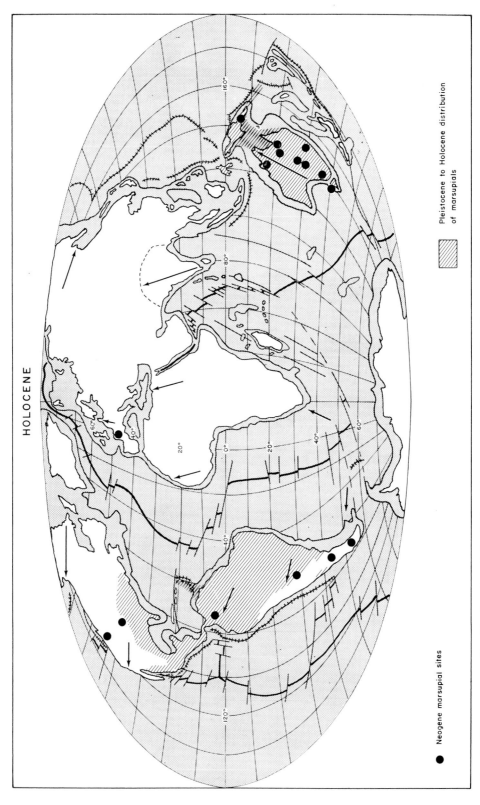

Fig. 4.—The present world with plate boundaries indicated by axes of sea floor spreading (heavy solid lines) offset by transform faults and ocean trenches or subduction zones (barred lines), following Dietz and Holden (1970), with additional details added in the Pacific to make the presentation coordinate with Figures 1–3. Arrows show plate motion and rate.

rians by the term "therians of metatherian-eutherian grade" (see Fox, 1971, for fuller discussion), rather than trying to ally them specifically to later groups. Recent discoveries have shown that mammals of this grade persisted into the Late Cretaceous (Campanian) in North America (*Potamotelses* Fox, 1972) and Mongolia (the Deltatheridiidae, Butler and Kielan-Jaworowska, 1973), where they were contemporary with their probable descendants among the earliest recognized marsupials (order Marsupicarnivora) and placentals (order Insectivora), including those types ancestral to Cenozoic orders. The evidence now strongly suggests differentiation of marsupials and placentals from a common stock of therians of metatherian-eutherian grade between Albian and Campanian time. The place in which this divergence occurred is a matter of conjecture, although the Laurasian occurrence of the ancestral and descendant groups suggest Laurasia as the site (Clemens, 1968, 1971). Such circumstantial evidence has been widely accepted as indicating that the higher therians originated in the northern hemisphere, but, in view of the close geographic relationships among the Late Jurassic-Early Cretaceous continents (fig. 1) and the widespread faunal and floral similarity noted above, this conclusion may be misleading.

Lillegraven (1969) has given an excellent detailed review of embryogenesis, morphology, and function in living marsupials and placentals. He concluded that this evidence together with that from the fossil record suggests that the common therian ancestor of the higher mammals was probably more metatherian than eutherian in reproductive organization. Dental specializations that enable us to identify a given fossil as a placental or marsupial may have considerably postdated the development of a reproductive system we could identify as marsupial. If we equate the appearance of certain dental characteristics with the presence of chorioallantoic placentation, then the placentals acquired their unique urogenital morphology and reproductive physiology by medial Cretaceous time, probably from ancestors with the "marsupial" mode of reproduction. Parallel evolution of placentation of this morphological type is known in three Australian marsupial families (bandicoots, wombats, and koalas), but endocrine secretions necessary to extend intrauterine existence beyond the length of the oestrous cycle are unknown in these marsupials. Nevertheless, the presence of such structures suggests the possibility of polyphyletic development of this characteristic eutherian feature, even among the placental orders. The specific conditions that led

to the development of chorioallantoic placentation can only be surmised. Modern studies (Sharman, 1970; Lillegraven, 1969) do not support the idea that this mode of reproduction is superior to the marsupial mode for small insectivorous mammals, although it certainly facilitated invasion of environments barred to marsupials. The dentitions of the earliest marsupials and placentals do not suggest markedly different feeding mechanisms or adaptations (Crompton and Hiiemae, 1970). Clearly such animals would have been in competition, a competition that may have become important in shaping the continental mammalian faunas by Late Cretaceous and Cenozoic time.

Because it is impossible in paleontology to use the mode of reproduction as a means of recognizing fossil marsupials or placentals, I use the terms here according to their usual dental definitions. Both groups have fully tribosphenic cheek teeth, but marsupial upper molars can usually be distinguished by the prominent labial cingular shelves studded with stylar cusps and a metacone labial to and often larger than the paracone; by the close approximation of the hypoconulid and entoconid in the lower molars; by their characteristic dental formula (normal maximum count: I5/4C1P3M4) and by the possession of only a single deciduous premolar. As far as known, these features characterize teeth of the Campanian marsupials and they are assumed to have been characteristic of the teeth of the ancestors of all known marsupials. Such dental features characterize those families of Late Cretaceous and Cenozoic marsupials that preserve a large number of primitive therian osteological and soft part characters, for example, members of the order Marsupicarnivora (Ride, 1964), and especially members of the family Didelphidae known in the New World from the Late Cretaceous to the Recent. Slaughter (1968) has referred the Albian *Holoclemensia* to the Didelphidae; while this may be expedient, the combination of features of the stylar shelf (very large stylar cusp C, weak stylocone and paracrista) and the labial position of the small metacone have not been observed together in any other didelphid, or in any family within the order Marsupicarnivora.

MARSUPIAL ZOOGEOGRAPHY

The distribution of land and sea in the Late Cretaceous is critical to the history of the Cenozoic land mammal faunas, because at that time the geographical bases for the continental faunas were established. Late Cretaceous mammal faunas are the best known of all Mesozoic mammals faunas, but the limited geographic sampling of the marsupial and placental groups ancestral to the Cenozoic fauna is still inadequate to give more than a few clues as to the sites of origin and dispersal.

North America.—In Late Cretaceous time North America was split into two regions by the transcontinental seaway. The western region, where the bulk of the fossil vertebrate sites occur, was continuous with eastern Asia to the north via the Bering Strait shelf, or Beringia. The eastern part of the continent was continuous with Europe across the yet unopened North Atlantic. These two "islands" acquired their own biological characteristics, so that by latest Cretaceous time it is possible to distinguish each area palynologically (Tschudy, 1970). The Late Cretaceous dinosaur fauna of Europe and eastern North America contrasts with that of western North America, especially in its lack of ceratopsians and absence of diversity among the hadrosaurs. Fossil mammals are rare in the Late Cretaceous of this eastern "island," but eutherians (Ledoux and others, 1966) are known. The lack of marsupials in the diverse Paleocene faunas of Europe (Russell, 1964), most of which have been sampled by techniques favoring recovery of small mammal remains, suggests that they may have actually been absent there until early Eocene (Sparnacian) time.

In the western part of North America mammal faunas of Campanian to Maastrichtian age are now known (see Clemens, 1970, 1971, for summaries). Typically, these were dominated by marsupials and multituberculates until the very latest Maastrichtian, when the number of eutherians markedly increased, apparently through immigration, and the older marsupial and multituberculate assemblages suffered nearly complete extinction. The North American Late Cretaceous marsupial fauna gives us the first comprehensive view of this group. Analyses of these animals by Clemens (1966, 1968) and Fox (1971) reveals some diversity. Three families are represented: the Didelphidae, including a generalized central stock with a primitive tribosphenic dentition referred to the Cenozoic subfamilies Didelphinae (characterized by the genus *Alphadon* Simpson, 1927) and the peculiar bunodont Glasbiinae; the Pediomyidae, whose upper molars virtually lack the characteristic marsupial stylar cusps; and a predaceous group, the Stagodontidae, the largest known Cretaceous marsupials with enlarged crushing premolars. Except for the didelphines, all of these groups became extinct at the close of the Cretaceous. The cause of extinction may be attributed to a combination of climatic changes leading to increasingly seasonal terrestrial climates at mid-latitudes (Axelrod and Bailey, 1968), decreasing mean temperature (reflected in marine isotopic temperature studies summarized by Stevens and Clayton, 1971), and competition from the invading eutherian fauna from northern North America and eastern Asia, which heralds the striking turnover in faunal composition at the beginning of the Cenozoic. It seems significant that the only North American marsupials to survive the Cretaceous belong to the generalized subfamily Didelphinae; by late Paleocene time they had extended their range into the temperate north so as to be able to participate in the Sparnacian invasion of Europe along with a variety of placentals (McKenna, 1971). Thus the marsupials gained a toehold on the Eurasian continent in the west, but were barred from further eastward penetration by the transasiatic epicontinental seaway, the Turgai Strait.

Asia.—The Campanian marsupial-like Deltatheridiidae (Butler and Kielan-Jaworowska, 1973) may have had a long history in Asia as a member of the widely distributed therians of metatherian-eutherian grade, but further evidence is needed to determine their role, if any, in the evolution and dispersal of the Marsupicarnivora. Early Tertiary mammal faunas of eastern Asia are now well enough known from West Pakistan, Burma, China, Mongolia, and Kazakstan to suggest that the marsupials were absent. The high latitude Bering route (Szalay and McKenna, 1971) may have posed a climatic barrier for the didelphines of North America. Had the Marsupicarnivora been in Asia they would have been unable to utilize the island-hopping southeast Asian route of dispersal to Australia as suggested by Matthew (1915). Such a route seems highly improbable in the plate tectonic model of the Late Cretaceous and Paleogene world. The volcanic arc behind the western Pacific subduction zone might have provided ephemeral island stepping stones across the equator into the southwestern Pacific. However, the continental portion of the Australian plate remained far to the south in high latitudes and out of reach of favorable currents until northward drift in Neogene time propelled it into the proximity of Asia.

South America.—The significance of the South American continent in the Mesozoic history of the mammals has not been considered adequately by Matthewian zoogeographers, partly because this history is almost totally undocumented, but mostly because of the assumption that the southern continents represent distributional dead-ends for lineages originating in the north. The size of South America, its latitudinal and altitudinal range, its emergent character in the late Mesozoic and Cenozoic, and its early connections to the north and south would demand consideration in any historical zoogeography of the mammals.

The little known vertebrate faunas of the Early Cretaceous in South America indicate a general similarity in composition to those of Laurasia (Von Huene, 1929). The mammalian component of these South American faunas likely shared some of the therian elements known to the north. However, biological filtering across the Middle America archipelago apparently excluded the allotherian multituberculates so common in the North American Upper Jurassic and Cretaceous, for, had they been present in the south, they surely would have persisted into Tertiary time there, just as they did in Holarctica.

Only a single Cretaceous mammal fauna, the Laguna Umayo local fauna from the Vilquechico Formation in the Andean Altiplano, Peru (Sigé, 1971, 1972), has been described from South America. The same rocks yielded dinosaur eggs (Sigé, 1968) and Late Cretaceous charophytes (Grambast and others, 1967), the latter suggesting a Late Cretaceous age for this earliest known South American mammal fauna. The mammal remains represent the two major elements characteristic of the Tertiary fauna of that continent, metatherian Marsupicarnivora and eutherian Protungulata (Condylarthra). The condylarth *Perutherium* Thaler, 1967 (in Grambast and others, 1967), the sole eutherian so far described, appears to be a member of the early Tertiary (Ricochican and Casamayoran) family Didolodontidae and is close to the Paleocene-early Eocene genus *Ernestokokenia* Ameghino, 1901. These remains indicate that by Late Cretaceous time South American protungulate evolution was already advanced in the direction of the endemic South American radiation and was well removed from the contemporary, and more primitive, arctocyonid condylarths of North America (*Protungulatum* Sloan and Val Valen, 1965).

The South American marsupials, however, do resemble those of the Late Cretaceous of North America, especially the didelphine *Alphadon* (*A. austrinum* Sigé, 1971, is close to the Lance species, *A. lulli* Clemens, 1966), and a single specimen is questionably attributed by Sigé to the Pediomyidae. These remains suggest that by Late Cretaceous time the mammal fauna of

South America had already acquired its characteristic features: carnivore and herbivore adaptations were divided between the Marsupicarnivora and Protungulata respectively, as in early Tertiary time. This glimpse into the Late Cretaceous provides an extremely limited view of the extent of the mammal radiation that was apparently already well underway in South America. Much about the history of the marsupials of that continent may only be inferred from the later Paleocene faunas of Brazil (Itaborai, State of Rio de Janiero) and Patagonia (Rio Chico, Chubut, Argentina) or the early Eocene faunas of Patagonia (Casamayor, Chubut).

The most diverse and best preserved remains, described by Carlos de Paula Couto (1952a, 1952b, 1961, 1962, 1969) and Simpson (1947), come from sediments filling limestone fissures at Itaborai. These remains belong to the orders Marsupicarnivora and Paucituberculata (superfamily Caenolestoidea). Representatives of the latter have not yet been found in Cretaceous rocks, but the recent karyological and serological studies of living caenolestids (Hayman and others, 1971) and their distinctive osteology, particularly that of the early Tertiary caenolestoid family Polydolopidae, suggest that the paucituberculates represent a very old group. The serological evidence indicates a greater affinity between the living Australian and South American marsupicarnivores than between either of these groups and the living caenolestid genera tested (*Caenolestes* Thomas, 1895, and *Lestoros* Ochser, 1934). These facts may be interpreted as indicating that the paucituberculates arose in South America at about the same time as the marsupicarnivores, indirectly suggesting a complex Cretaceous history for the marsupials on that continent. The caenolestoids early evolved an herbivorous group, the polydolopids, that converged with the multituberculates of Laurasia and, like the latter, may have held the niche later occupied by the rodents. The caenolestids themselves were insectivorous-omnivorous forms of shrew-like habitus that, together with the smaller didelphines, occupied the niches held by the Insectivora of Laurasia.

The Brazilian Paleocene fauna contained a great variety of small didelphids whose dental adaptations parallel those seen among the Late Cretaceous Lance marsupials of North America (see Clemens, 1966, p. 20–22 for such comparisons). The Brazilian forms include a generalized didelphine group (e.g., *Didelphopsis* Paula Couto, 1952, *Marmosopsis* Paula Couto 1962), bunodont glasbiine-like forms (*Guggenheimia*

Paula Couto, 1952, *Mirandatherium* Paula Couto, 1952, and *Caroloameghinia* Ameghino, 1901, of Patagonia), possible representatives of the subfamily Microbiotheriinae (*Schaefferia* Paula Couto, 1952, holotype only), and species with enlarged premolars approaching those of the stagodontids (*Gaylordia* Paula Couto, 1952). The largest early Tertiary Marsupicarnivora were members of the predaceous family Borhyaenidae; they are present in typical form (*Patene* Simpson, 1953) as early as the Paleocene in Argentina and Brazil. The upper molars of these animals have wide stylar shelves but show reduction of the stylar cusps. Some early Eocene borhyaenids (*Arminiheringia* Ameghino, 1902) have reduced shelf and stylar cusps so that the pattern resembles that of the North American Cretaceous pediomyids and the Australian thylacinids.

Thus the Late Cretaceous and Paleocene Marsupicarnivora of both North America and South America show a similar range of dental morphologies and presumed adaptations. The extent to which this represents parallel or direct phyletic relationship is not presently known, but close comparison suggests that many, if not all, of these resemblances could have arisen as parallel trends of adaptation on both continents. Both adaptive radiations could have had their origin in didelphines of the dental grade of *Alphadon*. Knowledge of the Mesozoic marsupials of the New World is fragmentary, but I do emphasize that the attribution of some North American Albian mammals to the Metatheria is insufficient proof that these forms (e.g., *Holoclemensia*, see comments above) are involved in the origin of the didelphines or that North America is the site of origin of forms ancestral to the Cenozoic Metatheria of the southern continents. In view of the geographic isolation of both the northern and southern portions of the Americas plate in Late Cretaceous time (fig. 2) and the composition of the marsupial faunas of both areas, dispersal from a South American center could have provided the nucleus for both the North American and Australian radiations. The scope of the South American marsupial radiation, as far as evidenced by the Late Cretaceous and early Tertiary record, suggests that marsupials may have been on that continent for a long time, possibly from early in the Cretaceous. In contrast the unified structure of the North American Late Cretaceous marsupicarnivores indicates a radiation of limited scope and more recent origin (Late Cretaceous, but pre-Campanian; see Fox, 1971) evolving in isolation, possibly from a southern didelphine migrant close to, or congeneric with,

Alphadon. It must be borne in mind that this hypothesis, like that of a Holarctic origin for the marsupials (most recently discussed by Clemens, 1971), rests only on interpretation of a very meager fossil record. It is offered as a serious alternative to be considered and tested against new evidence as it becomes available.

The Cenozoic history of the marsupials in South America is comparatively well known (Patterson and Pascual, 1968). The didelphids were probably more abundant and varied in the tropical portion of the continent, as they are today. This group invaded Middle and North America at the close of the Tertiary, and a single species (*Didelphis marsupialis* Linnaeus, 1760) of remarkable tolerance ranged from tropical Middle America to the cool temperate forests of northeastern North America. The borhyaenids occupied the medium to large carnivore niches (sharing the latter with phororhachoid birds), and by Pliocene time one lineage had developed a sabre-tooth adaptation remarkably convergent on the machairodont cats of Holarctica. In late Tertiary time the borhyaenids dwindled in diversity, and some of the niches they left vacant were occupied for a short time, before the Pleistocene placental invasion, by a group of predaceous didelphids, the Sparassocyninae.

The paucituberculates have been restricted to South America, and today the caenolestid species occupy temperate environments along the Andean cordillera. A caenolestid (*Rhyncolestes* Osgood, 1924), a didelphine (*Lestodelphys* Tate, 1934), and a microbiothere (*Dromiciops* Thomas, 1894) are at present the most southerly occurring marsupials in South America, living at latitude 45°–47°S in the northern part of the equable maritime beech forest belts and adjacent savannas of Chile and Patagonia. Polydolopids are unknown in the fossil record after the early Eocene (Casamayoran). The enigmatic gliriform groberiids, known only from the early Oligocene (Deseadan), may represent another marsupial invasion of the rodent niche that persisted until the caviomorph rodents appeared in South America. Other phyletically isolated endemic marsupials appeared in the South American Tertiary record from time to time (the molelike, possibly fossorial, early Miocene Necrolestidae and the kangaroo-rat-like late Pliocene-early Pleistocene Argyrolagidae) suggesting greater dimensions of the marsupial radiation on that continent than are presently known.

Australia.—In the Cretaceous and early Tertiary, Australia formed a northward jutting peninsula of the Antarctic continent according to data from paleomagnetism and sea floor spreading (Le Pichon and Heirtzler, 1968; Le Pichon, 1968). Surface geology supports the inference that the Westralian and East Antarctic Cratons were a single nucleus (McElhinny and Wellman, 1969). The Paleozoic and early Mesozoic mobile belts of the east line up with their Antarctic counterparts as Hamilton (1967) and Griffiths (1971) have noted. Arranged along the Pacific margin of the Australoantarctic continent was a late Mesozoic-Cenozoic mobile belt (Griffiths, 1971), the details of which are not yet clear. Work by Dalziel and Elliot (1971) and Barker (1970) have shown that in Cretaceous and early Cenozoic time the sinuous Scotia Island chain formed a continuous orogenic zone with the Andes to the north and the Antarctic Peninsula to the south. This Andean orogenic zone may be traced south through West Antarctica to New Zealand with enough continuity to support the idea of a circum-South Pacific mobile belt (Halpern, 1968; see LeMasurier, 1971, for qualifications), which probably developed behind a now-extinct subduction zone that was consuming Mesozoic and early Cenozoic crust generated along the East Pacific Rise (figs. 1 and 2).

The present archipelagic configuration of West Antarctica beneath its glacial cap suggests that the connecting links between the southern tip of South America and the Cretaceous-early Tertiary Australoantarctic continent may have been via a volcanic island chain rather than continuous land. Westward extension of the East Pacific Rise in the Late Cretaceous separated the Campbell Plateau, containing New Zealand, from Marie Byrd Land (Griffiths and Varne, 1971) and isolated the eastern Australian orogenic belt from West Antarctica. Archipelagic conditions seem to have been maintained for much of New Zealand's Mesozoic and all its Cenozoic history (Fleming, 1962); its proximity to the Australoantarctic continent in the Cretaceous and subsequent greater separation account for much of the unusual character of its terrestrial biota (Raven and Axelrod, 1972).

A high latitude dispersal route 60° to 80° in Late Cretaceous; McElhinny and Wellman, 1969), even if continuous land, probably acted as a climatic filter. The geographic barriers imposed by an archipelagic route would have intensified the filter effect and necessitated sweepstakes dispersal for certain types of organisms such as terrestrial mammals. Despite these difficulties, there is much biological evidence in favor of such a route (Darlington, 1965; Raven and Axelrod, 1972). The paleon-

tological and geological evidence of the paleoclimate of this high latitude region, although scant and indirect, suggests milder conditions than at present, at least along the coast. If the West Antarctic region was archipelagic, more equable temperate climates might be expected because of a maritime influence. Broad affinities of the Early Cretaceous Australian flora with those of South America and Laurasia have been noted (Dettman and Playford, 1969). Paleogene *Nothofagus* and araucarian pine forests have been recorded on the Antarctic peninsula (Cranwell, 1959), and early Cenozoic pollens from McMurdo Sound (Cranwell and others, 1960) and the West Ice Shelf (Kemp, 1972) indicate the occurrence of similar forests in eastern Antarctica. The Late Cretaceous and early Tertiary floras of southern Australia and New Zealand have similar compositions, at the generic level, with contemporary floras of southern South America and Antarctica, suggesting continuity of vegetation and paleoclimate (Raven and Axelrod, 1972). The climate may have been warmer than that favored by the beech-pine forests of the temperate southern continents today. This is suggested by the wide occurrence of early Tertiary pollens of the *Nothofagus brassi* group that today inhabits only the warm-temperate, equable uplands of New Guinea and New Caledonia.

Oxygen isotope studies on Jurassic and Cretaceous belemnites from New Zealand (Stevens and Clayton, 1971) indicate the presence of warm-temperate seas surrounding the archipelago up to about 80 m.y.a., after which a cooling trend began that continued into early Cenozoic time before being reversed. There is a significant drop in oxygen isotope paleotemperatures of benthonic Foraminifera in the late Paleogene of Australia (Dorman, 1968) and New Zealand (Devereux, 1968) and a decrease in the number of planktonic Foraminifera species in New Zealand (Jenkins, 1968). These changes may be related to the development of an Antarctic glacial cap and the initiation of peri-Antarctic ocean circulation following the northward drift of Australia and the opening of Drake's Passage. Mountain, and even continental glacier buildup apparently began in the early Cenozoic (42 ± 9 m.y.a., LeMasurier, 1970; Margolis and Kennett, 1970), and in time this would have provided an insuperable barrier to dispersal.

Unfortunately, we have no record of early Cenozoic or late Mesozoic marsupials in Australia. We know that the late Cenozoic families there had a long history, for they were osteologically distinct from one another by early

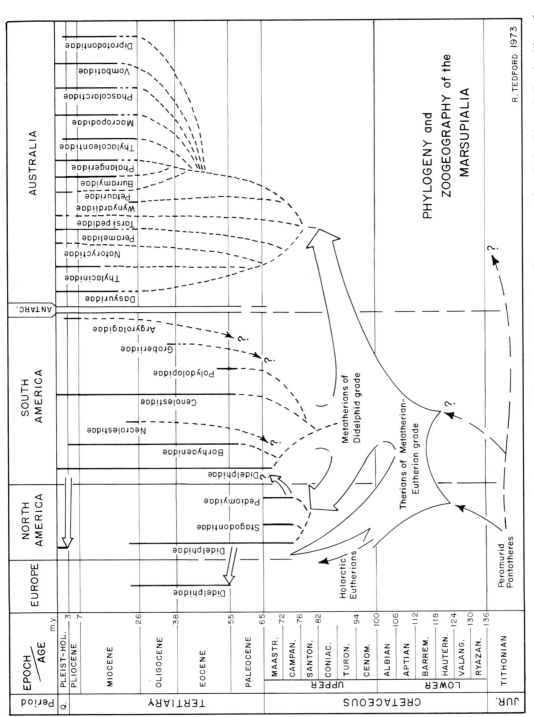

Fig. 5.—Diagram showing the known geological ranges and the inferred phyletic and zoogeographic relationships of the families of marsupials. Dashed borders between continent columns show that chance for dispersal between adjacent continents decreased through the Cretaceous and early Tertiary, becoming disjunct due to interposition of oceanic crust and development of a climatic barrier of increas-

Miocene time (Stirton and others, 1968, and fig. 5). The notion that the Australian radiation was initiated by an invading insectivorous form of didelphine grade is well entrenched in the literature (see especially Bensley, 1903), and it seems still warranted by the evidence. Serological studies (Kirsch, 1968) indicate that all the living Australian families are closer to one another than they are to any New World marsupial family, suggesting derivation from a common stock. This is an old idea and one not so far controverted by paleontological evidence. The dental morphologies of the Australian marsupicarnivoran dasyurids (presumably those closest in structure to the progenitors of the Australian radiation) consistently differ in stylar cusp structure from their analogues in the New World. The bony auditory regions of most living Australian marsupials are more complex than their New World counterparts, except for certain Australian fossil forms such as the early Miocene *Wynyardia* Spencer, 1900, whose ear region resembles those of the didelphines (Ride, 1964). These tenuous clues suggest that the Australian radiation had its roots in a closely-knit stock of small predaceous or insectivorous forms of didelphine grade adapted to dispersal across temperate regions. These immigrant forms dispersed during the Late Cretaceous or Paleocene and became isolated climatically, and finally geographically, as Australia began its northward voyage away from Antarctica in Eocene time (Le Pichon and Heirtzler, 1968).

The northward drift of Australia into warmer latitudes was undoubtedly accompanied by considerable vegetational change, especially as the continent entered the dry horse latitudes (Raven and Axelrod, 1972). Widespread beech-pine forests of the early Cenozoic would have been restricted to the southern edge of the continent as warm dry savannas and schlerophyl forests developed, and later as rain forests became established along the eastern ranges of the continent. Such climatic and vegetational changes presented new opportunities, especially for herbivorous marsupials. Many of the families of the order Diprotodonta may have arisen in mid-Tertiary time in response to these major changes in environment (as suggested in fig. 5). Phyletically isolated forms, such as the fossil *Wynyardia* or the living nectar-feeding *Tarsipes* Gervais and Verreaux, 1842, whose blood proteins are distinct from other diprotodontans (Kirsch, 1968), may represent some of the products of an earlier radiation of marsupials that became adapted to a herbivorous mode of life in the temperate forests of Late Cretaceous or early Tertiary Australoantarctica.

Africa and India.—The time of formation of the southwestern Indian Ocean has been difficult to determine, but evidence from paleomagnetics (Franchetaeau and Sclater, 1969) and sea-floor spreading (Smith and Hallam, 1970) suggests that the rifting and drift of the African and Indian plates northward from east Antarctica was underway in Jurassic time and that significant water barriers to the dispersal of terrestrial vertebrates were in existence by the beginning of the Cretaceous (pre-Valanginian) (Smith and Hallam, 1970). Evidence for a lingering contact or narrow watergap studded with volcanic islands between northeastern South America and West Africa (fig. 1) before the opening of the central Atlantic in mid-Cretaceous time (Smith and Hallam, 1970) suggests the possibility of biotic exchanges between these continents well into the Cretaceous (Raven and Axelrod, 1972). Mammals may have taken part in these exchanges at equatorial latitudes if a means of dispersal had been present. The oldest known faunas of Africa (late Eocene and Oligocene, North Africa) show that by that time the carnivore-insectivore niche was filled by hyaenodontid creodonts, which, like the artiodactyls in the same faunas, are of Holarctic origin. If there were any aboriginal marsupials or protungulates in Africa during early Tertiary, they were apparently displaced before the late Eocene by northern placental invaders.

The historical zoogeography of peninsular India seems to contradict the isolation of the continental part of the Indian plate as interpreted from sea-floor spreading and paleomagnetic evidence (Le Pichon and Heirtzler, 1968; Dietz and Holden, 1970; McKenzie and Slater, 1971). India shared the major elements of the Late Cretaceous dinosaur fauna of the southern continents (Von Huene and Matley, 1933). These terrestrial animals must have reached India overland or across short water gaps, for the nature of the Indian fauna implies closer relationships of that continent with Madagascar and Africa during Cretaceous time. The Holarctic affinities of the Eocene mammals of the Indian plate are also surprising in view of the isolation of the continent from Africa and Asia as depicted in plate tectonic models (McKenzie and Sclater, 1971). Perhaps, like the Cretaceous faunas, zoogeographic ties between Africa and India were maintained across the Malagasy and Seychelle-Mascarine microcontinents into early Tertiary time.

CONCLUSIONS

The dynamic model of plate tectonics provides the geological basis for a new concept of paleogeography and a set of physical constraints on biogeographic theory. Principles of dispersal formulated under the stable continent model (Simpson, 1940) may be applied to the dynamic model with logical modifications and extensions (McKenna, 1973). In addition, the new continental relationships imposed by plate tectonics necessitate a critical examination of the role of each continent in the development of the world's fauna. Plate tectonic models of the Mesozoic and Cenozoic history of the world have attracted the attention of a growing number of vertebrate zoogeographers (Kurtén, 1969; Cox, 1970; Hoffstetter, 1970a, 1970b, 1972; Tedford, 1971; Jardine and McKenzie, 1972; Fooden, 1972; Raven and Axelrod, 1972), all of whom have embraced the idea of southern continent dispersal of marsupials; at least one author (Tedford, 1971) has suggested a southern continent origin for this group. Important consequences of the new geography are the reduction in probability for some zoogeographic hypotheses and the increase in probability for others. With respect to the marsupials, the Matthewian Holarctic dispersal route through Indonesia to Australia now seems much less likely than an Antarctic one. Island arc festoons behind the western Pacific subduction zone would have provided ephemeral stepping stones into the South Pacific from Asia, but the chances of successful dispersal along this route into temperate southern latitudes seems improbable for terrestrial mammals until Australia reached the proximity of Asia in late Tertiary time. The preceding pages review the history of the marsupials in some detail and propose as a viable and likely hypothesis a Late Cretaceous southern continental (specifically South American) origin for the progenitors of the Late Cretaceous and Cenozoic marsupial radiations of the Americas and Australia.

REFERENCES CITED

AIR, G. M., E. O. P. THOMPSON, B. J. RICHARDSON, AND G. B. SHARMAN. 1971. Amino-acid sequences of kangaroo myoglobin and haemoglobin and the date of marsupial-eutherian divergence. Nature. 229:391–394.

ATWATER, T. 1970. Implications of plate tectonics for the Cenozoic tectonic evolution of western North America. Bull. geol. Soc. Am. 81:3513–3536.

AXELROD, D. I., AND H. P. BAILEY. 1968. Cretaceous dinosaur extinction. Evolution. 22:595–611.

BARKER, P. F. 1970. Plate tectonics of the Scotia Sea region. Nature. 228:1293–1296.

BARSBOLD, R., Y. I. VORONIN, AND V. I. ZHEGALLO. 1971. The work of the Soviet-Mongolian Paleontological Expedition. Paleont. Zh. 5(2):273. (A.G.I. translation)

BENSLEY, B. A. 1903. On the evolution of the Australian Marsupialia: with remarks on the relationship of the marsupials in general. Trans. Linn. Soc. Lond. Zoology. 9:83–217.

BUTLER, P. M., AND Z. KIELAN-JAWOROWSKA. 1973. Is *Deltatheridium* a marsupial? Nature. 245:105–106.

CASAMIQUELA, R. M. 1961. Sobre la presencia de un mamifero en el primer elenca (icnologico) de vertebrados del Jurasico de la Patagonia. Physis. 22:225–233.

CHARIG, A. J. 1969. Faunal provinces on land: evidence based on the distribution of fossil tetrapods, with especial reference to the reptiles of the Permian and Mesozoic. *In* MIDDLEMISS, F. A., P. E. RAWSON AND G. NEWALL, Eds. Faunal provinces in space and time. Geol. J. Spec. Issue 4: pp. 111–128.

CHASE, C. G. 1971. Tectonic history of the Fiji Plateau. Bull. geol. Soc. Am. 82:3087–3110.

CHURKIN, M., JR. 1972. Western boundary of the North American continental plate in Asia. Ibid. 83:1027–1036.

CLEMENS, W. A. 1966. Fossil mammals of the type Lance Formation, Wyoming. Part II. Marsupialia. Univ. Calif. Publs. geol. Sci. 62:1–122

———. 1968. Origin and early evolution of marsupials. Evolution. 22:1–18.

———. 1970. Mesozoic mammalian evolution. Ann. Rev. Ecol. System. 1:357–390.

———. 1971. Mammalian evolution in the Cretaceous. *In* KERMACK, D. M. AND K. A. KERMACK, Eds. Early Mammals. J. Linn. Soc. Zoology. 50 Suppl. No. 1:165–180.

——— AND J. R. E. MILLS. 1971. Review of *Peramus tenuirostris* Owen (Eupantotheria, Mammalia). Bull. Br. Mus. nat. Hist., Geology. 20:89–113, 4 pls.

COLBERT, E. H. 1971. Tetrapods and continents. Q. Rev. Biol. 46:250–269.

COX, B. 1970. Migrating marsupials and drifting continents. Nature. 226:767–770.

CRANWELL, L. M. 1959. Fossil pollen from Seymour Island, Antarctica. Ibid. 184:1782–1785.

———, H. J. HARRINGTON AND I. G. SPEDEN. 1960. Lower Tertiary microfossils from McMudo Sound, Antarctica. Ibid. 186:700–702.

CROMPTON, A. W., AND K. HIEMAE. 1970. Molar occlusion and mandibular movements during occlusion in the American opossum, *Didelphis marsupialis* L. J. Linn. Soc. Zoology. 49:21–47, 1 pl.

DALZIEL, I. W. D., AND D. H. ELLIOT. 1971. Evolution of the Scotia Arc. Nature. 233:246–252.

DARLINGTON, P. J., JR. 1957. Zoogeography: the geographical distribution of animals. i–xi, 1–675 p. John Wiley and Sons, New York.

———. 1965. Biogeography of the southern end of the world. i–x, 1–236 p. McGraw-Hill Book Co., New York.

DAVIES, H. L., AND I. E. SMITH. 1971. Geology of eastern Papua. Bull. geol. Soc. Amer. 82:3299–3312.

DETTMAN, M. E., AND G. PLAYFORD. 1969. Palynology of the Australian Cretaceous: A review. In CAMP-BELL, K., Ed. Stratigraphy and Paleontology. Essays in honor of Dorothy Hill. P. 174–210, Pls. 11–13. Aust. Natl. Univ. Press, Canberra.

DEVEREUX, I. 1968. Oxygen isotope paleotemperatures from the Tertiary of New Zealand. Tuatara. 16:41–44.

DIETZ, R. S., AND J. C. HOLDEN. 1970. Reconstruction of Pangaea: Breakup and dispersion of continents, Permian to present. J. geophys. Res. 75:4939–4956.

DORMAN, F. H. 1968. Some Australian oxygen isotope temperatures and a theory for a 30 million-year world-temperature cycle. J. Geol. 76:297–313.

DU TOIT, A. L. 1937. Our wandering continents: an hypothesis of continental drift. Oliver and Boyd, Edinburgh. 366 p.

FLEMING, C. A. 1962. New Zealand biogeography: a paleontologist's approach. Tuatara. 10:53–108.

FOODEN, J. 1972. Breakup of Pangaea and isolation of relict mammals in Australia, South America, and Madagascar. Science. 175:894–898.

FOX, R. C. 1971. Marsupial mammals from the early Campanian Milk River Formation, Alberta, Canada. In KERMACK, D. M., AND K. A. KERMACK, Eds. Early Mammals. J. Linn. Soc. Zoology. 50 Suppl. No. 1:145–164, 6 pls.

FRANCHETEAU, J., AND J. G. SCLATER. 1969. Paleomagnetism of the southern continents and plate tectonics. Earth and Planet. Sci. Letters. 6:93–106.

FUNNELL, B. M., AND A. G. SMITH. 1968. Opening of the Atlantic Ocean. Nature. 219:1328–1333.

GRAMBAST, L., M. MARTINEZ, M. MATTAUER, AND L. THALER. 1967. Perutherium altiplanese, nov. gen., nov. sp., premier mammifère Mésozoïque d'Amérique du Sud. C. r. Acad. Sci. Paris. 264:707–710.

GREEN, A. G. 1972. Sea floor spreading in the Mozambique channel. Nature. 236:19–21, 32.

GREGORY, W. K. 1910. The orders of mammals. Bull. Am. Mus. nat. Hist. 27:1–524.

GRIFFITHS, J. R. 1971. Reconstruction of the south-west Pacific margin of Gondwanaland. Nature. 234:203–207.

———, AND R. VARNE. 1972. Evolution of the Tasman Sea, Macquarie Ridge and Alpine Fault. Ibid. 235:83–86.

HALPERN, M. 1968. Ages of Antarctic and Argentine rocks bearing on continental drift. Earth Planet. Sci. Letters. 5:159–167.

HAMILTON, W. 1967. Tectonics of Antarctica. Tectonophysics. 4:555–568.

HAYMAN, D. L., J. A. W. KIRSCH, P. G. MARTIN, AND P. F. WALLER. 1971. Chromosomal and serological studies of the Caenolestidae and their implications for marsupial evolution. Nature. 231:194–195.

HERRON, E. M. 1972. Sea-floor spreading and the Cenozoic history of the East Central Pacific. Bull. geol. Soc. Am. 83(6):1671–1692.

HOFFSTETTER, R. 1970a. Radiation initiale des mammifères placentaires et biogéographie. C. r. Acad. Sci. Paris. 270:3027–3030.

———. 1970b. L'Histiore biogéographique des marsupiaux et la dichotomie marsupiaux-placentaires. Ibid. 271:388–391.

———. 1972. Données et hypotheses concernant l'origine et l'histoire biogéographique des Marsupiaux. Ibid. 274:2635–2638.

JARDINE, N., AND D. MCKENZIE. 1972. Continental drift and the dispersal and evolution of organisms. Nature. 235:20–24.

JENKINS, D. G. 1968. Planktonic Foraminiferida as indicators of New Zealand Tertiary paleotemperatures. Tuatara. 16:32–37.

KEMP, E. M. 1972. Reworked palynomorphs from the West Ice Shelf area, east Antarctica, and their possible geological and palaeoclimatological significance. Mar. Geol. 13(3):145–157.

KIRSCH, J. A. W. 1968. Prodromus of the comparative serology of Marsupialia. Nature. 217:418–420.

KUMMEL, B. 1961. History of the earth, an introduction to historical geology. 2nd ed. W. H. Freeman, San Francisco. p. i–xix, 1–707.

KURTÉN, B. 1969. Continental drift and evolution. Scient. Am. 220:54–63.

LILLEGRAVEN, J. A. 1969. Latest Cretaceous mammals of upper part of Edmonton Formation of Alberta, Canada, and review of marsupial-placental dichotomy in mammalian evolution. Paleont. Contr. Univ. Kans. Art. 50 (Vertebrata 12), 122 p.

LEDOUX, J., J. HARTENBERGER, J. MICHAUX, J. SUDRE, AND L. THALER. 1966. Decoverte d'un mammifère dans le Cretacé Superieur à dinosaures de Champ-Garimond près de Fons (Gard). C. r. Hebd. Séanc. Acad. Sci. Paris. 262:1925–1928.

LEMASURIER, W. E. 1970. Volcanic evidence for early Tertiary glaciation in Marie Byrd Land. Antarct. J. 5:154–155.

———. 1971. Spatial variation in Cenozoic volcanism of Marie Byrd Land and Ellsworth Land. Ibid. 6:187–188.

LE PICHON, X. 1968. Sea-floor spreading and continental drift. J. geophys. Res. 73:3661–3697.

——— AND J. R. HEIRTZLER. 1968. Magnetic anomalies in the Indian Ocean and sea-floor spreading. Ibid. 73:2101–2117.

MALFAIT, B. T., AND M. G. DINKELMAN. 1972. Circum-Caribbean tectonic and igneous activity and evolution of the Caribbean plate. Bull. geol. Soc. Am. 83:251–272.

MARGOLIS, S. V., AND J. P. KENNETT. 1970. Antarctic glaciation during the Tertiary recorded in sub-Antarctic deep-sea cores. Science. 170:1085–1087.

MATTHEW, W. D. 1906. Hypothetical outlines of the continents in Tertiary times. Bull. Am. Mus. nat. Hist. 22:353–383.

———. 1915. Climate and evolution. Ann. N. Y. Acad. Sci. 24:171–318, Reprinted, E. M. SCHLAIKJER, Ed. Spec. Publs., N.Y. Acad. Sci. 1:i–xii, 1–223 (1939).

MCELHINNY, M. W., AND P. WELLMAN. 1969. Polar wandering and sea-floor spreading in the southern Indian Ocean. Earth Planet. Sci. Letters. 6:198–204.

McKenna, M. C. 1971. Fossil mammals and the Eocene demise of the De Geer north Atlantic dispersal route. Abstr. geol. Soc. Am. 3(7):664.

————. 1973. Sweepstakes, filters, corridors, Noah's arks, and beached Viking funeral ships in palaeogeography. *In* Tarling, D. H., and S. K. Runcorn, Eds. Implications of continental drift to the earth sciences. Academic Press, London and New York. 1.

McKenzie, D., and J. G. Sclater. 1971. The evolution of the Indian Ocean since the Late Cretaceous. Geophys. J. Roy. astr. Soc. 25:437–528.

Osborn, H. F. 1910. The age of mammals in Europe, Asia and North America, Macmillan, New York. i–xvii, 1–635 p.

Patterson, B., and R. Pasqual. 1968. Evolution of mammals on southern continents. V. The fossil mammal fauna of South America. Q. Rev. Biol. 43:409–451.

Paula Couto, C. de. 1952a. Fossil mammals from the beginning of the Cenozoic in Brazil. Marsupialia: Polydolopidae and Borhyaenidae. Am. Mus. Novit. 1559, 1–27.

————. 1952b. Fossil mammals from the beginning of the Cenozoic in Brazil. Marsupialia: Didelphidae. Ibid. 1567:1–26.

————. 1961. Marsupiais fósseis do Paleoceno do Brasil. Anais Acad. bras. Cienc. 33:321–333.

————. 1962. Didelfideos fosiles del Paleoceno de Brasil. Revta Mus. argent. de Cienc. nat. Bernardo Rivadavia. 8:135–166.

————. 1969. News on the fossil marsupials from the Riochican of Brazil. Anais Acad. bras. Cienc. 42:19–34.

Pitman, W. C., III, and M. Talwani. 1972. Sea floor spreading in the north Atlantic. Bull. geol. Soc. Am. 83:619–646.

Raven, P. H., and D. I. Axelrod. 1972. Plate tectonics and Australasian paleobiogeography. Science. 176:1379–1386.

Ride, W. D. L. 1964. A review of Australian fossil marsupials. J. Proc. R. Soc. West. Aust. 47:97–131.

Russell, D. E. 1964. Les mammifères Paléocènes d'Europe. Mém. mus. natn. Hist. nat. Paris n.s., C. 13:1–324, 14 pls.

Sharman, G. B. 1970. Reproductive physiology of marsupials. Science. 167:1221–1228.

Sigé, B. 1968. Dents de micromammifères et fragments de coquilles d'oeufs de dinosauriens dans la fauna de vertébraés du Crétacé superieur de Laguna Umago (Andes peruviennis). C. r. Acad. Sci. Paris. 267:1495–1498.

————. 1971. Les Didelphoidea de Laguna Umayo (formation Vilquechico, Crétacé superieur, Pérun), et le peuplement marsupial d'Amerique du Sud. Ibid. 273:2479–2481.

————. 1972. La faunule de Mammifères du Crétacé supérieur de Laguna Umayo (Andes Péruvienres). Bull. Mus. Nat. Hist. Naturelle, Sci. de la Terre. 19:375–409.

Simpson, G. G. 1940. Mammals and land bridges. J. Wash. Acad. Sci. 30:137–163.

————. 1941. The affinities of the Borhyaenidae. Amer. Mus. Novit. 1118, 1–6.

————. 1947. A new Eocene marsupial from Brazil. Ibid. 1357, 1–7 p.

————. 1965. The geography of evolution: collected essays. Chilton Books, New York. i–x, 1–249 p.

Sinclair, W. J. 1906. Mammalia of the Santa Cruz beds, Marsupialia. Rep. Princeton Univ. Exped. Patagonia. 4:333–459.

Slaughter, B. H. 1968. Earliest known marsupials. Science. 162:254–255.

————. 1971. Mid-Cretaceous (Albian) therians of the Butler Farm local fauna, Texas. *In* Kermack, D. M., and K. A. Kermack, Eds. Early Mammals. J. Linn. Soc. Zoology 50 Suppl. No. 1:131–143. 10 pls.

Smith, A. G., and A. Hallam. 1970. The fit of the southern continents. Nature. 225:139–144.

Stevens, G. R., and R. N. Clayton. 1971. Oxygen isotope studies on Jurassic and Cretaceous belemnites from New Zealand and their biogeographic significance. N. Z. Jl. Geol. Geophys. 14:829–897.

Stirton, R. A., R. H. Tedford, and M. O. Woodburne. 1968. Australian Tertiary deposits containing terrestrial mammals. Univ. Calif. Publs. geol. Sci. 77:1–30.

Szalay, F. S., and M. C. McKenna. 1971. Beginning of the Age of Mammals in Asia: the late Paleocene Gashato fauna, Mongolia. Bull. Am. Mus. nat. Hist. 144:271–317.

Tedford, R. H. 1971. Marsupials and global tectonics. Abstr. geol. Soc. Am. 3(7):730–731.

Tschudy, R. H. 1970. Palynology of the Cretaceous-Tertiary boundary in the northern Rocky Mountain and Mississippi Embayment regions. Spec. Pap. geol. Soc. Am. 127:65–111, 6 pls.

Von Huene, F. 1929. Los saurisquios y ornithisquios del Cretáceo Argentino. An. Mus. La Plata. 3:1–196, 44 pls.

———— and C. A. Matley. 1933. The Cretaceous Saurischia and Ornithischia of the central provinces of India. Mem. geol. Surv. India Paleont. Indica. 21:1–74, 24 pls.

Wegener, A. 1967. The origin of continents and oceans. Methuen, London. 248 p. (new translation of 1929 edition).

Wood, H. E., II. 1924. The position of the "sparassodonts": with notes on the relationships and history of the Marsupialia. Bull. Am. Mus. nat. Hist. 51:77–86.

PROVINCIAL ASPECTS OF SOME NEOGENE OSTRACODA OF THE UNITED STATES

FREDERICK M. SWAIN

Department of Geology and Geophysics, University of Minnesota, Minneapolis, MN 55455
and Department of Geology, University of Delaware, Newark, DE 19711

ABSTRACT—Provincially developed species or species-groups represent only a small part of the Neogene Ostracoda in the United States. Possible examples of provincial groups are cited from the Neogene fresh-water deposits of the Great Basin and the central interior United States and the marine Neogene of the southeastern and Pacific coast states.

Causes of provinciality in the freshwater Ostracoda are uncertain but prolonged climatic stability, perhaps coupled with a furtive habitat of the species, is indicated. Provinciality in marine Neogene ostracodes probably results from the prolonged coincidence of cool and warm water masses; the provincial types seem to be related more to the warm water than to the cool water masses. Provinciality in benthonic marine ostracodes suggests minimum involvement of the area concerned with separation or rotation of crustal plates.

INTRODUCTION

Ostracoda that have persisted in a restricted area for an epoch or more without undergoing dispersal to other regions are believed to show some degree of provinciality (fig. 1). The provincial character of ostracodes is commonly emphasized by diversification within a genus or species. Because Neogene freshwater and near-shore marine ostracodes had many opportunities for dispersal by birds, fish, terrestrial or marine mammals and winds, development of provinciality was predictably limited at the generic level. Many examples of short-lived endemism at the species level, that could be cited, are omitted from the present discussion.

HABITATS OF OSTRACODA

Fresh-water Ostracodes.—Fresh-water ostracodes live most abundantly in vegetation-rich littoral, rather than profundal, zones of lakes and in shallow temporary ponds, ditches and springs. They are relatively scarce in offshore deeper parts of lakes except for detrital feeding species represented by important forms. Another small group lives in running water. Certain freshwater species lay their eggs at the waters edge and the eggs undergo a required dessication state followed by remoistening. Such forms are particularly accessible to dispersal by birds and by wind action, either as eggs or live individuals. Other nearshore ostracodes are susceptible to being picked up by wading and browsing birds. Several examples of live ostracodes in the guts of ducks have been recovered (Proctor, cited in Neale, and others, 1969, p. 243). Considering possible factors, the chances for freshwater ostracodes to be widely dispersed appears to be much better than for them to escape dispersal.

Some suggested factors acting to limit the dispersal of freshwater ostracodes are: (1) restricted site for eggs to be laid and hatched; (2) eggs can not tolerate significant variations in temperature or humidity; (3) juvenile instars require special food supplies; (4) juvenile instars require restricted conditions for growth; (5) adults require restricted conditions for reproduction; (6) adults survive only on special food supplies or in special environments; (7) burrowing or profundal habitat not available to transporting agents; (8) low tolerance to separation from habitat or to new environment following migration; (9) shell features are sensitive to native habitat and change to different shell form following migration; falsely suggesting that the species is restricted in distribution. Which of these or other possible factors are more plausible is unknown.

Marine Ostracodes.—The brackish water and marine environments are typified by a large variety of ostracodes. Estuarine and lagoonal species are commonly epiphytic on algae or pondweeds; a group of genera and species are characteristic of these habitats. Littoral and sublittoral habitats have abundant and generally characteristic, also apparently epiphytic, ostracodes marked by high diversity and locally abundant specimens; detritus feeders are also well represented. Outer sublittoral, shelf-edge, continental slope and particularly abyssal environments are typified by characteristic but progressively more scarce ostracodes. The deeper water forms are probably mainly detritus feeders.

The genera and species of the estuarine-lagoonal and the bathyal-abyssal environments in widely separated localities are closely similar and could be construed as ecologic variants.

127

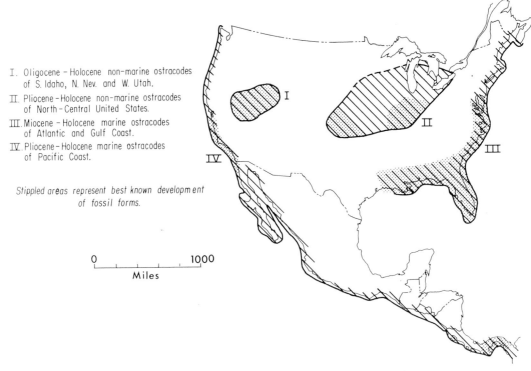

I. Oligocene – Holocene non-marine ostracodes of S. Idaho, N. Nev. and W. Utah.

II. Pliocene – Holocene non-marine ostracodes of North – Central United States.

III. Miocene – Holocene marine ostracodes of Atlantic and Gulf Coast.

IV. Pliocene – Holocene marine ostracodes of Pacific Coast.

Stippled areas represent best known development of fossil forms.

0 ———————— 1000
Miles

Fig. 1—Areas showing provincial development of Neogene ostracode faunas discussed in this paper.

Explanation of Plate 1

Fig. *1a,b—Tuberocypris* sp. aff. *T. centronotus* Swain. Right side and ventral views of shell, ×37.5, Middle Esmeralda Formation (Miocene), 2 miles west of Black Springs, Mineral County, Nevada. *2a,b—Tuberocypris centronotus* Swain. Left side and ventral views of shell, ×37.5, 75 feet above base of Colton-Green River Transition Beds, (lower Eocene), near west end of Raven Ridge, Uinta County, Utah. *3,4,6—Tuberocypris centronotus* subsp. 1, 3–4. Left sides of two shells, ×47; 6, Left valve nested in a larger right valve, ×47, Lower Humboldt Formation (Miocene), Palisades, secs. 17, 20, T. 31 N., R. 52 E, Elko County, Nevada. *5—Tuberocypris centronotus* subsp. 2. Right side of elongate shell, ×54, Lower Humboldt Formation (Miocene), same locality as preceding. *7,8,11—Elkocythereis bramlettei* Dickinson and Swain. Oblique dorsal view, right side and ventral views, ×94. Upper Humboldt Formation (Pliocene-Pleistocene), 2 miles north of Twin Bridges, Elko County, Nevada. *9,10—Elkocythereis minutidontis* Dickinson and Swain. Left side and ventral views of shells, ×94, Upper Humboldt Formation, (Pliocene-Pleistocene) 1 mile south of Elko, Elko County, Nevada.

Explanation of Plate 2

Figs. *1,2—Bairdoppilata triangulata* Edwards. Left side and dorsal views, ×93, Yorktown Formation, upper Miocene, 4.1 mile west of Kissimmee River, Canal C-41A, Highlands County, Florida. *3,4—Proteoconcha multipunctata* (Edwards). Left side, ×100 and dorsal view, ×94, of two shells, Duplin Formation upper Miocene, Duplin County, North Carolina. *5—Proteoconcha* cf. *P. gigantica* (Edwards). Left side of shell, ×94, Duplin Formation, upper Miocene, Duplin County, North Carolina. *6—Campylocythere* (C.) *laeva* Edwards. Left side of shell, ×90, Duplin Formation, upper Miocene, Duplin County, North Carolina. *7—Pontocythere (Hulingsina) ashermani* (Ulrich and Bassler). Left side of shell, ×95, Pungo River Formation, middle Miocene, "Onslow Bay," Atlantic Ocean, Station K-15. *8a,b—Proteoconcha* sp. aff. *P. gigantica* (Edwards). Right side of shell, ×93, and enlargement of surface showing sieve plates, ×940, Duplin Formation, upper Miocene, Duplin County, North Carolina.

PLATE 1.

PLATE 2.

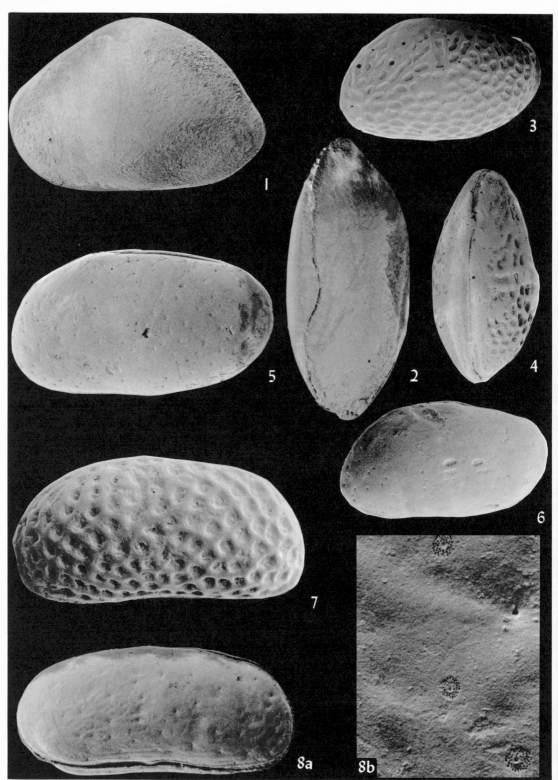

PLATE 3.

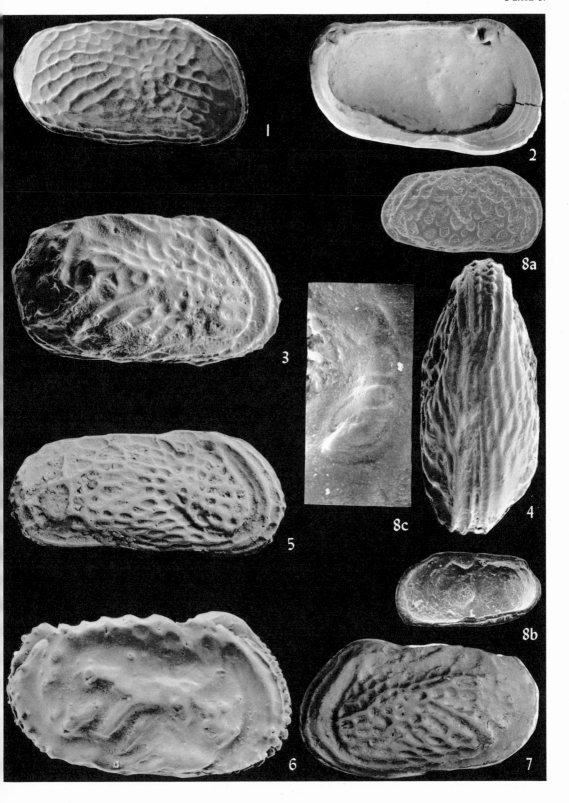

PLATE 4.

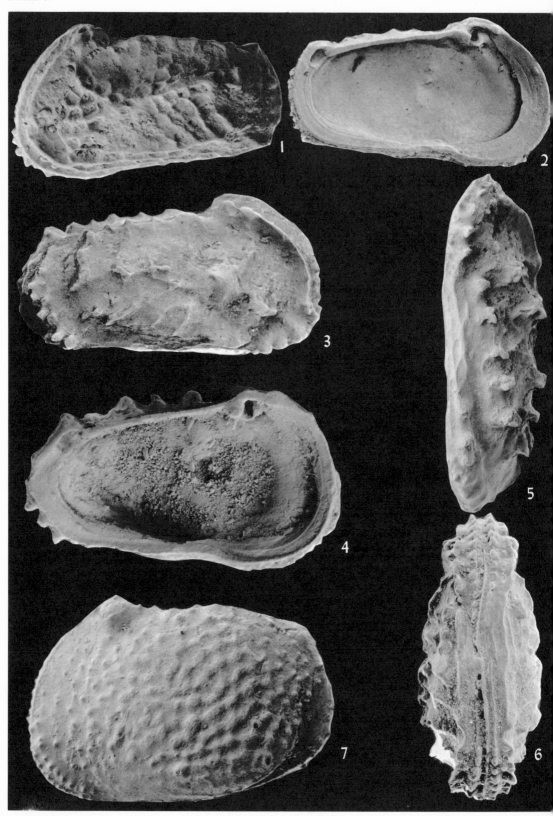

TABLE 1.—NEOGENE NONMARINE OSTRACODA OF WESTERN
UNITED STATES HAVING PROVINCIAL CHARACTERISTICS

Species	Occurrence	How long in area	Acme zone	Lineage development
Tuberocypris spp.	Utah, Nevada, Idaho	Eocene-Miocene	None	Eocene forms apparently gave rise to younger species
Elkocythereis spp.	Nevada	Pliocene-Pleistocene	None	Derived from *Limnocythere* sp.

PROVINCIALLY RESTRICTED NEOGENE FRESHWATER
OSTRACODA OF THE WESTERN UNITED STATES

Ostracode-bearing early Neogene-late Paleogene lake beds attain 2000 meters or more in thickness in Nevada, western Utah and southern Idaho (Swain, and others, 1971) (fig. 1). These are represented by the so-called Lower Humboldt, Middle Esmeralda Formations and by related formations in: (1) littoral, calcitic arenaceous and diatomaceous facies, and (2) profundal dark shale, siltstone and laminated carbonate and oil shale facies. The ostracodes of those lake beds comprise about 32 species, mostly undescribed. Eight genera are represented in the littoral facies and two in the profundal facies. Only one genus, *Tuberocypris,* appears to be provincially restricted (table 1). *Tuberocypris* appears in the Paleogene Green River lake beds (Eocene) of eastern Utah and western Colorado (Swain, 1964 a,b). It is ecologically restricted to early eutrophic-stage lake facies in the Green River Formation but different species reappear in the late Paleogene or early Neogene Lower Humboldt beds near Cobre, Nevada. The lower Miocene of Elko County, Nevada and Oneida County, Idaho has other species of *Tuberocypris*. In the upper Miocene Salt Lake Formation of northwestern Utah, southern Idaho and near Elko, Nevada, other species of *Tuberocypris* occur. The Middle Esmeralda Formation (Miocene of west-central Nevada) also contains a species of *Tuberocypris*. It is not recorded, however, in Pliocene deposits from northwestern Wyoming (Sohn, 1956). Thus the genus persists for approximately 3 epochs in the western United States before disappearing and is not known to occur outside this area. It is associated with other freshwater ostracode genera, species of which occur in Neogene deposits in Europe, Asia and Australia. Why these other ostracodes underwent such widespread distribution in the Cenozoic is unknown, but dispersal by birds is the most plausible explanation. Both eggs and sexually mature individuals can be, at present, transported on the feet or in the gut of migratory birds. Considering the apparent ease with which many freshwater ostracodes at the generic level can undergo dispersal it is difficult to explain how *Tuberocypris* remained restricted to the western United States during the Eocene, Oligocene, and Miocene Epochs.

A second genus not recorded outside the area of the Upper Humboldt of northern Nevada and representing Pliocene and early Pleistocene epochs is *Elkocythereis* (Dickinson and Swain,

EXPLANATION OF PLATE 3

FIGS. *1,2,5—Murrayina howei* Puri. 1, Right side of female shell, ×76; 2, interior of female left valve, ×86; 5, right side of male shell, ×91, Pungo River Formation, middle Miocene, Texas Gulf sulphur pit, Beaufort County, North Carolina. *3,4,6,7—Murrayina gunteri* (Howe and Chambers). *3,* Right side of shell, ×95; *4,* ventral view of shell, ×92; *6,* right side of abraded shell, ×95; *7,* left side of shell, ×86, middle Miocene, Choptank Farm, Peach Blossom, Virginia. *8a–c—Bensonocythere whitei* (Swain). *a,* Exterior of right valve, ×54.5; *b,c,* detail of adductor muscle scar, ×365 and interior of right valve, ×54.5, Yorktown Formation, upper Miocene, Nansemond County, Virginia.

EXPLANATION OF PLATE 4

FIGS. *1,2—Cletocythereis mundorffi* (Swain). 1, Exterior of left valve, ×91; 2, interior of left valve, ×84, Yorktown Formation, upper Miocene, Quankey Creek, Halifax County, North Carolina. *3–6—Actinocythereis exanthemata* (Ulrich and Bassler). *3,* Exterior of right valve, ×85.5; *4,* interior of left valve, ×88; *5,* dorsal view of right valve, ×93; *6,* ventral view of shell, ×94, Pungo River Formation, middle Miocene, "Onslow Bay," Atlantic Ocean, Station K-15. *7—Echinocythereis clarkana* (Ulrich and Bassler). Exterior of right valve, ×79, Same locality and horizon as preceding.

TABLE 2.—LATE NEOGENE FRESHWATER OSTRACODA OF CENTRAL
UNITED STATES HAVING PROVINCIAL CHARACTERISTICS

Species	Occurrence by state	How long in area	Acme zone	Lineage development
Candona acuta	Ks, Ia, Il, Oh, Mi	Kansan-Holocene	Holocene?	Not known
Candona scopulosa	Il, Oh	Illinoian-Holocene	Holocene?	Not known
Candona sigmoides	Il, Oh, Mn?	Illinoian-Holocene	Holocene?	Not known
Candona simpsoni	Il, Oh, In	Nebraskan-Holocene	Not known	*C. ohioensis, C. exilis*, and *C. reflexa* may be derived forms
Candona truncata	Il, Oh, Mi, Ont	Illinoian-Holocene	Not known	Not known, became larger in Holocene
Candona crogmaniana	Ks, Oh, Il, Mi	(?Upper Triassic) Pliocene-Holocene	Holocene?	*C. subtriangulata*, a derived form
Cypria maculata	Il, In, Ne, Ks	Kansan-Holocene	Holocene?	*Physocypria dentifera* may be a derivative
Cypricerus tuberculata	Ks, Il, In	Aftonian-Holocene	Holocene?	Not known
Eucypris meadensis	Ks	Late Wisconsinan-Holocene	Not developed	Not known
Limnocythere reticulata	Il, In, Ia	Illinoian-Holocene	Not developed	*L. pseudoreticulata* may be a derived form

1967).[1] The genus, represented by two species, appears to have evolved from a *Limnocythere* (table 1). The rocks in which *Elkocythereis* occurs consist of about 1000–1500 meters of sands, clays and marls that also contain 11 other genera. These other genera occur in Europe and Asia in deposits of the same age. *Elkocythereis* has not been recorded in the Pliocene of northwestern Wyoming or in Kansas (Sohn, 1956; Gutentag and Benson, 1962). Thus a problem exists in the non-dispersal of *Elkocythereis,* as with *Tuberocypris,* although the geologic range of the former was relatively shorter.

PLEISTOCENE AND HOLOCENE OF THE
CENTRAL UNITED STATES

Several species of freshwater Ostracoda of the central United States (Staplin, 1963 a,b; and Teeter, 1970) are not known to occur elsewhere and range through a large part of the Pleistocene and Holocene of that area (fig. 1). Those that range at least from Illinoian to Recent are: *Candona acuta* Hoff (Kansan-Recent), *C. scopulosa* Furtos (Illinoian-Recent), *C. sigmoides* Sharpe (Illinoian-Recent), *C. simpsoni* Sharpe (Nebraskan-Recent), *C. truncata* Furtos (Illinoian-Recent), *Cypria maculata* Hoff (Kansan-Recent), and *Limnocythere reticulata* Sharpe (Illinoian-Recent) (table 2). In addition, Staplin found numerous species

[1] *Limnocythere (Denticulocythere) asymmetrica* Carbonnel and Ritzkowski (1969) from the Oligocene of Germany may be congeneric with *Elkocythereis*. The German form occurs with *Cytheridella* which, like the *Elkocythereis* fauna, suggests brackish water conditions.

that were restricted to the Pleistocene of the area.

Gutentag and Benson (1962) did not cite provincially developed freshwater ostracodes in Pliocene to Holocene deposits from Kansas, Texas, Oklahoma, and Wisconsin. Among these species, however, *Candona crogmaniana* Turner is said by Benson and MacDonald (1963) to range in the central United States from the Pliocene to the Recent.

Benson (1967) has cited at least two freshwater Pleistocene to Holocene species of the central United States that appear to be provincially restricted. *Cypricercus tuberculatus* (Sharpe) of late Kansan or Yarmouthian age in Kansas is still living in the Great Lakes region. *Eucypris meadensis* (Gutentag and Benson) of Wisconsin age in Kansas is still living in western Kansas.

PROVINCIALLY RESTRICTED NEOGENE MARINE
OSTRACODA OF THE EASTERN UNITED STATES

In a review of the described species of Miocene to Holocene Ostracoda of the Atlantic coastal plain, nine species or species-groups appear to have developed some degree of provincialism (table 3). These forms seem to have developed in the Virginian, Carolinian or Floridian Provinces, or perhaps in the eastern Gulf of Mexico in later Paleogene or earlier Neogene times and to have persisted only in those general areas for an epoch or more (fig. 1). A semblance of lineage-formation also seems to have occurred in several of the taxa. One additional species-group, *Murrayina* spp., had a shorter history, middle and upper Miocene, but deserves mention because of its uniqueness.

Two taxa, *Actinocythereis exanthemata* (Ulrich and Bassler) and *Echinocythereis clarkana* (Ulrich and Bassler) or their close ancestors appeared in the Oligocene, became plentiful by the middle Miocene in the seas covering the eastern and southeastern Atlantic states, and continued to the Holocene for the former species and the upper Miocene for the latter species. Forms related to *Actinocythereis exanthemata* spread westward to Mississippi and Louisiana (Butler, 1963). Both species were sublittoral and had no noticeable barriers to dispersal other than existing ocean currents, yet they did not disperse widely. Other associated forms, such as *Haplocytheridea* spp., *Orionina* spp., and *Aurila* spp., spread widely from this area or migrated into it from elsewhere.

Four taxa appeared by middle Miocene time, three ranging to the Holocene, *Acuticythereis laevissima* (Edwards) (somewhat doubtful in the middle Miocene), *Bensonocythere whitei* (Swain), and *Pontocythere (Hulingsina) ashermani* (Ulrich and Bassler) and one stopping in the Miocene (*Murrayina* spp.) (Swain, 1973). Of these *P. (H.) ashermani* ranged into the Gulf of Mexico and northern Caribbean from the Carolinian Province and *Bensonocythere whitei* occurs at present in the Fundyan Province as well as in the Carolinian and Floridian Provinces. *A. laevissima* and *Murrayina* spp., including *M. howei, M. gunteri,* and *Murrayina* n. spp. seem to have been located in the Carolinian and Floridian Provinces.

Four taxa appeared in the upper Miocene in the Carolinian or Floridian Provinces and remained there until Pliocene or Holocene time: *Bairdoppilata triangulata* Edwards, *Proteoconcha gigantica* (Edwards), *Campylocythere laeva* Edwards, and *Cletocythereis mundorffi* (Swain).

Both the middle and upper Miocene taxa were sublittoral and no barriers are known, other than the ocean currents of the present day, to their becoming widely dispersed, as were species of several associated genera, such as *Radimella, Thaerocythere*. Many other species were more restricted in vertical distribution in the area, but are not known outside it. The reason why these were less successful than the provincially developed species is not known.

PROVINCIALLY RESTRICTED MARINE NEOGENE OSTRACODE OF THE PACIFIC COAST OF THE UNITED STATES

Of the nearly 200 known species of Holocene Ostracoda of the Pacific coastal region of North America only a few can be cited as possibly provincial in character (fig. 1). The forms identified as *Ambostracon glauca* (Skogsberg) are represented (as *Trachyleberis glauca*) in the middle Pliocene of San Diego County, California, the upper Pliocene of Santa Barbara and Orange Counties, California, and the undifferentiated Pliocene of Los Angeles and Orange Counties, California (Crouch, 1949) (table 4). This species was recorded as *Trachyleberis glauca* (LeRoy, 1943) and *Urocythereis glauca* (Hazel, 1962) in the lower Pleistocene Lomita Marl at San Pedro, California.

TABLE 3.—NEOGENE MARINE OSTRACODA IN THE EASTERN UNITED STATES HAVING PROVINCIAL CHARACTERISTICS

Species	Area of occurrence	How long in area	Acme zone	Lineage development
Actinocythereis exanthemata	Md, Va, NC, SC, Fl, Gulf Mexico	Oligocene?- M. Miocene-Holocene	M. Miocene	From *A. rosefieldensis,* Oligocene of Gulf of Mexico Region
Acuticythereis laevissima	Md, Va, NC, SC, Gulf Mexico	M. Miocene?, U. Miocene-Holocene	U. Miocene	In Carolinian Province
Bairdoppilata triangulata	Va, NC, Fl, Gulf Mexico	U. Miocene-Holocene	Not developed	From pre-Miocene *Bairdoppilata* in Carolinian Province
Bensonocythere whitei	Md, Va, NC, SC, Atlantic Ocean	M. Miocene-Holocene	?U. Miocene	Of Boreal origin
Campylocythere laeva.	Va, NC, SC, Gulf Mexico	U. Miocene-Holocene	U. Miocene	Of Carolinian origin
Cletocythereis mundorffi	Va, NC, SC, Atlantic Ocean?	U. Miocene-Pliocene, Holocene?	U. Miocene	Of Carolinian origin
Echinocythereis clarkana	Md, Va, NC, SC	Oligocene?, M.-U. Miocene	M. Miocene	Of European or Carolinian origin
Murrayina spp.	Md, Va, NC, SC, Fl	M.-U. Miocene	M. Miocene	Of Carolinian origin
Pontocythere ashermani	Md, Va, NC, SC, Fl, Gulf Mexico	M. Miocene-Holocene	M. Miocene	Of Boreal or Carolinian origin
Proteoconcha gigantica	NC, SC	U. Miocene-Pliocene	Not developed	Of Carolinian origin

TABLE 4.—NEOGENE MARINE OSTRACODA OF THE WESTERN
UNITED STATES HAVING PROVINCIAL CHARACTERISTICS

Species	Area of occurrence	How long in area	Acme zone	Lineage development
Ambostracon glauca	Ca, Baja Ca, Nicaragua	Pliocene-Holocene	Holocene	Of Californian origin
Hemicythere californiensis	Ca, Baja, Ca	Pliocene?-Holocene	Holocene	Of Californian origin
Pterygocythereis delicata	Panama to Ca	Miocene-Holocene	Not developed	Of Panamanian origin

It occurs living at many places along the Pacific coast from Coos Bay, Oregon, to central Baja California, the Gulf of California and Nicaragua. Whether or not its pre-Holocene distribution was as great as at present is not known. It has not been recorded from the Caribbean region. Several other Holocene species of *Ambostracon* occur along the Pacific coast: *A. vermillionensis* Swain (1967) from the Gulf of California; *A. hulingsensis* McKenzie and Swain (1967) from Baja California, Mexico; *Ambostracon* sp. (Swain and Gilby, 1967) from Nicaragua; and *Ambostracon* sp. (Swain, 1969) from Baja, California. Diversification of *Ambostracon* seems to be taking place along the Pacific coast of North and Central America at the present time. Hazel (informal communication) suggests that *Cytherina calceolata* Costa of the Miocene to Pliocene of Italy, and *Cythere porticula* Capeder (=*Cypridina ungeri* Reuss) of the Tortonian (middle upper Miocene) of Italy and Sicily may belong in *Ambostracon*. If so, these occurrences detract from the provincial value of the genus.

A second species restricted to the Pacific coast of North America from Pliocene to modern time is *"Hemicythere" californiensis* LeRoy. The species is noteworthy because of its unique shell characteristics and its dimorphism. Although only the one species has been recorded from the area, its restriction seems to be of provincial nature.

A third species, *Pterygocythereis delicata* (Coryell and Fields), occurs in the Miocene of Panama and during the Pliocene spread into California where it is still living. A similar form *Pterygocythereis jonesi* (Baird) is living in the North Atlantic and its occurrence, if related to *Pterygocythereis delicata,* detracts from the provincial value of the latter species. The genus itself ranges widely in the Cenozoic and late Mesozoic.

A number of other Ostracoda of the Pacific coast Holocene of North and Central America and of northern South America exhibit a certain degree of provinciality, in particular *Aurila* Pokorny, 1955, *Basslerites* Howe, 1937, and *Radimella* Pokorny, 1968. Each genus was marked by a diversification of species in this region during the Holocene as compared to their pre-Holocene representatives.

EXAMPLES OF PROVINCIALLY DEVELOPED NEOGENE
OSTRACODA IN OTHER AREAS

Detailed discussion of other areas is beyond the scope of this paper, but several examples of possible provincially developed Neogene ostracode faunas are mentioned as deserving of future consideration (table 5). In South Africa several Holocene freshwater ostracode genera are not at present found elsewhere (McKenzie, 1971) and are known to occur in fossil deposits as far back as the Pliocene. A collection of Pliocene age from Mseleni, northern Zululand, South Africa, submitted by Professor J. J. Frankel, University of New South Wales, contained *Acocypris* sp. aff. *A. hyalina* Lowndes, *Hemicypris* sp. aff. *H. pyxidata* Moniez, *Sclerocypris* sp. aff. *S. clavularis* Sars, *Zonocypris* sp., and *Z. madagascarensis* Müller. Except for the *Hemicypris* which occurs in South America, southeast Asia and northern Africa (Bate, 1970)

EXPLANATION OF PLATE 5

FIGS. *1a,b*—*Ambostracon glauca* (Skogsberg). *a,* Left side of shell, ×97; Holocene, Crescent City, California; *b,* detail of anteroventral margin, ×970. *2*—*Pterygocythereis delicata* Coryell and Fields. Exterior of immature right valve, ×177, Holocene, South Bahia Sebastian Vizcaino, Baja California. *3a,b*—*Hemicythere californiensis* LeRoy. *a,* Right side of male shell, ×94; *b,* detail of normal pore showing sieve plate and normal pore seta, ×1820, Holocene, Depoe Bay, Oregon. *4,5*—*Basslerites delrayensis,* LeRoy. *4,* Right side of shell, ×175; *5,* interior of right valve, ×175, Holocene, Bahia Sebastian Vizcaino, Baja California.

PLATE 5.

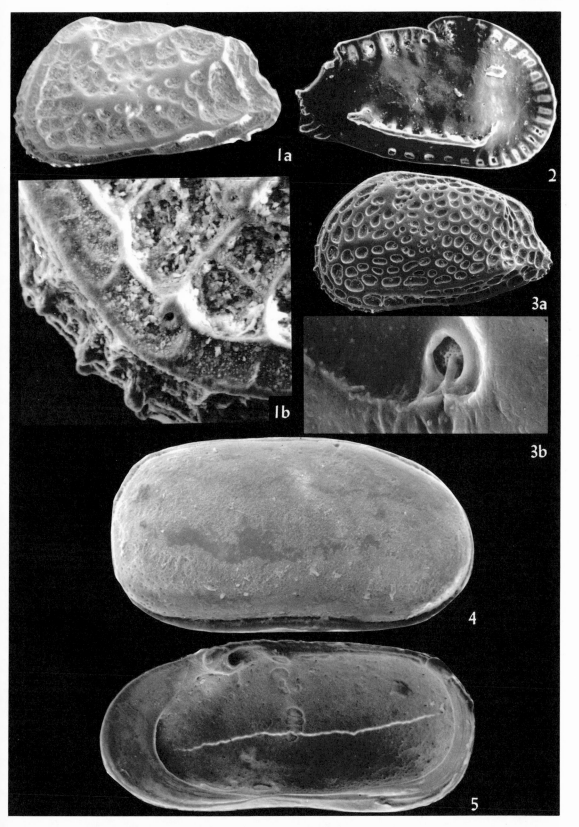

TABLE 5.—EXAMPLE OF PROVINCIALLY RESTRICTED NEOGENE OSTRACODA IN OTHER AREAS

Taxon	Occurrence	How long in area	Habitat
Acocypris spp.	South Africa	Pliocene-Holocene	Lacustrine
Sclerocypris spp.	South Africa	Pliocene-Holocene	Lacustrine
Zonocypris spp.	South Africa	Pliocene-Holocene	Lacustrine
Chrysocythere spp.	W. African-Mediterranean	U. Miocene-Holocene	Nearshore marine
Kuiperiana spp.	Germany, Belgium, France	Oligocene-Miocene	Nearshore marine
Urocythereis spp.	France, Italy, Germany	Miocene?-Pliocene	Nearshore marine
Ambocythere spp.	Caribbean	Oligocene?-Holocene	Offshore marine (at present in deep sea)

the other three genera are not known to occur outside Africa and appear to be of provincial character.

In marine strata of Neogene age in West Africa and the Mediterranean region, *Chrysocythere* seems to be of provincial nature (van den Bold, 1966). Two species, *C. cataphracta* Ruggieri and *C. foveostriata* (Brady) occur in the lower and upper Miocene, respectively, of Gabon and are still living in the seas of that area.

In the marine Oligocene and Miocene of Germany, France, and Belgium, *Kuiperiana* seems to be provincially developed (Bassiouni, 1962; Keij, 1957). *Kuiperiana*, a loxoconchoid genus, occurs in the Miocene Hemmoorer Schichten and Reinbek-Dingdener Schichten of northwestern Germany and related forms are found in the Oligocene and Miocene of France and Belgium. *Urocythereis* spp. may be provincial in distribution in the Miocene and Pliocene beds of France and Italy (Keij, 1957). Records of this genus in the Miocene of northern Germany, however, may not be correct (Bassiouni, 1962). The genus has been recorded by Hazel (1962) from the Pleistocene of California, so that the provincial value of the genus may be limited.

In the Caribbean region certain species of *Ambocythere* apparently have provincial development in the Neogene (van den Bold, 1965) and are living in the Gulf of Panama (Gunther, 1967). The genus occurs in the Holocene of Japan (Ishizaki, 1968) but the species there is somewhat atypical. R. H. Benson (oral communication) also finds *Ambocythere* to be widespread in the oceans so that the Caribbean *Ambocythere* may have only localized value as provincial indicators.

CAUSES OF RECOGNIZED PROVINCIALISM
IN NEOGENE OSTRACODA

Consideration of the possible causes of provincialism, listed under "Habitats of Ostracoda," suggests specialized environments and food supplies as plausibly the major causes of

such restriction. These in turn are very likely of geoclimatic origin.

The freshwater Paleogene and Neogene Ostracoda of the Colorado Plateau-Great Basin areas, western United States, developed in a long-term system of large lakes that persisted for perhaps 60 million years. For such a prolonged limnological regime to occur, a continental climate with well developed climatic belts, established drainage patterns, and precipitation is indicated. The suggestions by Cifelli (1969) for a major but short-lived world climatic cooling in the early Paleocene and late Eocene, as reflected in the planktonic foraminiferal assemblages of the oceans, may also apply to the freshwater ostracode assemblages.

The Paleogene ostracodes of the western United States include several evolutionary series that became extinct by Neogene time. In the Oligocene the loci of great lake development shifted from eastern Utah, Colorado and Wyoming westward to western Utah, Nevada and southern Idaho. In the new lake system another series of ostracode assemblages developed and persisted to Pleistocene and perhaps Holocene time. Specifically what factors of food, substrate, bottom conditions, etc. may have been responsible for species development and diversification in the "Humboldt" lakes are not known. Assuming that this area of the western United States lay in the prevailing westerly belt a climatic barrier to dispersal of the ostracode species and their possible transporting agents may have existed.

A recent study by Cole and Minckley (1972) on endemic aquatic arthropods in an isolated valley in Mexico may have a bearing on the provincial nature of the freshwater ostracodes discussed above. Cole and Minckley found that an interstitial furtive habitat and nocturnal feeding in springs and small caves characterized a specialized group of isopods and other aquatic arthropods they studied. The shifting lacustrine environments, common development of algal reef and hot spring deposits that typified the

Neogene lacustrine deposits of the western United States may have provided a protective interstitial furtive habitat for *Tuberocypris* and *Elkocythereis* that seem to have been provincially restricted. No explanation other than a possible furtive habitat can at present be cited for the Pliocene, Pleistocene and Holocene provincial ostracodes from the north-central United States.

The marine, provincially restricted species have their fossil representatives best developed in areas near the conjunction with a different major ocean current than that in which the provincial species seem to have developed. The *Actinocythereis-Campylocythereis-Murrayina* assemblage of the early Neogene of the middle Atlantic United States appears to have developed in the Gulf Stream in the Floridian Province or somewhat to the west and to have moved northward to beyond present day Cape Hatteras where at present a discontinuity in ostracode populations occurs (Swain, 1968; Valentine, 1971; Hazel, 1971). The northern extent was perhaps as far as Georges Bank (Hazel, 1971), at which latitude further development was probably stopped by the ancestral Laborador Current. Thus the assemblage was mainly thermophilic and was held in a provincial pattern for a geologic epoch or more by water-mass properties that developed in the region.

The Pacific coast *"Hemicythere" californiensis-Ambostracon* spp.-*Pterygocythereis delicata* assemblage also seems to have been a thermophilic group originating in coastal North Equatorial Current waters and moving northward until stopped near or south of Point Conception, California by the cool California Current.

Thus the marine provincial faunas may be thermophilic and held in provincial patterns by environmental pressures relating to water mass differences. Furtive habitats may have characterised provincial marine species. Cryophilic ostracodes, on the other hand, possibly excepting the deeper water form, *Ambocythere,* of the Caribbean, seem to have been less susceptible to provincial restriction.

ACKNOWLEDGMENTS

Appreciation is expressed for the assistance provided by grant No. 485-0100-4909-02, Graduate School, University of Minnesota, and to the University of Delaware for the use of its scanning electron microscope. Helpful comments were received from R. H. Benson, L. S. Kornicker and I. G. Sohn.

REFERENCES CITED

BASSIOUNI, M. A. A. 1962. Ostracoden aus dem Mittelmiozän in N. W. Deutschland. Roemeriana. 3:1–99, 9 pls.

BATE, R. H. 1970. A new species of *Hemicypris* (Ostracoden) from ancient beach sediments of Lake Rudolf, Kenya. Palaeontology. 13:289–296, pl. 52.

BENSON, R. H. 1967. Muscle-scar patterns of Pleistocene (Kansan) ostracodes. *In*, TEICHERT, C. AND E. L. YOCHELSON, Eds. Essays in Paleontology and Stratigraphy. Spec. Publs. Univ. Kans. Dept. Geol. 2: 211–241.

———, AND H. C. McDONALD. 1963. Postglacial (Holocene) ostracodes from Lake Erie. Paleont. Contr. Univ. Kans. Arth. Art. 4:1–26, pls. 1–4.

BUTLER, E. A. 1963. Ostracoda and correlation of the upper and middle Frio from Louisiana to Florida. Bull. La. geol. Surv. 39:1–100, 6 pls.

CARBONNEL, G., AND S. RITZKOWSKI. 1964. Ostracodes lacustres de l'Oligocene, (Melanienton de la Hesse (Allemagne). Archs. Sci. phys. nat. 22:55–82. 5 pls.

CIFELLI, R. 1969. Radiation of Cenozoic planktonic Foraminifera. Syst. Zool. 18:154–168.

COLE, G. A., AND W. L. MINCKLEY. 1972. Stenasellid isopod Crustacea in the western hemisphere—a new genus and species from Mexico—with a preview of other North American freshwater isopod genera. Proc. biol. Soc. Wash. 84:313–326.

CROUCH, R. W. 1949. Pliocene Ostracoda from southern California. J. Paleont. 23:594–599, 1 pl.

DICKINSON, K. A., AND F. M. SWAIN. 1967. Late Cenozoic freshwater Ostracoda and Cladocera from northwestern Nevada. Ibid. 41:335–350, pls. 35–39.

GUNTHER, F. J. 1967. Ostracoda of the Gulf of Panama and Bahia San Miguel. M.S. Thesis unpubl. Univ. Minn. 204 p., 8 pls.

GUTENTAG, E. D., AND R. H. BENSON. 1962. Neogene (Plio-Pleistocene) freshwater ostracodes from the central High Plains. Bull. Kans. geol. Surv. 57(4):1–60, 2 pls.

HAZEL, J. E. 1962. Two new hemicytherid ostracodes from the lower Pleistocene of California. J. Paleont. 36:822–826.

———. 1971. Ostracode biostratigraphy of the Yorktown Formation (upper Miocene and lower Pliocene) of Virginia and North Carolina. Prof. Pap. U.S. geol. Surv. 704:1–13.

ISHIZAKI, K. 1968. Ostracodes from Uranouchi Bay, Kichi Prefecture, Japan. Sci. Rep. Tôhoku Univ. ser. 2 40:1–45, pls. 1–9.

KEIJ, A. J. 1957. Eocene and Oligocene Ostracoda of Belgium. Mem. Inst. r. Sci. nat. Belg. 136:1–210, pls. 23.

LEROY, L. W. 1943. Pleistocene and Pliocene Ostracoda of the coastal region of Southern California. J. Paleont. 17:354–373, pls. 58–62.

McKENZIE, K. G. 1971. Species list of freshwater Ostracoda with an appendix listing museum collections and some further determinations. Ann. S. Afr. Mus. 57:157–213.

————, AND F. M. SWAIN. 1967. Recent Ostracoda from Scammon Lagoon, Baja California. J. Paleont. 41: 281–305, pls. 29, 30.

NEALE, J. W. 1969. The taxonomy, morphology and ecology of Recent Ostracoda. Oliver and Boyd, Edinburgh. 553 p.

POKORNY, V. 1968. The Genus *Radimella* Pokorny, 1969 (Ostracoda, Crustacea) in the Galapagos Islands. Acta Univ. Carol. Geologica 4:293–334, 10 pls.

SOHN, I. G. 1956. Pliocene ostracodes from Jackson Hole, Wyoming. Wyo. geol. Ass. 11th Ann. Field Conf. Guidebook, p. 120–121, 1 pl.

STAPLIN, F. L. 1963a. Pleistocene Ostracoda of Illinois. Pt. I. Subfamilies Candoninae, Cyprinae, general ecology, morphology. J. Paleont. 37:758–797, pls. 91–94.

————. 1963b. Pleistocene Ostracoda of Illinois. Pt. II. Subfamilies Cyclocyprinae, Cypridopsinae, Ilyocyprinae; Families Darwinulidae and Cytheridae, stratigraphic ranges and assemblage patterns. J. Paleont. 37:1164–1203, pls. 159–160.

SWAIN, F. M. 1964a. Early Tertiary freshwater Ostracoda from Colorado, Nevada, and Utah, and their stratigraphic distribution. J. Paleont. 38:256–280, pls. 41–44.

————. 1964b. Tertiary freshwater Ostracoda of the Uinta Basin and related forms from southern Wyoming, western Utah, Idaho, and Wyoming. Intermount. Assoc. Pet. Geol., 13th Ann. Field Guidebook (1964), p. 173–180, 2 pls.

————. 1967. Ostracoda from the Gulf of California. Mem. geol. Soc. Am. 101:1–139, 9 pls.

————. 1968. Ostracoda from the upper Tertiary Waccamaw Formation of North Carolina and South Carolina. Prof. Pap. U.S. geol. Surv. 573-D:1–37, 7 pls.

————. 1969. Taxonomy and ecology of Recent Ostracoda from the Pacific coast of North and Central America. *In,* NEALE, J. H., Ed. Taronomy, morphology and ecology of Recent Ostracoda. Oliver and Boyd Ltd., Edinburgh. p. 423–474, 11 pls.

————. 1973. Some upper Miocene and Pliocene Ostracoda of the Atlantic coastal region and their use in hydrogeologic studies. Prof. Pap. U.S. geol. Surv. 821:1–45, 13 pls.

————, J. BECKER, AND K. A. DICKINSON. 1971. Paleoecology of Tertiary and fossil Quaternary non-marine Ostracoda from the western-interior United States. *In,* OERTLI, H. J., Ed. Paleoecologie des Ostracodes. Bull. Cent. Rech. Pau, 5 (supplement):461–487, 5 pls.

———— AND J. M. GILBY. 1967. Recent Ostracoda from Corinto Bay, western Nicaragua and their relationship to some other assemblages of the Pacific coast. J. Paleont. 41:306–334, pls. 31–34.

TEETER, J. W. 1970. Paleoecology of a Pleistocene microfossil assemblage at the Fairlawn, Ohio mastodon site. Am. Midl. Nat. 83:583–594.

VALENTINE, P. C. 1971. Climatic implication of a late Pleistocene ostracode assemblage from southeastern Virginia. Prof. Pap. U.S. geol. Surv. 683-D:1–28, 4 pls.

VAN DEN BOLD, W. A. 1965. New Species of the Ostracoda genus *Ambocythere.* Ann. Mag. nat. Hist. ser. 13. 8:1–18, 2 pls.

————. 1966. Les Ostracodes du Neogene du Gabon. Revue Inst. fr. Pétrole 21:155–188, 6 pls.

PHYSICAL CONTROLS ON MARINE BIOTIC DISTRIBUTION IN THE JURASSIC PERIOD

W. A. GORDON

University of Saskatchewan, Regina, Saskatchewan, Canada S4S OA2

ABSTRACT—The Jurassic Period was a time of only moderate latitudinal variation in temperature. On land, vegetation and animal life were broadly similar over great distances, but in the sea invertebrate life showed evidence of provincialism from the very beginning. This provincialism intensified as the period progressed. The provincialism is considered to result primarily from the influence of latitudinal temperature gradients. These temperature gradients declined away from the tropical Tethyan zone more sharply in the northern hemisphere than in the southern hemisphere. The changing configuration of land and sea under the effects of continental drift seems to be the cause of gradually strengthening climatic differentiation as the Arctic Ocean became more and more enclosed by land, and so became a semi-isolated reservoir of cool water. Marine currents were a significant influence on the distribution of the life of the time. The principal center of evolution and dispersal in Jurassic seas was the Tethys.

INTRODUCTION

From the time that paleontologists first noticed geographic differences among fossil faunas, they have argued about the underlying physical causes. The debate has been fruitful in many ways, and yet it has also proved to be inconclusive. As far as the Jurassic is concerned, the argument began with work published by Melchior Neumayr (1872, 1883). Neumayr's work was extensively criticized by Ortmann (1896) and the discussion has continued ever since. Good recent summaries of many of the ideas put forward will be found in the work of Imlay (1965), Hallam (1969), and Stevens (1971).

The long debate over relationships between Jurassic biota and their physical environment has tended to divide students of the problem into advocates of either temperature differentials or physical barriers as the primary biogeographic determinants, although, of course, it has been suggested also that the two may operate together. The physical barriers which are invoked are sometimes land barriers, and sometimes ocean deeps. Recently, Hallam (1969) has introduced the suggestion that substantial reduction of marine salinity on a regional scale may account for some of the observed biogeographic differences of Jurassic time. Fleming (1967) has attempted to correlate orogenic events in the southwestern Pacific during the Mesozoic with migrations of organisms that required shallow water marine routes for their dispersal. Whatever the solutions offered to the problems of Jurassic biogeography, these authors are agreed that many of the organisms were clearly separated into a series of realms and provinces whose boundaries fluctuated from time to time.

It is useful at the present time to review the topic of physical influences on Jurassic biogeographic patterns for at least two reasons. One reason is simply the timeliness of looking at the whole problem again during the wave of biogeographic enthusiasm that has been sweeping through the science of paleontology for the last half decade. The other more profound reason is the wide acceptance and detailed understanding of continental drift that has come about through recent developments in a wide range of geotectonic studies. Restoration of the continental masses to their Jurassic positions can now be made with some degree of certainty, and this has provided a whole new framework upon which biogeographic analysis of the Jurassic can rest. A good example of the new approaches made available to biogeography by advances in geotectonic theory is provided by the work of Douglas, Moullade, and Nairn (1972). With reference to the Cretaceous Period, they have attempted to relate changes of volume of the ocean basins brought about by activity of the mid-oceanic ridges to marine transgression and regression, and thus to changing biogeographic developments. In other words biogeographic problems, including those of the Jurassic, have been reopened to study in a completely new context.

The approach taken in the present paper will be first of all to establish the new context by delineating the land and sea areas of Jurassic time, taking into account the effects of continental drift. Second, the evidence for climatic zonation will be reviewed. Subsequently, I will suggest a likely ocean current system for the Jurassic, and then discuss the part played by the Tethys Sea as an evolutionary and dispersal center for the Period.

136

DISTRIBUTION OF LAND AND SEA

When physical controls on Jurassic marine biota are examined, first consideration must be given to the distribution of land and sea. Modern work on seafloor spreading, paleomagnetism, and plate tectonics, as well as older ideas on continental fit, necessitate the repositioning of the continental masses if a realistic view is to be obtained of the paleogeography of the Jurassic world. Opinions on continental drift have converged to such a degree in recent years that it would be erroneous to omit its effects in trying to reconstruct the physical environment of Jurassic time. Hallam (1967) reviewed a wide range of Mesozoic biogeographic data and found that much of it is difficult to explain without invoking continental drift, and none of it is incompatible with drift. Thus, considerable paleontological evidence can be adduced to support the concept of large scale continental displacements, for which the physical geological evidence is already overwhelming.

The distribution of land and sea for four intervals of Jurassic time shown on figures 1, 2, 3, and 5 has been developed from the basic framework of continental dispositions produced by Dietz and Holden (1970). Dietz and Holden have made a series of maps showing successive positions of the continents during the Mesozoic, usually outlined at the 1000 fathom isobath. These maps have been composed from widely drawn data interpreted principally in the light of plate tectonics and seafloor spreading theory

to show the actual position through time of each continent in terms of present day latitude and longitude. Dietz and Holden differ in detail from conclusions reached by some other workers, for example in their placement in the early Mesozoic of Madagascar on the east coast of Africa against Tanzania rather than against Mozambique, but in general their results fall within the broad consensus obtained in recent years with regard to continental drift. Their maps provide a good basis upon which more detailed paleogeographic outlines can be drawn. The maps in the present work are redrawn from Dietz and Holden's figures 3 and 4, retaining the Aitoff equal area projection that they used. Detailed coastlines superimposed on the basic maps have been drawn from Arkell (1956); Brinkmann (1954); Brown, Campbell, and Crook (1968); Harrington (1962); Termier and Termier (1952); and Wills (1951).

The resulting maps leave several areas of uncertainty, although in most respects these do not greatly affect the present study. The modern East and West Indies present particular difficulties arising from their complex history, the paucity of relevant geologic information, and palinspastic considerations. It is sufficient for present purposes to know that in Jurassic time the East Indies were a complex of marine troughs and islands (Umbgrove, 1938) and that the West Indies seem to have been similar (Woodring, 1964). The Bering Strait region also presents difficulty because of insufficient

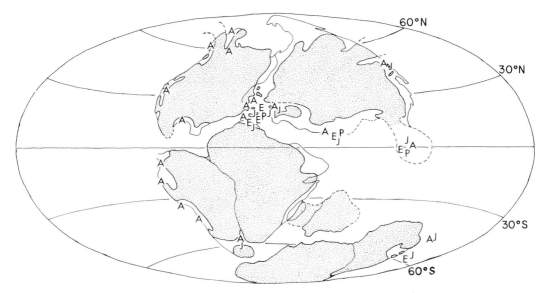

FIG. 1—Distribution of selected ammonoids in the Early Jurassic. A, Arietitidae; E, Ectocentritidae; J, Juraphyllitidae; P, Pleuroacanthitidae. Coastlines drawn for Pliensbachian time, land areas shaded. Edges of continental masses shown in fine outline.

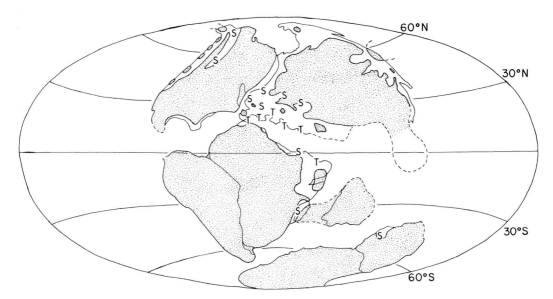

FIG. 2—Distribution of Middle Jurassic foraminiferal assemblages. S, Shelf assemblages; T, Tethyan assemblages. Coastlines drawn for Bathonian time, land areas shaded. Edges of continental masses shown in fine outline.

evidence, but north-south seaways between the Arctic and Pacific Oceans of the time were probably fairly restricted. In a series of paleo-geographic maps, Termier and Termier (1952) suggest that the Bering Strait region itself was commonly a land area, but that at times in the Jurassic a marine strait existed either to the east or the west of it.

One of the most important features of Ju-rassic paleogeography is the absence of either a North or a South Atlantic Ocean in the modern sense. Initial rifting between Africa and South America was apparently in progress by late in the Jurassic, but it has little biogeographic sig-nificance until the Cretaceous. Opening of the southern end of the North Atlantic basin during Jurassic time is more important because it forms part of the Tethys Sea. The Tethys in Jurassic time occupied a roughly east-west posi-tion between the northern and southern group-ings of continents, more or less along the contemporary tropical belt. As will become ap-parent later, the Tethys had a key role to play in Jurassic and indeed in all Mesozoic biogeo-graphic development as a center of organic evolution and dispersal.

A point of divergence between the conclu-sions of Dietz and Holden (1970) and those of workers such as King (1958), van Hilten (1964), and Irving (1967) is with respect to the position of Antarctica during the Jurassic. King (1958) from a study of major suboceanic ridges and from consideration of ancient cli-

matic belts has developed a configuration for the components of Gondwanaland which places Antarctica almost entirely north of latitude 60°S during the Late Jurassic and Early Cre-taceous. Van Hilten (1964) and Irving (1967) using paleomagnetic data as their principal cri-teria reach roughly the same conclusion. Irving agrees with King in placing Antarctica largely north of 60°S during the Jurassic, although with the continent differently oriented, while van Hilten shows approximately the same posi-tion and orientation for Antarctica as does Irving. Dietz and Holden, however, suggest that Antarctica was situated over the South Pole throughout Mesozoic and Cenozoic time, and that its movement as a continental mass was largely confined to westward rotation over the same spot.

To be consistent in my paleogeographic re-constructions, I have followed the placement of the Antarctic continent proposed by Dietz and Holden. On the other hand, interpretations of continental position based on quantitative data such as paleomagnetism presumably have a high degree of reliability and cannot easily be dis-missed. Dietz and Holden used paleomagnetism only as a secondary constraint on their analysis. In view of the distribution of Jurassic marine organisms and its climatic implications, it seems preferable to accept a position for Antarctica away from the South Pole during Jurassic time. Stevens (1971), in his discussion of Jurassic and Cretaceous faunal realms, similarly groups

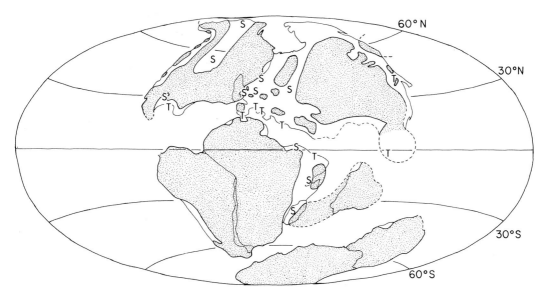

FIG. 3—Distribution of Late Jurassic foraminiferal assemblages. S, Shelf assemblages; T, Tethyan assemblages. Coastlines drawn for Oxfordian time, land areas shaded. Edges of continental masses shown in fine outline.

the southern continents including Antarctica away from the Pole.

As I will discuss in the following section, Jurassic climate was more equable from low to high latitude than that of today. Nevertheless, climatic zoning existed and it was more sharply differentiated in the northern than in the southern hemisphere. If Antarctica were to have been situated over the Jurassic South Pole, its relative thermal isolation from the rest of the world would presumably have made it into a center of cold climate. This would have caused it to generate a sharper latitudinal temperature gradient in the southern hemisphere than actually was the case. Ewing and Donn (1956) have pointed out that, if the poles were situated over open ocean, free interchange of water by means of ocean currents between low and high latitudes would tend to promote climatic equability such as existed in Jurassic time. Consequently, it seems most likely that Antarctica was situated away from the South Pole during the Jurassic, rather than over it. The apparently sharper climatic gradient in the northern hemisphere can probably be attributed to increasing thermal isolation of the Arctic Ocean during the Jurassic as continental drift moved Eurasia and North America into higher northern latitudes. A boreal marine faunal assemblage became ever more sharply differentiated in the northern hemisphere, apparently as the Arctic Ocean was more and more separated from the

world ocean and so became a largely land-enclosed body of cool water.

CLIMATIC ZONATION IN THE JURASSIC

The decline of mean temperature from the equator to the poles is one of the most important determinants of biogeographic distributions. Familiar modern examples of organisms whose distribution is controlled primarily by temperature include planktonic foraminifera and reef-building corals. Among vertebrates, an interesting case is that of the penguins, a group principally confined to high latitudes in the southern hemisphere but living on the equator in the Galapagos Islands which are cooled by the northflowing Peru Current. Land plants are plainly distributed latitudinally. Studies by Stehli and Helsley (1963) and by Stehli, McAlester, and Helsley (1967) on living planktonic foraminifera and pelecypods respectively have quantitatively documented the primacy of latitudinal temperature control on global distribution patterns of these organisms.

Similar latitudinal temperature control is generally agreed to have influenced biogeographic patterns among Cenozoic and Cretaceous biota, even though temperature gradients may have been more gentle than in modern time. For the Jurassic there is a common tendency to stress the equability of climate and to minimize the effects of a temperature gradient. At least a partial cause for this viewpoint is traceable to

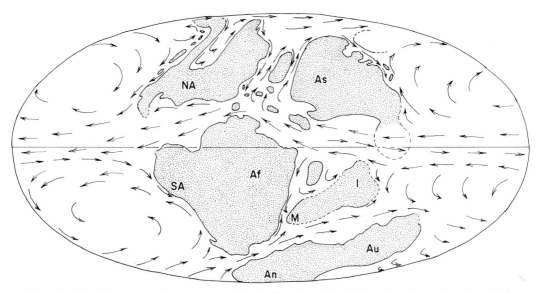

Fig. 4—Inferred ocean surface currents of Oxfordian time. Af, Africa; An, Antarctica; As, Asia; Au, Australia; I, India; M, Madagascar; NA, North America; SA, South America.

the widespread superficial uniformity of Jurassic land floras which may not be as meaningful as it seems to be. It cannot be doubted that in Jurassic time there was a greater similarity of plant life across the world than now exists, but recent studies show that some variation occurs. In view of the fact that strong geographic differences have long been recognized among Jurassic marine invertebrates, it is important to review this question carefully.

Jurassic foraminiferal assemblages are clearly differentiable into Tethyan and non-Tethyan or shelf faunas (Gordon, 1970), especially during the middle and later parts of the period (figs. 2, 3). Some Tethyan forms reach into higher latitudes, such as to Japan in the Upper Jurassic, but these can be explained by the influence of warm, poleward moving currents comparable to the modern Kuroshio (Japan Current) if the Tethyan assemblages are accepted as tropical. That the Tethyan assemblages may be interpreted as being tropical is indicated by the geographic situation of the Tethys and also by comparison with the much better known Cretaceous faunas. Bergquist (1971), Dilley (1971), and Scheibnerová (1971a) have shown that Cretaceous foraminiferal assemblages are arranged roughly parallel to latitude and are controlled by climatic zonation.

Ammonoids also are distributed provincially during the Jurassic. Arkell (1956) recognized the existence of three marine realms among ammonoids in the Middle and Late Jurassic,

but he believed that during the early part of the Period the ammonoids were cosmopolitan. However, Donovan (1967) has been able to show that Early Jurassic distribution records indicate a separation into northern and southern regions at that time, at least in Europe. In a statistical analysis, 30 genera of ammonoids were found to be chiefly or entirely northern, 67 were southern, and 76 were unrestricted. Provincialism was most marked during the later Pliensbachian. The northern or Boreal Realm is characterized both at this time and later by the relative poverty of its fauna compared with that of the Tethys. Figure 1 shows the distribution of three ammonoid families typical of the Early Jurassic Tethyan Realm, together with the Arietitidae, a contemporary but thoroughly cosmopolitan family. The distributions are compiled from Arkell, Kummel, and Wright (1957), as are those shown on figure 5. Donovan (1967) concluded that the Early Jurassic ammonoid distributions that he had studied were controlled largely by temperature.

On the modern globe, the Middle and Late Jurassic realms recognized by Arkell (1956) include the Boreal Realm in middle to high northern latitudes sharply distinguished from the Tethyan and Pacific Realms over most of the rest of the world. Because the Tethyan and Pacific Realms are less sharply distinguished from each other than from the Boreal Realm, it is possible to look upon the ammonoid biogeography of the Middle and Late Jurassic as being primarily controlled by latitude. The separation of the Boreal Realm from the remainder of the world ocean became especially clear from the end of Kimmeridgian time onward. Typical boreal ammonoids of the latest Jurassic include the Craspeditidae and two subfamilies of perisphinctids, the Dorsoplanitinae and the Virgatitinae. The distribution of such forms is in strong contrast with that of other ammonoids of the Late Jurassic which are characteristic of the Tethyan and Pacific Realms, such as the Berriasellidae (fig. 5).

The belemnoids are another group of marine Jurassic organisms that show a pattern of provincial distribution. Stevens (1963) classified them into three marine realms in the Late Jurassic: the Boreal, Tethyan, and Indo-Pacific. The Boreal and Tethyan Realms correspond fairly closely to the ammonoid realms of the same name. They were separated by a fairly stable boundary zone which Stevens considered to be the result of climatic control. The Indo-Pacific Belemnoid Realm is less sharply delineated than the other two and its fluctuating boundary may be explicable in terms of deep water barriers that could have restricted migration of the possibly shelf-living belemnoids.

In assemblages older than the Callovian, Stevens could find no evidence of provincialism among belemnoids. Nevertheless, his Early and Middle Jurassic maps (Stevens, 1963, p. 482, 484) could suggest that the Tethys Sea was typified by a greater variety of belemnoids than

the regions to the north and south. In the Early Jurassic, *Atractites, Hastites,* and *Rhabdobelus* are characteristic of the Tethys. Although evidence is inconclusive, being negative rather than positive in its nature, it may show a latitudinal arrangement of belemnoid distributions as far back as Early Jurassic time.

Among marine invertebrates other than the foraminifera and the cephalopods already discussed there remain many which are provincial in distribution. A number of gastropods including *Discohelix* are confined to the Tethys. Reef-building corals are most abundant there. Ager (1967) has pointed out that costate and sulcate brachiopods appear to be almost entirely restricted to the Tethys from the Early Jurassic onward, although he cautions that this distribution pattern may in part be caused by inadequate records. Smooth, rectimarginate brachiopods dominate in non-Tethyan areas.

Especially helpful in a discussion of climatic zonation for the Late Jurassic are the rudist pelecypods. Throughout their history, the rudists are confined to the Tethyan region or to extensions from it which can be related to temporary spread of warm water conditions. They are well documented tropical forms in the Cretaceous. In Jurassic rocks they almost all belong to the single Family Diceratidae and they range upward from the Oxfordian (Cox *et al.,* 1969). The Jurassic forms occur along the Tethys zone from France, Switzerland, and North Africa to the Crimea.

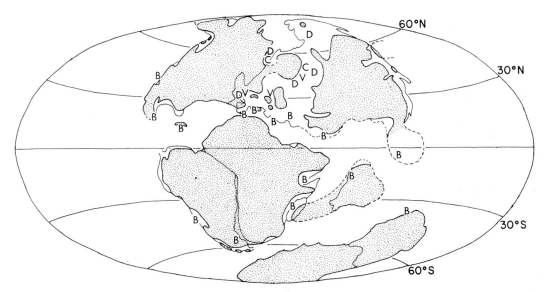

Fig. 5—Distribution of selected ammonoids in the post-Kimmeridgian Jurassic. B, Berriasellidae; C, Craspeditidae; D, Dorsoplanitinae; V, Virgatitinae. Coastlines drawn for Portlandian time, land areas shaded. Edges of continental masses shown in fine outline.

Turning to animal life on land, the most striking feature is the worldwide similarity of the reptiles, particularly in the Upper Jurassic where the record is much the best. Distribution data from Colbert (1962; 1969) and Romer (1966) show that there was an unusually wide belt of warm climate suitable for the existence of terrestrial reptiles at the time. When the effect of continental drift is taken into consideration, reptile distribution seems to have extended into higher latitudes in the southern hemisphere than in the northern. Jurassic reptile remains are known from Patagonia, southern Africa, and Australia, all presumably situated farther south than now. This distribution pattern conforms to a more gradual temperature decline toward the South Pole than existed in the northern hemisphere, although the evidence is not strong because of the small number of vertebrate localities.

The apparent similarity of land floras over wide areas of the Jurassic world is partly accounted for by the chance of preservation being better in certain preferred environments. Seward (1933) and Edwards (1955) have both concluded that the uniformity may well be illusory. Axelrod (1963) recognized a symmetry of floras arranged north and south from the tropics, citing the greater abundance of conifers at higher latitudes in each hemisphere than at lower latitudes. Strakhov (1962) in reviewing the history of Jurassic floras concluded that in Eurasia uniformity in the Early Jurassic was succeeded by provinciality in the Late Jurassic. This conclusion agrees with the increasing provincialism already noted among marine invertebrates.

Isotopic paleotemperature data provides useful supplementary information in the discussion of Jurassic climatic zonation, but it must be treated with due caution. Stevens (1965) has pointed out that considerable uncertainties are introduced by biological factors such as depth ranges and migration habits of the organisms from which temperatures are derived, as well as by problems relating to diagenesis and the effects of the original marine salinity. Similarly, Spaeth, Hoefs, and Vetter (1971) have shown that the isotopic balance in the environment of the time may not be properly recorded in the skeletal material of an analysed specimen for a number of reasons related to life processes and subsequent preservation.

With these limitations in mind, it remains worthy to note that Bowen (1961) reviewed a number of isotopic paleotemperature results and concluded that the mean temperature differential between the tropics and the poles in Ju-

rassic time was about 20°C. This should be compared with a figure of about 28°C for modern seas (Scheibnerová, 1971a). More recently, Stevens and Clayton (1971) found from isotopic paleotemperature determinations that the temperature in New Zealand waters during the Late Jurassic was slightly cooler than now. They also discussed the lack of evidence for a Jurassic anti-Boreal fauna in the southern hemisphere. They concluded from the lack of notably cool isotopic temperatures in the New Zealand seas of the time that the water was probably not as cool there as it was in the Boreal Realm.

Other physical evidence relating to Jurassic climatic zonation includes the virtual absence of carbonate beds in the Middle and Upper Jurassic of the arctic region (Arkell, 1956, p. 616). This contrasts markedly with the abundance of carbonate rock in the Jurassic of southern England, France, Germany and other areas to the south.

In summary, a number of lines of evidence indicate that climatic zonation existed throughout the Jurassic Period. Latitudinal temperature gradients seem to have become progressively steeper as the Period progressed. By the Late Jurassic the criteria are as good as those which have long been accepted as indicators of Cretaceous climatic differentiation. A sharper differentiation is fairly clear northward from the Jurassic tropical belt than southward. This latter conclusion in part is based upon rather poor southern hemisphere evidence, however, the configuration of land and sea at the time appears to make it likely in view of the influence that ocean currents would have had on heat interchange in the more openly connected seas of the south.

Before leaving the question of temperature control and climatic zonation, it is essential to consider if some physical factor other than temperature could have brought about the same biogeographic patterns. Such environmental factors as water turbulence, oxygenation, turbidity, and nature of the substrate profoundly influence the distribution of marine organisms, but they are essentially local ecologic controls that would influence world distribution patterns only in detail. The influence of physical barriers such as ocean deeps and land barriers should usually be distinguishable from the effects of latitudinal temperature control. In addition, the differing poleward penetration of warm water organisms on the east and west sides of a landmass may provide a particular opportunity to test the significance of temperature control on biotic dispersal when the influence of ocean currents is taken into account. There seems to remain only one physical factor in the environment that might cause distribution patterns that could be confused with the influence of temperature. This factor is salinity, which varies on a regional scale in modern oceans.

The effects of reduced salinity on marine communities are similar to those of reduced temperature in diminishing biotic diversity without diminishing abundance. The Boreal Realm among Jurassic marine invertebrates shows a reduced diversity of species and genera among a wide range of taxonomic groups. For this reason, Hallam (1969) suggested that a salinity reduction to perhaps 30‰ may account for most of its observed characteristics and that temperature may have played only a minor part in differentiation of the Boreal Realm. Support for this contention includes the pattern of sedimentary deposition which agrees with a northern sea entered by many rivers, the presence at times of pollen and spores which indicate an inshore environment, and possibly some of the foraminifera in the Boreal Realm. Salinity is the only factor other than temperature which may be capable of bringing about a widespread gradient in faunal diversity and composition. It is true also that in the modern ocean, surface salinity values decline from lower middle latitudes towards the polar regions (Sverdrup, Johnson, Fleming, 1942). Close to the antarctic ice pack surface salinities are usually below 34‰, while scattered data from high northern latitudes show that some open sea salinities may fall below 33‰.

On the other hand, the balance of evidence seems to be against the hypothesis that reduced salinity is the determining influence on the Jurassic Boreal Realm. The Boreal Realm persisted in essential continuity from the Jurassic into the Cretaceous, a time when the foraminifera demonstrate the presence of a southern hemisphere counterpart of the Boreal in the north (Bergquist, 1971; Scheibnerová, 1971b). This would be difficult to explain on the basis of salinity variations. The primary determining factor then must have been temperature. In the Jurassic, the Middle and Upper Jurassic foraminiferal assemblages to the north and the south of the Tethys are essentially similar. To cite a particular instance, the foraminiferal faunas of the Callovian and Oxfordian of northern Scotland (Cordey, 1962; Gordon, 1967) are very similar to those of Egypt (Said and Barakat, 1958) and Somalia (Macfadyen, 1935), a fact that suggests no unusual salinity differential between these points. It seems most reasonable to conclude that the low diversity of the Jurassic Boreal Realm is primarily a function of reduced temperature. Stevens (1971) has reached the same conclusion from several lines of evidence, including the general agreement of paleotemperature data based on both the Ca/Mg and the oxygen isotope methods. The land-enclosed Arctic Ocean with its scatter of islands in the bordering European shelf sea could still have had considerable variation of salinity such as occurs in the modern seas of the Malaysian-Indonesian archipelago.

OCEANIC CIRCULATION

The existence of climatic belts in Jurassic time suggests a corresponding planetary system of winds. Opdyke and Runcorn (1960) suggest that the Mesozoic wind system was comparable to the modern system and that cross bedding data show that North America and Europe were moving out of the tradewind belt into the westerly wind belt during later Mesozoic time. The generally warmer climate of the earth during the Jurassic together with its greater equability from equator to poles probably resulted in an extension of the tradewind belts into higher latitudes than at the present day. In turn, the westerly wind belts may have been displaced poleward. Therefore, there may have been no room for the polar anticyclones that in modern time are associated with high latitude belts of easterly winds. With this difference, most students of the planetary wind system of the Mesozoic accept that the atmospheric circulation was much like that of today.

Working in association with density variations such as occur in modern seas, the planetary wind system under the influence of a rotating earth would have produced a system of ocean surface currents which also would have had similarities with the modern system. Equatorial currents ancestral to those of modern time must have existed, but during most if not all of the Jurassic they would have formed a world-encircling girdle across the central Pacific Ocean and through the Tethys Sea. Within the equatorial westbound flow an eastbound counter current would have existed just as it does today. In each hemisphere the coriolis force would have induced current gyres, and at high latitudes in each hemisphere a West Wind Drift would have existed as it does today in the Antarctic Ocean. As indicated earlier, some uncertainty exists about the precise position of Antarctica in the Jurassic, but a West Wind Drift in some form must have existed in the south. Figure 4 shows the world system of ocean surface currents as I infer it to have been during Oxfordian time. The pattern is probably quite representative of the Jurassic as a whole.

By analogy with modern oceanic circulation, the suggested Oxfordian current system involved only the upper layers of ocean water. This would include only the upper 1000 feet, and often a much lesser thickness, of water. Ocean surface currents are extremely important as distributors of heat from low latitudes to middle and high latitudes. Because many Jurassic forms of marine life were influenced by water temperature, they provide support for the suggested circulation pattern which initially was derived by uniformitarian comparison with modern oceans. For example, the homogeneity of faunas of both the Tethyan and the Boreal Realms suggests that each is encompassed by a continuously circulating and hence homogeneous body of water as shown. The Jurassic Arctic Ocean was larger than today's and would have had sufficient area for a circumglobal West Wind Drift around the pole which would have reinforced its significance as a northern reservoir of cool water. The Tethys on the other hand was the tropical sea of the Jurassic. Extensions of Oxfordian Tethyan organisms including perisphinctid ammonoids from the Tethys to Japan and Madagascar (Arkell, 1956, p. 611) are an indication that poleward warm currents reached these points. Sato (1960) suggested on the basis of ammonoid distributions that the warm Kuroshio (Japan Current) was also reaching Japan during the Pliensbachian and Callovian, Early and Middle Jurassic respectively. He also took the presence of Boreal ammonoids in Japan at those times to mean that a cold current comparable to the south-flowing Oyashio of today was washing the inner side of the Japanese islands. Similarly, the presence of Boreal cardioceratid ammonoids in eastern Greenland during the Oxfordian suggests the existence there of a cold current flowing south from the Arctic Ocean under the right-turn influence of the coriolis force.

In the southern hemisphere, the presence of an austral West Wind Drift is supported by similarities of upper Oxfordian to Kimmeridgian foraminiferal faunas from southern Chile, Madagascar, and India (Sigal and others, 1970). The Late Jurassic belemnoid faunas of the south are also sufficiently similar (Stevens, 1963) that they could represent a southern equivalent of the Boreal Realm in the austral West Wind Drift zone although evidence is not available from areas which are critical to the suggestion. The presence of Tethyan perisphinctids in the Oxfordian of Peru does not agree with significant influence from a north-

bound, cool Peru Current, but could be explained if the Pacific Counter Equatorial Current penetrated that far south.

The position of the landmass of Africa and South America during the Oxfordian and probably throughout the Jurassic must have been important in diverting warm water northwards into the European area, much as Cape San Roque, South America, deflects the South Atlantic Equatorial Current today. Taken together with the influence of the coriolis force, this must have resulted in the oceanic thermal equator being situated considerably north of the geographic equator in the region of the Tethys Sea. In turn, this would agree with the seemingly sharper temperature gradient that existed between the Tethys and the Arctic Ocean than between the Tethys and the more open southern seas.

The absence or, at most, extremely weak development of an Austral Realm during the Jurassic demands explanation because such an anti-Boreal Realm was characteristic of the succeeding Cretaceous time. During the Permian, brachiopods were strongly bipolar in distribution (Stehli and Grant, 1971), and yet by Jurassic time this fundamental biogeographic pattern had been lost. The answer seems to lie in the configuration of land and sea during Jurassic time, with Antarctica probably not situated over the South Pole, and in the pattern of ocean currents that maintained rather similar water conditions southward from the tropical seas into fairly high latitudes.

TETHYS AS A CENTER OF EVOLUTION

One aspect of the relationship of physical features of the Jurassic world to the biotic features remains to be discussed. This is the central part played by the Tethys Sea not only in the geographic but in the evolutionary sense. Many Mesozoic invertebrates are known first from the Tethyan region and seem to have originated there. These include planktonic foraminifera, scleractinian corals, rudist and other pelecypods, some gastropods, and many ammonoid families. Ager (1956) in a study of middle Lias brachiopods in Britain found that the most important invasion of outside forms was from the south. Stevens (1963) in a series of maps postulates a number of outward migrations of belemnoids from the Tethys during the Jurassic. Reid (1967) concluded that the profuse Late Cretaceous sponge faunas of northwestern Europe had their provenance in the Tethys. By contrast, very few forms seem to have invaded other areas from a boreal center of dispersal.

The progressive increase in biotic diversity from high to low latitudes among both terrestrial and marine forms has long been known. Pianka (1966) has for example reviewed many of the theories that have been advanced to explain it. Stehli, Douglas, and Newell (1969) have shown that it is characteristic not only of the present day but also of the past back at least to the Permian. They were able to demonstrate from selected examples that evolutionary rates are higher in the tropics than elsewhere, and that for this reason the latitudinal diversity gradient among different levels of taxa tends to be maintained through time. Tropical forms seem to be much more successful than extratropical forms in spreading to new environments and in eventually becoming cosmopolitan in distribution. The ancestral forms of many taxa should therefore be expected to have originated in the tropical zone. Just why rapid evolution and the most successful colonizers are characteristic of the tropics is not clear, but Stehli, Douglas, and Newell (1969) suggested a possible response of the organisms to the high and more constant solar energy level.

Darlington (1957, p. 620) stated with particular reference to land vertebrates that the more dominant animals tend to evolve in and disperse from the largest, most favorable areas. Briggs (1966) also emphasized the importance of favorable, central locations for the evolution of species which are likely to be successful in terms of having a phyletic future. He suggested that the broad, tropical regions of the modern world are the principal centers for successful evolution and that the relatively stable ecosystems of the tropics are a significant contributing factor in this. Briggs (1966) differed from Stehli, Douglas, and Newell (1969) in stressing the significance of relatively slow rates of evolution in producing successful forms.

Whatever the underlying cause, observational data and theoretical considerations both show the Tethys Sea was the principal center for evolution and dispersal of successful new marine species and higher taxa during Mesozoic time. The circumglobal belt of the Tethys and the central Pacific was the favorable, relatively homogeneous and ecologically stable center from which successive outward waves of migration emanated.

SUMMARY

1. Reconstruction of the global distribution of land and sea for Jurassic time must take into account the subsequent changes brought about by continental drift. The Tethys Sea and the mid-Pacific Ocean formed a circumglobal tropical seaway throughout the Period. Antarctica seems not to have been situated over the South Pole during the Jurassic. The Arctic Ocean became progressively more enclosed by land as time went on because of the northward component involved in continental drift.

2. Although Jurassic time was characterized by greater climatic equability than now exists, the provincial distribution of marine life shows that climatic zonation existed throughout the Period. This climatic zonation, or at the very least the evidence for it, sharpened progressively from the beginning to the end of the Jurassic. The progressive change is believed to be linked to the increasing isolation of the Arctic Ocean from the world ocean of the time.

3. On the world scale, temperature was the primary agent controlling the distribution of Jurassic life. The temperature gradient northward from the Tethyan zone appears to have been sharper than the temperature gradient southward. Hence, the marine faunas of the Tethyan Realm are less sharply differentiated from the southern hemisphere faunas than they are from the faunas of the Boreal Realm.

4. Regional variation from a latitudinal distribution of Jurassic marine organisms can usually be attributed to temperature anomalies introduced by marine currents. This, together with comparisons drawn from modern oceanic circulation, makes it possible to delineate a system of ocean surface currents for the Jurassic. Significant features of the inferred current system include circumglobal currents in the Tethyan and mid-Pacific zone, and current gyres comparable to those of modern oceans in the Jurassic North and South Pacific Oceans.

5. The principal center for evolution of marine organisms that were most likely to adapt to and invade other regions was the Tethys Sea. Large numbers of new forms developed in the Tethys, and many of these spread outward into other marine realms in successive waves of migration.

ACKNOWLEDGMENT

I acknowledge with thanks financial support from the National Research Council of Canada, grant number A 7955, which has enabled me to undertake and complete this study.

REFERENCES CITED

AGER, D. V. 1956. The geographical distribution of brachiopods in the British Middle Lias. Q. Jl. geol. Soc. Lond. 112:157–188.

———. 1967. Some Mesozoic brachiopods in the Tethys region. *In,* ADAMS, C. G. AND D. V. AGER, Eds. Aspects of Tethyan biogeography. Systematics Ass. Publ. 7:135–151.

ARKELL, W. J. 1956. Jurassic geology of the world. Oliver and Boyd, Edinburgh and London. 806 p.

———, BERNHARD KUMMEL, AND C. W. WRIGHT. 1957. Mesozoic Ammonoidea. *In,* MOORE, R. C., Ed. Treatise on Invertebrate Paleontology. Geol. Soc. Am. and Univ. Kansas Press. p. L80–L437.

AXELROD, D. I. 1963. Fossil floras suggest stable, not drifting, continents. J. geophys. Res. 68:3257–3263.

BERGQUIST, H. R. 1971. Biogeographical review of Cretaceous Foraminifera of the western hemisphere. North Amer. Paleont. Conv. Proc. pt. L:1565–1609.

BOWEN, ROBERT. 1961. Paleotemperature analyses of Belemnoidea and Jurassic paleoclimatology. J. Geol. 69: 309–320.

BRIGGS, J. C. 1966. Zoogeography and evolution. Evolution. 20:281–289.

BRINKMANN, ROLAND. 1954. Abriss der Geologie, v. 2, Historische Geologie. Ferdinand Enke Verlag, Stuttgart. 359 p.

BROWN, D. A., K. S. W. CAMPBELL, AND K. A. W. CROOK. 1968. The geological evolution of Australia and New Zealand. Pergamon, Oxford. 409 p.

COLBERT, E H. 1962. Dinosaurs: their discovery and their world. Hutchinson, London. 288 p.

———. 1969. Evolution of the vertebrates. Wiley, New York, 535 p.

CORDEY, W. G. 1962. Foraminifera from the Oxford Clay of Staffin Bay, Isle of Skye, Scotland. Senckenberg. leth. 43(5):375–409.

COX, L. R., AND OTHERS. 1969. Bivalvia. *In,* MOORE, R. C., Ed. Treatise on Invertebrate Paleontology. Geol. Soc. Am. and Univ. Kansas Press. 2:N491–N952.

DARLINGTON, P. J., JR. 1957. Zoogeography: the geographical distribution of animals. Wiley, New York. 675 p.

DIETZ, R. S., AND J. C. HOLDEN. 1970. Reconstruction of Pangaea: breakup and dispersion of continents, Permian to present. J. geophys. Res. 75:4939–4956.

DILLEY, F. C. 1971. Cretaceous foraminiferal biogeography. *In,* MIDDLEMISS, F. A., P. F. RAWSON, AND G. NEWALL, Eds. Faunal provinces in space and time. Geol. J. Spec. Issue 4:169–190.

DONOVAN, D. T. 1967. The geographical distribution of Lower Jurassic ammonites in Europe and adjacent areas. *In,* ADAMS, C. G., AND D. V. AGER, Eds. Aspects of Tethyan biogeography. Systematics Ass. Publ. 7:11–134.

DOUGLAS, R. G., M. MOULLADE, AND A. E. M. NAIRN. 1972. Model of Cretaceous paleogeography and its consequences (abstr.). Bull. Am. Ass. Petrol. Geol. 56:614–615.

EDWARDS, W. N. 1955. The geographical distribution of past floras. Advance Sci. 12:165–176.

EWING, MAURICE, AND W. L. DONN. 1956. A theory of Ice Ages. Science. 123:1061–1066.

FLEMING, C. A. 1967. Biogeographic change related to Mesozoic orogenic history in the south-west Pacific. Tectonophysics. 4:419–427.

GORDON, W. A. 1967. Foraminifera from the Callovian (Middle Jurassic) of Brora, Scotland. Micropaleontology. 13:445–464.

———. 1970. Biogeography of Jurassic Foraminifera. Bull. Geol. Soc. Am. 81:1689–1704.

HALLAM, ANTHONY. 1967. The bearing of certain paleozoogeographic data on continental drift. Palaeogeogr., Palaeoclimat., Palaeoecol. 3:201–241.

———. 1969. Faunal realms and facies in the Jurassic. Palaeontology. 12:1–18.

HARRINGTON, H. J. 1962. Paleogeographic development of South America. Bull. Am. Ass. Petrol. Geol. 46: 1773–1814.

HILTEN, D. VAN. 1964. Evaluation of some geotectonic hypotheses by paleomagnetism. Tectonophysics. 1:3–71.

IMLAY, R. W. 1965. Jurassic marine faunal differentiation in North America. J. Paleont. 39:1023–1038.

IRVING, EDWARD. 1967. Palaeomagnetic evidence for shear along the Tethys. *In,* ADAMS, C. G., AND D. V. AGER, Eds. Aspects of Tethyan biogeography. Systematics Ass. Publ. 7:59–76.

KING, L. C. 1958. Basic palaeogeography of Gondwanaland during the late Palaeozoic. Q. Jl. geol. Soc. Lond. 114:47–77.

MACFADYEN, W. A. 1935. I. Jurassic Foraminifera. *In,* The Mesozoic palaeontology of British Somaliland. Pt. II of the geology and palaeontology of British Somaliland. London. p. 7–20.

NEUMAYR, MELCHIOR. 1872. Ueber Jura-Provinzen. Verh. K. K. geol. Reichsanst. Wien. 1872:54–57.

———. 1883. Über klimatische Zonen während der Jura- und Kreidezeit. Kaiserlichen Akad. Wissenschaft. Wien, Math-Naturwiss. Classe, Denkschr. 47:277–310.

OPDYKE, N. D., AND S. K. RUNCORN. 1960. Wind direction in the western United States in the late Paleozoic. Bull. geol. Soc. Am. 71:959–972.

ORTMANN, A. E. 1896. An examination of the arguments given by Neumayr for the existence of climatic zones in Jurassic times. Am. J. Sci. ser. 4. 1:257–270.

PIANKA, E. R. 1966. Latitudinal gradients in species diversity: a review of concepts. Am. Nat. 100:35–46.

REID, R. E. H. 1967. Tethys and the zoogeography of some modern and Mesozoic Porifera. *In,* ADAMS, C. G., AND D. V. AGER, Eds. Aspects of Tethyan biogeography. Systematics Ass. Publ. 7:171–181.

ROMER, A. S. 1966. Vertebrate paleontology. Univ. Chicago Press, Chicago. 468 p.

SAID, RUSHDI, AND M. G. BARAKAT. 1958. Jurassic microfossils from Gebel Maghara, Sinai, Egypt. Micropaleontology. 4:231–272.

SATO, TADASHI. 1960. A propos des courants oceaniques froids prouvé par l'éxistence des ammonites d'origine arctique dans le Jurassique japonais. 21st. Int. Geol. Congr. Copenhagen. pt. 12:165–169.

SCHEIBNEROVÁ, VIERA. 1971a. Palaeoecology and palaeogeography of Cretaceous deposits of the Great Artesian Basin (Australia). Rec. geol. Surv. N. S. W. 13:5–48.

———. 1971b. Implications of deep sea drilling in the Atlantic for studies in Australia and New Zealand—some new views on Cretaceous and Cainozoic palaeogeography and biostratigraphy. Search. 2:251–254.

SEWARD, A. C. 1933. Plant life through the ages. Cambridge Univ. Press, Cambridge. 603 p.

SIGAL, JACQUES, NICOLAS GREKOFF, N. P. SINGH, A. CAÑON, AND M. ERNST. 1970. Sur l'âge et les affinités "gondwaniennes" de microfaunes (foraminifères et ostracodes) malgaches, indiennes et chiliennes au sommet du Jurassique et à la base du Cretacé. C. r. hebd. Séanc. Acad. Sci. Paris. 271:24–72.

SPAETH, C., J. HOEFS, AND U. VETTER. 1971. Some aspects of isotopic composition of belemnites and related paleotemperatures. Bull. geol. Soc. Am. 82:3139–3150.

STEHLI, F. G., R. G. DOUGLAS, AND N. D. NEWELL. 1969. Generation and maintenance of gradients in taxonomic diversity. Science. 164:947–949.

———, AND R. E. GRANT. 1971. Permian brachiopods from Axel Heiberg Island, Canada, and an index of sampling efficiency. J. Paleont. 45:502–521.

———, AND C. E. HELSLEY. 1963. Paleontologic technique for defining ancient Pole positions. Science. 142: 1057–1059.

———, A. L. MCALESTER, AND C. E. HELSLEY. 1967. Taxonomic diversity of recent bivalves and some implications for geology. Bull. geol. Soc. Am. 78:455–466.

STEVENS, G. R. 1963. Faunal realms in Jurassic and Cretaceous belemnites. Geol. Mag. 100:481–497.

———. 1965. Faunal realms in Jurassic and Cretaceous belemnites. Ibid. 102:175–178.

———. 1971. Relationship of isotopic temperatures and faunal realms to Jurassic-Cretaceous paleogeography, particularly of the south-west Pacific. J. R. Soc. N. Z. 1:145–158.

———, AND R. N. CLAYTON. 1971. Oxygen isotope studies on Jurassic and Cretaceous belemnites from New Zealand and their biogeographic significance N. Z. Jl. Geol. Geophys. 14:829–897.

STRAKHOV, N. M. 1962. Principles of historical geology. Israel Progr. Sci. Transl. Jerusalem. 2 vols. 257 and 432 p.

SVERDRUP, H. U., M. W. JOHNSON, AND R. H. FLEMING. 1942. The oceans. Prentice-Hall, New York. 1087 p.

TERMIER, HENRI, AND GENEVIÈVE TERMIER. 1952. Histoire géologique de la biosphère; la vie et les sédiments dans les géographies successives. Masson, Paris. 721 p.

UMBGROVE, J. H. F. 1938. Geological history of the East Indies. Bull. Am. Ass. Petrol. Geol. 22:1–70.

WILLS, L. J. 1951. A palaeogeographical atlas of the British Isles and adjacent parts of Europe. Blackie, London. 64 p.

WOODRING, W. P. 1964. Caribbean land and sea through the ages. Bull. geol. Soc. Am. 65:719–732.

PERMIAN PALYNOFLORAS AND THEIR BEARING ON CONTINENTAL DRIFT

GEORGE F. HART

Department of Geology, Louisiana State University, Baton Rouge, LA 70803

ABSTRACT—The megafloral and palynofloral evidence for the existence of botanical provinces during the Permian Period over the Euroasiatic landmass is discussed. Data suggest the flora were latitudinally controlled and imply a rotational pole in northeastern Siberia. Paleobotanical evidence can be of some use in elucidating the past latitudinal position of a landmass, but, as yet, the variation observed in assemblages has not been adequately partitioned into its component sources of variation.

INTRODUCTION

One of the important changes in present scientific thought is the acceptance that the relative position of continents now observed is different from that in past periods of geological time. The theory of continental drift, held by so few for many decades and recently strengthened by the theory of sea floor spreading, has given rise to the current ideas on plate tectonics.

Today much paleobiological evidence could be brought to bear on the problem of continental relationships. A major deterrent to global synthesis of paleobiologic data is the lack of uniformity in systematic practices and the methods of noting area and temporal location. Recently, Meyen (1970) synthesized the Permian megafloral and Permian palynofloral data respectively for Euroasia. The present contribution:

1, discusses the relationship between the megafloral-palynofloral evidence and latitudinal botanical belts;

2, defines the palynofloral characteristics of each latitudinal botanical zone and suggests a hypothesis called the Old World Hypothesis for the latitudinal distribution of palynoflora during the Permian Period.

Traditionally (Seward, 1933; Plumstead, 1973) botanical theory separates the floras of the Permian Period into four distinctive provinces:

1, Euroamerican;
2, Angaran;
3, Cathaysian; and
4, Gondwanian.

Many different types of plant remains have been used to synthesize these flora but they are readily determined using either the leaf genera or the palynoflora. For the Euroasian area the synthesis of the leaf genera distribution (Meyen, 1970) allows the greatest precision in locating the provincial boundaries and also re-

vision of their relationship. Meyen (1970: p. 111) recognized four phases in the evolution of the Euroasian flora in the Permian rocks:

phase 1, lower Lower Permian flora;
phase 2, upper Lower Permian flora;
phase 3, lower Upper Permian flora; and
phase 4, upper Upper Permian flora.

The flora of the lower part of the Lower Permian is divided into five characteristic floral associations each of which has a specific geographic distribution (fig. 1). These are: the Angaran Province, consisting of the Angaran association of northeastern Siberia; the Amerosinian Province, consisting of (1) Euroamerican or Atlantian association of Europe, (2) Middle Asian association of Middle Asia and Kazakhstan, and (3) the Cathaysian association of China; and the Gondwana Province, consisting of the Gondwana association of India.

In the lower part of the Upper Permian (fig. 2) Meyen recognized similar associations in the provinces but, in addition, subdivided the Angaran Province into (1) Angaran association, (2) Pechoran association, and (3) Uralian-Kazakhstanian association.

In the lower part of the Upper Permian (fig. 3) Meyen recognized in addition the further growth and differentiation of the Angaran Province into the (1) true Angaran or Siberian association, (2) Tungusk-Verkhoyansk association, (3) Taimyr-Kuznets association, (4) far-eastern association, (5) Pechorian association, and (6) the east European association. In this phase he also recognized the Cathaysian flora as sufficiently well differentiated to be elevated to the level of the Cathaysian Province. Meyen recognized the same associations during the upper part of the Upper Permian Period (fig. 4) as existed for phase three.

On the basis of Meyen's (1970) work, the typical distribution of floras over Euroasia during the Kungurian or Kazanian Stages of the Permian Period are:

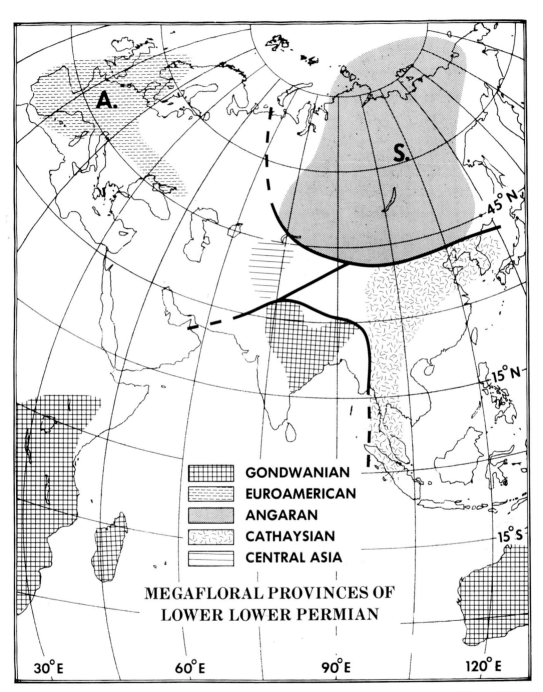

Fig. 1—Distribution of lower assemblages of Lower Permian flora over Euroasia (after Meyen, 1970).

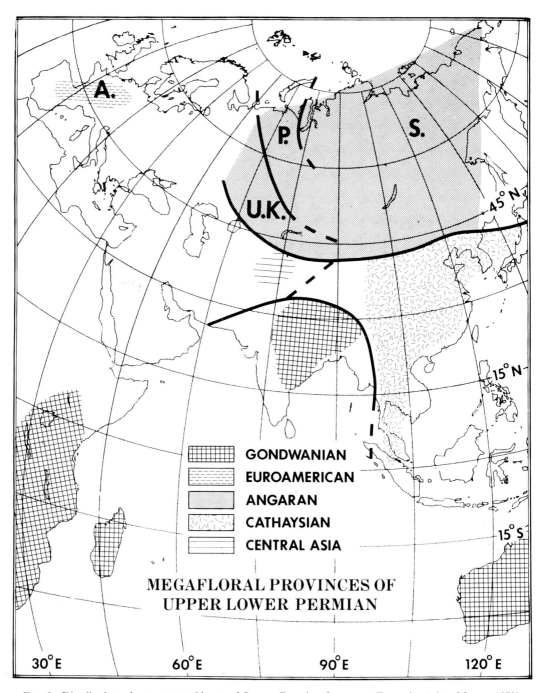

Fig. 2—Distribution of upper assemblages of Lower Permian flora over Euroasia (after Meyen, 1970).

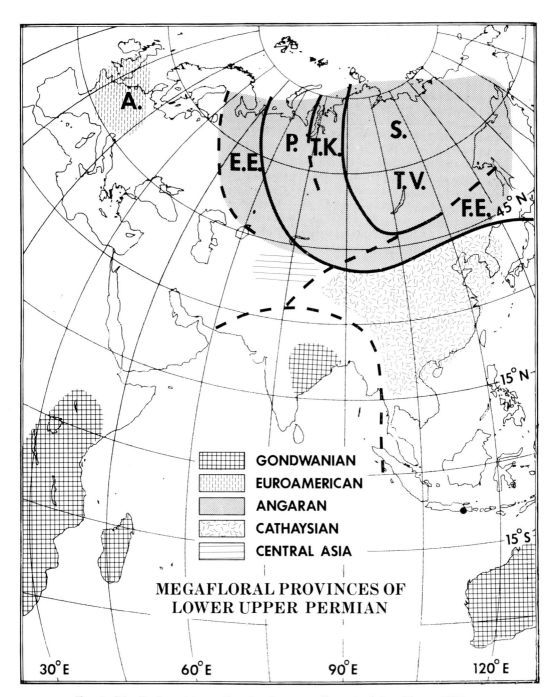

FIG. 3—Distribution of lower Permian flora over Euroasia (after Meyen, 1970).

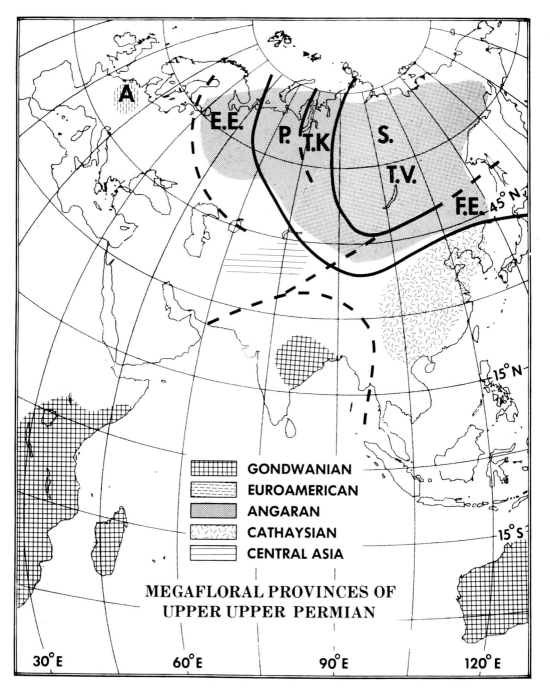

Fig. 4—Distribution of upper Upper Permian flora over Euroasia (after Meyen, 1970).

Angara Province
  1, Siberian association;
  2, Tungusk-Verkhoyansk association;
  3, Taimyr-Kuznets association;
  4, far eastern association;
  5, Pechorian association; and
  6, east European association.

Gondwana Province
  1, Indian association.

Cathaysian Province
  1, Chinese association.

Euroamerican Province
  1, Atlantian association and
  2, central Asian Kazakhstanian association.

The boundaries of the associations of the Angaran Province were defined by Meyen (1970) with considerable precision. The distribution of associations of the Angaran Province suggests that they originally extended as concentric belts around a pole located somewhere in northeastern Siberia. Thus, Meyen's Siberian and Tungusk-Verkhoyansk associations appear to represent a polar flora, herein termed the Siberian Flora, distributed circumpolarly similar to the present Arctic Flora. In this model Meyen's Taimyr-Kuznets and Pechora associations represent a high latitude flora herein termed the Taimyrian Flora and would correspond to the present subarctic and cold temperate flora respectively.

The region to the south of the Aralian Sea and Lake Balkhash which corresponds to Meyen's central Asian association would correspond to a middle latitudinal belt. Its equivalent on the Russian Platform would be Meyen's east European association. Although Meyen indicates his east European association is essentially part of the general Angaran Flora this is inconclusive according to the palynoflora. The east European palynoflora and the Kazakhstanian, central Asian palynoflora show similarities, particularly until the middle part of the Permian Period. The central Asian association is here referred to as the Uzbekian Flora and the east European Russian Platform association as the Russian Flora.

The Atlantian association of Meyen corresponds to the low latitude belt and varied from a subtropical to an arid flora. It is herein termed the Anatolian Flora. The palynoflora from the Turkish area and the Arabian Peninsula indicated an equatorial belt and is presumed to correspond to a humid tropical flora.

PERMIAN BOTANICAL PROVINCES AND THEIR RELATIONSHIP TO EUROASIAN CRUSTAL BLOCKS

The generalized distribution pattern for the floral zones existing during the Permian Period is given in figure 5. From this the Cathaysian Flora and the Gondwanian Flora appear to be misfits. Hart (1965, 1969) pointed out this irregularity and suggested the Cathaysian Flora occurred in the equatorial belt during the Permian Period as shown by the close similarity of the Lower Permian palynoflora of China with that of Turkey. The Cathaysian Flora probably developed on a continental plate separate from that of Euroasia. Since the early part of the Permian Period, this Sinian Plate has moved from an equatorial position.

The Gondwana Flora of India is believed to represent the southern middle latitudinal belt of a subtropical flora. My interpretation of Balme's (1970) evidence suggests the Salt Range of India lay near the equatorial belt. The Gondwana Flora of southern Africa and Australia probably represents a more southern latitudinal belt (i.e., temperate) than does India (Hart, in press).

Indian Block

Petrushevsky's (1971) review of the tectonic activity in southern Euroasia emphasizes the Himalayan Chain. He summarized much of the evidence indicating the pre-Neogene rocks of the present Himalayas formed on part of the Epi-Proterozoic Indian Platform. Only the Tibetian Himalayas were formed off this platform and their rocks were deposited in association with a fault trough which formed along the northern boundary of the platform between the Main Himalayan Fault and the Main Boundary Fault. Only in this region does a complete sequence of Paleozoic-Mesozoic deposits exist (6,000 m. thick). Petrushevsky (p. 32) suggested this area developed on the boundary between sharply different crustal elements.

All the palynological work on India discussed herein concerns rocks deposited on the Indian Block. Of particular importance is the study by Balme (1970) of the Permian palynology of the Salt Range and Surghar Range of West Pakistan. These areas were part of the Indian Block during the Permian Period. From palynological and megaflora data the Indian Block is distinct from the Central Asiatic Block during the Permian Period and probably moved to its present position only after the Permian Period. Packham and Falvey (1971) discussing

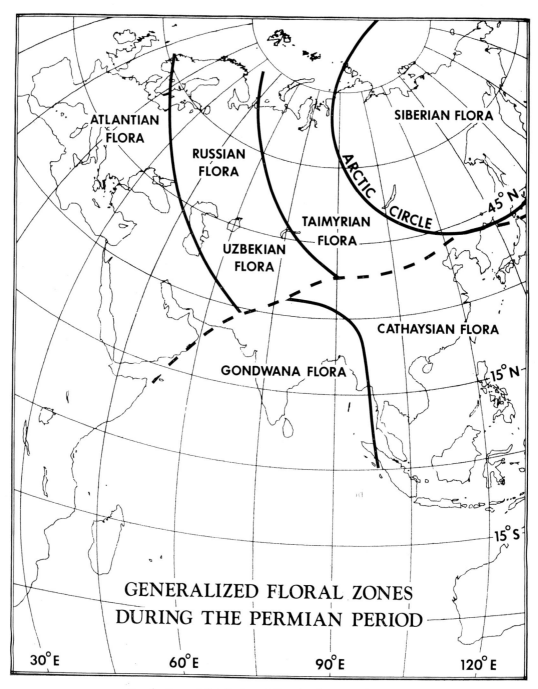

FIG. 5—General distribution of Permian flora over Euroasia.

the marginal seas of the Pacific note "the direct interaction of the Indian sub-continental block with Eurasia first occurred in the late Cretaceous to early Eocene."

Central Asian Block

G. P. Tamrazyan (1971) in discussing Siberian continental drift outlined a fracture zone separating the European and Asiatic continents. Movement along the Siberian Fracture Zone was mainly pre-Mesozoic but according to Tamrazyan (1971, p. 435) is continuing today. The main Paleozoic coal basins formed along the eastern and western margins of this fracture zone, and it is in these coal basins that the major palynological work has been concentrated. However, palynological data, so far, does not provide the resolution to determine the existence or nonexistence of this fracture zone during the Permian Period. Nevertheless the unifying characteristics of the Angaran Palynoflora on the Central Asian Block are distinct.

Euroamerican Block

G. P. Tamrazyan (1971) suggested the separation of the Euroamerican Block from the Central Asian Block took place at about the Paleozoic-Mesozoic boundary (200–210 m.y.a.), whereas, the split of Europe from North America took place later. Palynological evidence indicates a great difference between the Euroamerican Block, as represented by the Atlantian Flora, and the Asiatic blocks, as represented by the palynofloras of the Indian Block and Central Asian Block.

Sinian Block

Palynological distribution patterns (Hart, 1965, 1969) suggest south China lay in the equatorial belt during the Permian Period. This interpretation suggests either drift has occurred to reposition the Central Asian Block and Euroamerican Block or independent northward movement of a Sinian Block took place commencing during the middle Permian. The latter alternative is favored here. The distribution of the Cathaysian Flora suggests the Sinian Block rotated clockwise as it moved northwards.

Paleobotanical and palynological data suggest a distribution of crustal blocks during the Permian Period as outlined in figure 6 to form eastern Pangaea.

PALYNOFLORAL CHARACTERISTICS OF THE
LATITUDINAL BELTS DURING THE
PERMIAN PERIOD

A correlation chart for the Permian deposits of the Central Asian Block is given in figure 7.

The names given in the chart will be used in the discussion with the presumed stratotype-equivalent parenthesized and following.

Polar Palynoflora

The polar palynoflora is typically represented by the Tungusk-Verkhoyansk and the Siberian associations. Representative palynofloras occur in the region of the Lower Tungusk and Ilimpa rivers and the Nordvik-Khatanga region. Medvedeva (1960) described palynofloras from the classic area of the Tungusk Basin, and Dibner (1958) described them from the Nordvik-Khatanga region. The vegetative zone is assumed to be arctic to subarctic.

Nordvik Region

Dibner (1958) studied 994 assemblages from the Nordvik area. These are discussed under the four phases noted in the Introduction.

Phase 1.—Dibner described Tustakhian assemblages (Orenburgian, Asselian, and Sakmarian stages of the stratotype) from boreholes of the Nordvik area. Monosaccites and Triletes are prominent, with fewer Disaccites and Monocolpates. Among the characteristic species are *Cycadopites retroflexus* (Luber & Valts) Hart, *Retrusotriletes nigritellus* (Luber & Valts) nov. comb., *Deltoidospora pyramidalis* (Luber & Valts) Hart, *Acanthotriletes rigidispinus* (Luber & Valts) nov. comb., *Lophotriletes gibbosis* (Ibrahim), *L. verrucosus* (Ibrahim), *L. scurrus* (Luber & Valts) Naumova, *Zonotriletes nigropunctatus* (Luber & Valts), and *Endosporites globiformis*(?) (Ibrahim) Schopf, Wilson & Bentall. Other prominent species include: *Deltoidospora subintortus* var. *rotundatus* (Luber & Valts), *Lophotriletes micrograniferus* (Luber & Valts), and *Punctatisporites? glaber* (Luber & Valts).

Phase 2.—In the same area the lower Zhevnikovian assemblage (upper part of Artinskian Stage and Kungurian Stage) was found in boreholes. Among the characteristic species are: *Retrusotriletes nigritellus* (Luber & Valts) nov. comb., *Deltoidospora pyramidalis* (Luber & Valts) Hart, *Lophotriletes verrucosus* (Ibrahim), *L. scurrus* (Luber & Valts), *Acanthotriletes rigidispinus* (Luber & Valts) nov. comb., *A. tenuispinosus* (Luber & Valts) Hart, *Zonotriletes nigropunctatus* (Luber & Valts), *Endosporites* cf *globiformis* (Ibrahim), *Periplecotriletes* aff. *contortereticulatus* (Sadkova), and *Cycadopites retroflexus* (Luber & Valts) Hart.

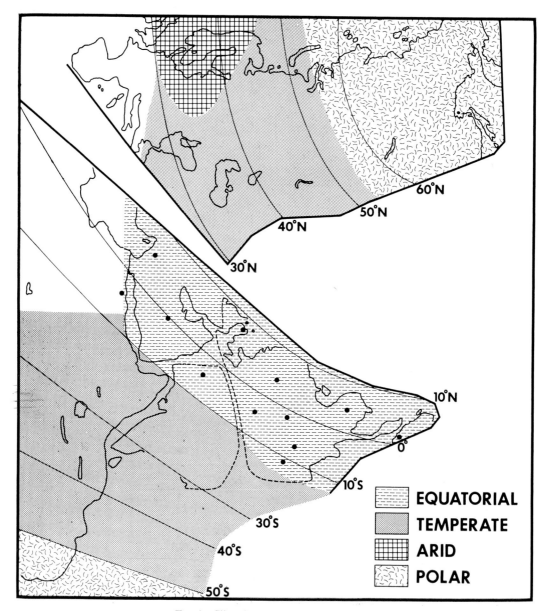

Fɪɢ. 6—Climatic zones of eastern Pangaea.

Phase 3.—In the Nordvik Region Dibner (1958, p. 78) described upper Zhevnikovian assemblages (Kazanian Stage) from boreholes. Among the characteristic species are *Deltoidospora nigrans* (Naumova) nov. comb., *Lophotriletes* aff. *notatus* (Luber & Valts), *Dictyotriletes angulosus* (Kara-Myza), *Cycadopites magna* (Naumova) nov. comb., and *Acanthotriletes spinosellus* (Luber & Valts). Associated and stratigraphically more widely distributed species include: *Leiotriletes glaber* (Luber & Valts), *L. subintortus* var. *rotundatus* (Luber

& Valts), *L. micrograniferus* (Luber & Valts), *Acanthotriletes rectispinus* (Luber & Valts) Hart, *A. parvispinus* (Luber & Valts), *A. obtusosaetosus* (Luber & Valts) Hart, *Cycadopites glaber* (Luber & Valts) Hart, *Cycadopites caperatus* (Luber & Valts) Hart, and *Cordaitina rotata* (Luber & Valts) Samoilovich.

Phase 4.—The Misailipian assemblages (Tatarian Stage) were described by Dibner (1967) from boreholes. Characteristic species are: *Dictoyotriletes angulosus* Kara-Myrza, *Lopho-*

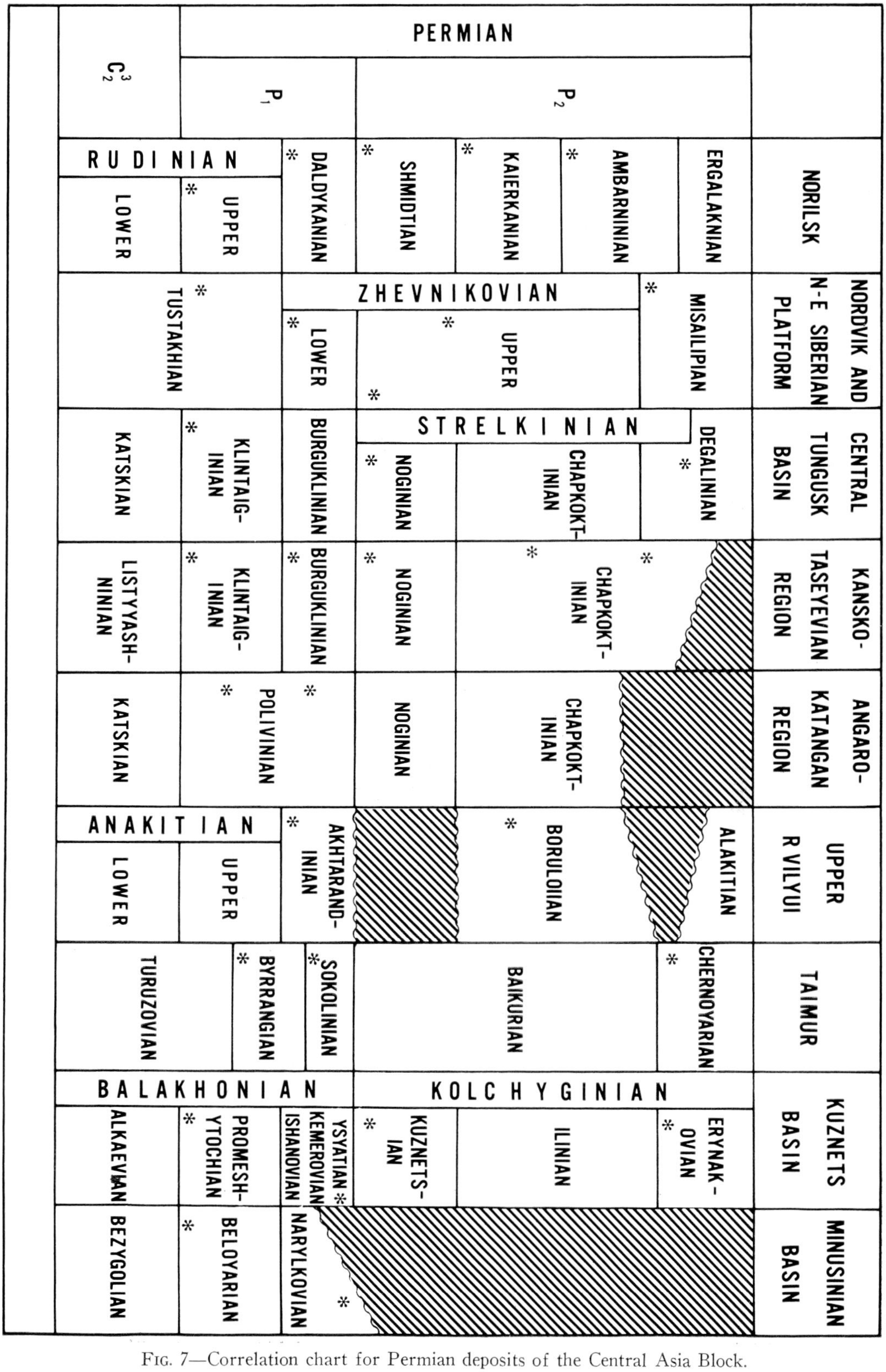

C₂³	PERMIAN						
	P₁				P₂		
RUDINIAN (LOWER / UPPER)	* DALDYKANIAN	* SHMIDTIAN	* KAIERKANIAN	* AMBARNINIAN	ERGALAKNIAN		NORILSK
TUSTAKHIAN	* ZHEVNIKOVIAN (LOWER / UPPER)				* MISAILIPIAN		NORDVIK AND N-E SIBERIAN PLATFORM
KATSKIAN	* KLINTAIGINIAN	BURGUKLINIAN	STRELKINIAN — NOGINIAN	CHAPKOKTINIAN	* DEGALINIAN		CENTRAL TUNGUSK BASIN
LISTYYASHNINIAN	* KLINTAIGINIAN	* BURGUKLINIAN	* NOGINIAN	* CHAPKOKTINIAN	*		KANSKO-TASEYEVIAN REGION
KATSKIAN	* POLIVINIAN	*	NOGINIAN	CHAPKOKTINIAN			ANGARO-KATANGAN REGION
ANAKITIAN (LOWER / UPPER)	* AKHTARANDINIAN		* BORULOIIAN		ALAKITIAN		UPPER R VILYUI
TURUZOVIAN	* BYRRANGIAN	*SOKOLINIAN	BAIKURIAN		* CHERNOYARIAN		TAIMUR
BALAKHONIAN		KOLCHYGINIAN					KUZNETS BASIN
ALKAEVIAN / BEZYGOLIAN	* PROMESH-YTOCHIAN / BELOYARIAN	* ISHANOVIAN / KEMEROVIAN / NARYLKOVIAN	* YSATIAN	KUZNETS-IAN	ILINIAN	* ERYNAK-OVIAN	MINUSINIAN BASIN

FIG. 7—Correlation chart for Permian deposits of the Central Asia Block.

triletes aff. *notatus* (Luber & Valts), and *Cyca-dopites magna* (Naumova) nov. comb.

The overlying Effusive-Tufogenic assemblages (Tatarian Stage) occurred in only one borehole. Additional characteristic species found here are *Leiotriletes nigrans* Naumova and *Acanthotriletes spinosellus* (Kara-Myrza).

Tungusk Basin

Medvedeva (1960) described a vertical sequence of eight miospore zones from Upper Carboniferous and Permian deposits of the Tungusk Basin. Of these, zones IV to VIII represent the Permian Period.

Phase 1.—The lower part of the Lower Permian of the Tungusk Basin is represented by Medvedeva's Zone IV and includes the following characteristic species: *Leiotriletes microrugosus* (Ibrahim), *L. simplicissimus* (Naumova), *L. subtriangulatus* (Luber & Valts), *Retrusotriletes nigritellus* (Luber & Valts), *Leiotriletes lemniscatus* Naumova, *L. trimodius* (Andreyeva), *Lophotriletes polypyrenus* (Ibrahim), *Lophotriletes larvatus* (Luber), *L. perpusillus* (Naumova), *L. microgranifer* (Ibrahim), *Cordaitina marginata* (Luber & Valts) Samoilovich, *C. varica* Naumova, *C. praestantis* Medvedeva, *C. neuburgae* Medvedeva, *C. rotata* (Luber & Valts) Samoilovich, *C. kenderlykensis* (Sadkova ex Luber) Hart, *Psilohymena psilopteris* (Luber & Valts) Hart & Harrison, in press, *Florinites? schopfi* Medvedeva, and *F. menneri* Medvedeva. Less common species include: *Lophotriletes resistens* (Luber & Valts), *L. trichacanthus* (Luber & Valts), *Acanthotriletes mediaspinous* (Andreyeva), *A. multisetus* (Luber & Valts), *A. rectispinus* (Ibrahim), and *Cycadopites glaber* (Luber & Valts) Hart.

Phase 2.—The upper part of the Lower Permian of the Tungusk Basin is represented by Medvedeva's Zone V from the Burgyklinian suite. The following species are characteristic: *Leiotriletes microrugosus* (Ibrahim) var. *minor* Luber, *U. trimoidus* (Luber) Naumova, *Lophotriletes polypyrenus* (Ibraham), *L. larvatus* (Luber & Valts), *L. microgranifer* (Ibrahim), *Acanthotriletes spinosus* Naumova, *A. multisetus* (Luber & Valts), *A. rectispinus* (Ibrahim), *Cordaitina praestantis* Medvedeva, *C. uralensis* (Luber & Valts) Samoilovich, *C. rugulifer* (Luber & Valts) Samoilovich, *C. kenderlykensis* (Sadkova ex Luber) Hart, and *Florinites? menneri* Medvedeva. More rarely the following are found: *Leiotriletes simplicissimus* Naumova, *Retrusotriletes nigritellus*,

Luber & Valts, *Lophotriletes cystostegius* (Andreyeva), *Cordaitina marginata* (Luber & Valts) Samoilovich, *Cycadopites glaber* (Luber & Valts) Hart, and *C. caperatus* (Luber & Valts) Hart.

Phase 3.—The lower part of the Upper Permian of the Tungusk Basin is represented by Medvedeva's Zones VI & VII from the lower and middle parts of the Strelkinian suite. Important species are: *Leiotriletes microrugosus* (Ibrahim), *L. microrugosus* f. *minor* (Luber) Naumova, *L. trimodius* (Luber) Naumova, *Lophotriletes polypyrenus* (Luber) Naumova, *L. subminor* Naumova, *L. cystostegius* (Andreyeva) Naumova, *L. rutilis* Medvedeva, *Acanthotriletes heterodontus* (Andreyeva) Naumova, *A. mediaspinosus* (Andreyeva) Naumova, *A. globulosus* (Andreyeva) Naumova, *A. identis* (Marzenko) Naumova, *A. spinosus* Naumova, *A. mirabilis* (Bessonova) Naumova, *A. multisetus* (Luber) Naumova, *A. rectispinus* (Ibrahim), *A. tschunisensis* Medvedeva, *Cycadopites glaber* (Luber & Valts) Hart, *C. involutus* (Samoilovich), *C. insubulum* (Luber & Valts) Hart, *C. caperatus* (Luber & Valts) Hart, and *C. erosus* (Luber & Valts) Hart. Species less commonly found include: *Leiotriletes subtriangulatus* (Luber & Valts), *Retrusotriletes nigritellus* (Luber & Valts), *Leiotriletes remniscatus* Naumova, *Lophotriletes larvatus* (Luber & Valts), *L. microgranifer* (Ibrahim) Naumova, *L. resistens* (Luber & Valts), *Acanthotriletes olligodontus* (Andreyeva) *Cordaitina praestantis* Medvedeva, *C. praetexta* (Luber & Valts) Hart, *C. rotata* (Luber & Valts) Samoilovich, *Caytonanthus tecturatus* (Luber & Valts), and *C. harrisis* Medvedeva.

Phase 4.—The upper part of the Upper Permian is represented in the Tungusk Basin by Medvedeva's Zone VIII from the upper Strelkinian suite. The characteristic species include: *Trachytriletes sibiricus* Medvedeva, *Acanthotriletes globulosus* Andreyeva, *Acanthotriletes mirabilis* (Besson) Naumova, *Acanthotriletes gongilocarpus* Andreyeva var. *grassispinus* Porth, *Acanthotriletes heterodontus* (Andreyeva), *Cordaitina elliptica* (Koval), *C. rotata* (Luber & Valts) Samoilovich, *Cycadopites procerus* (Medvedeva) nov. comb., *Acanthotriletes spinosus* Naumova, *Monosulcites subrotatus* (Luber & Valts) Hart, and *Cycadopites excellus* (Samoilovich).

Other important studies carried out in the Permian Arctic palynofloral area are Dibner (1961) from both the lower Tungusk area and the basins of the River Vilyuy and by Dibner

(1958) from the northeastern part of the Siberian Platform.

High Latitudinal Palynoflora

The high latitudinal palynoflora is typically represented by the Taimyr-Kuznets association. The palynofloras in the regions of the Norilsk Basin, western Taimyr, Kenderlyk Basin and Kuznets Basin are representative of these palynofloras. Andreyeva (1956) described palynofloras from the classic area of the Kuznets Basin, and Dibner (1967) described them from Norilsk and western Taimyr.

Norilsk and western Taimyr

Phase 1.—The lower part of the Lower Permian flora from the Norilsk region shows general similarities with the Arctic Flora except miospores with coniferous aspect (i.e., Disaccites) are absent. Locally the beds are referred to as the Upper Rudninian (Orenburgian-Asselian-Sakmarian). The species include: *Leiotriletes microrugosus* (Ibr.) Ischenko, *L. simplicissimus* Naumova, *Retrusotriletes nigritellus* (Luber & Valts), *Lophotriletes rarituberculatus* (Sadkova), *L. trichacanthus* (Luber & Valts), *L. gibberulus* (Luber & Valts), *L. verrucosus* (Ibrahim), *Acanthotriletes obtusosaetosus* (Luber) Hart, *A. tenuispinosus* (Luber & Valts), *Hymenozonotriletes papilatus* Naumova, *H. nigrus* (Kara-Myrza), *Cycadopites retroflexus* (Luber & Valts) Hart, *C. tunguskensis* (Luber & Valts) Hart, and *C. retroflexus* (Luber & Valts) Hart.

Phase 2.—The upper part of the Lower Permian is the Daldykanian suite (Artinskian-Kungurian Stages) with a significantly smaller relative abundance of Disaccites and Zonales than in the Arctic palynoflora. The characteristic species include: *Leiotriletes pyramidalis* (Luber & Valts), *Trachytriletes asperatus* (Kara-Myrza), *T. subasperatus* (Kara-Myrza) forma *tenuis* Kara-Myrza, *Lophotriletes scurrus* (Luber & Valts), *Azonaletes levis* (Luber & Valts), *A. plicatus* (Luber & Valts), *Cordaitina ornata* Samoilovich, *C. stiptica* (Luber & Valts), *C. varians* (Sadkova) Samoilovich, *Cycadapites erosus* (Luber) Samoilovich, and *C. subrotatus* (Luber) Samoilovich.

Phase 3.—The lower part of the Upper Permian is represented by the Shmidtian, Kaierkanian, and Ambarninian suites (Kazanian and lower part of Tatarian Stages). The abundance of *Psilohymena* provides an important difference

between the lower Upper Permian palynoflora of the subarctic and the arctic palynoflora. Species include *Leiotriletes glaber* Naumova var. *parva* Kara-Myrza, *Lophotriletes polypyrenus* (Luber & Valts), *Acanthotriletes parvispinus* (Luber) Ischenko, *Cordaitina rotata* (Luber & Vaults) forma *minutula* Kara-Myrza, *N. angustelimbata* (Luber & Valts), *Cycadopites glaber* (Luber) Hart, *C. magnus* (Naumova), *C. caperatus* (Luber & Valts) Hart, *Leiotriletes nigrans,* Naumova, *L. subtriangulatus* (Luber & Valts), *L. radiatus* Kara-Myrza, *L. rotundatus* Kara-Myrza, *Trachytriletes sibiricus* Medvedeva, *Lophotriletes ornata* Medvedeva, *Lophotriletes ornata* Kara-Myrza, *L. politus* Kara-Myrza, *L. gibberuliformis* Kara-Myrza, *L. graniferus* Kara-Myrza, *L. inflatus* L. cf. *notatus* (Luber & Valts), *A. spinosellus* (Luber & Valts), *A. heterodontus* (Andreyeva), *Dictyotriletes angulosus* Kara-Myrza, *Cordaitina rugulifera* (Luber & Valts) Samoilovich, *C. rotata* (Luber & Valts) Samoilovich, *C. minutula* (Kara-Myrza), *Cycadopites parvus* (Kara-Myrza), *C. obtusus* (Kara-Myrza), and *C. excellus* (Medvedeva).

Kuznets Basin

Andreyeva's (1956) study from the Kuznets Basin allowed a detailed subdivision and correlation of the coal measures of the Erynakova suite (upper part of Upper Permian) and Balakhonian suite (Lower Permian). An interesting difference between the Kuznets Basin and the areas to the north in the Arctic palynoflora is the presence of a species of Striatiti amongst the Disaccites in the Kuznets Basin. Further to the south in the Kenderlyk Basin (also in the subarctic palynoflora) more species of disaccite Striatiti are present in the upper part of the Lower Permian sequence.

Phase 1.—The lower part of the Lower Permian of the Kuznets Basin shows an increased number of Monosaccites and a decrease in Triletes. Typical taxa include *Psilohymena psiloptera* (Luber & Valts), *Cordaitina rotata* (Luber & Valts) Samoilovich, *Acanthotriletes trichacanthus* (Luber & Valts), *Leiotriletes microrugosus* (Ibrahim), *Laricoidites similis* (Luber & Valts) Hart, *Cycadopites caperatus* (Luber & Valts) Hart, *Cordaitina rugulifer* (Luber & Valts) Samoilovich, *Nuskosporites augustelimbatus* (Luber & Valts) Hart, *Cordaitina stipticus* (Luber & Valts), *Acanthotriletes obtusosaetosus* (Luber & Valts) Hart, *A. rectispinus* (Luber & Valts) Hart, *A. polypyrenus* (Luber & Valts), and *A. asperatus* (Luber & Valts) Hart.

Phase 2.—The upper part of the Lower Permian of the Kuznets Basin shows close similarities to the Norilsk region. Characteristic species include: *A. stimulosus* (Andreyeva) Hart, *A. obtusosaetosus* (Luber & Valts) Hart, *A. rectispinus* (Luber & Valts) Hart, *Cycadopites caperatus* (Luber & Valts) Hart, *Cordaitina rotata* (Luber & Valts) Samoilovich, *Cordaitina ruglifer,* (Luber & Valts) Samoilovich, *Acanthotriletes microrugusus* (Ibrahim), *Laricoidites similis* (Luber & Valts) Hart, *Nuskoisporites augustelimbatus* (Luber & Valts) Hart, *Acanthotriletes polypyrenus* (Luber & Valts), *Cycadopites glaber* (Luber & Valts) Hart, and *A. asperatus* (Luber & Valts) Hart.

Phase 3.—The lower part of the Upper Permian miospore assemblages were not described by Andreyeva (1956).

Phase 4.—The upper part of the Upper Permian miospores are those from the Erynakovian suite (Tatarian Stage). The Kuznets palynoflora shows a greater number of Monosaccites and a smaller number of Monocolpates than does the synchronous Arctic palynoflora. Characteristic species include *Acanthotriletes microrugosus* (Ibrahim) Luber & Valts, *Retrusotriletes nigritellus,* Luber & Valts, *Acanthotriletes polypyrenus* Luber & Valts, *A. asperatus,* Luber & Valts, *A. adspersus,* Andreyeva, *A. facerus* Andreyeva, *A. punctillosus* Andreyeva, *A. hirtellus* Andreyeva, *A. acutiusculus* Andreyeva, *A. tenuispinosus* (Luber & Valts), *A. heteromorphus* Anrreyeva, *A. gongilocarpus* Andreyeva, *Cordaitina rotata* (Luber & Valts) Samoilovich, *Cordaitina uralensis* (Luber & Valts) Samoilovich, *Cordaitina gemina* (Andreyeva) Hart, *Cordaitina rugulifer* (Luber & Valts) Samoilovich, *Psilohymena psiloptera* (Luber & Valts), *Laricoidites similis* (Luber & Valts) Hart, *Acanthotriletes gibberosus,* Andreyeva, *Cycadopites amphistomus* (Andreyeva) *Cycadopites caperatus* (Luber & Valts) Hart, *Cycadopites involutus* (Andreyeva), *Cycadopites conjunctur* (Andreyeva) Hart.

Middle Latitudinal Palynoflora

Pechora Basin

During the Lower Permian an assumed cold temperate flora existed as the Pechora association. This flora became warmer temperate to possible arid during the Middle Permian. The flora, as represented by palynofloras of the Pechora Basin, were described by Naumova (unpublished work) and Chalishev and Varyukina (1960). The Pechora palynoflora illus-trates the differences between the high latitude and the polar palynoflora. The work of Chalishev and Varyukina (1960) covers the Kungurian-Kazanian and Tatarian Stages of the Permian System. The major difference between the Kungurian palynofloras of the Pechora Basin and those of the rest of the Angara Province was in the general increase in Pollenites and the abundance of *Vittatina* in the Pechora Basin. In the Upper Permian deposits (Pechora and Buzovsk suites) the palynofloras in terms of presence of suprageneric taxa, were very similar to the upper Kungurian but the relative abundance of these taxa was extremely different. In the lower Kazanian deposits (lower Pechora suite) the Disaccites, particularly disaccate Striatiti, predominated, Sporites play a subdued role and Monocolpates is only poorly developed (0 to 5%). In the upper Pechora suite of uppermost Kazanian and lower Tatarian age the most remarkable increase is in Disaccites, particularly Caytoniales which may reach 70%.

Phase 2.—The Bolshepatokian suite (Kungurian Stage) is differentiated from the lower part of the Lower Permian deposits of the subarctic and arctic Permian palynoflora by the decreased abundance of Monasaccites and Triletes, and an increase in Zonales and particularly disaccate Striatiti (*Vittatina*). The characteristic species include: *Leiotriletes pyramidalis* (Luber & Valts), *Retrusotriletes nigritellus* (Luber & Valts), *L. verrucosus* (Ibrahim), *Psilohymena psiloptera* (Luber & Valts), *Endosporites globiformis* (Ibrahim), *Potoniesporites turboreticulatus* (Samoilovich) Hart, *Zonotriletes marginellus* (Luber & Valts), *Z. limpidus* Andreyeva, *Z. radiatus* (Luber & Valts), *Z. nigropunctatus* (Luber & Valts), *Cordaitina rotata* (Luber & Valts) Samoilovich, *Cordaitina ornata* Samoilovich, *Florinites luberae* Samoilovich, *Cycadopites retroflexus* (Luber & Valts) Hart, *Cycadopites erosus* (Luber & Valts) Hart, *Hamiapollenites bullaeformis* (Samoilovich) Jansonius, *Hamiapollenites tractiferinus* (Samoilovich) Jansonius emended Hart, *Vittatina vittifera* (Luber & Valts) Samoilovich, and *Vittatina striata* (Luber & Valts) Samoilovich.

Phase 3.—The Pechora Series (Kazanian Stage and lower part of Tatarian Stage) represents the lower part of the Upper Permian deposits of the Pechora Basin. From Chaliskev and Varyukhina (1960) comparison shows the arctic and subarctic palynofloras of the lower part of the Upper Permian with an increased abundance of Disaccites, Aletes, and Striatiti (*Vitta-*

tina) and a corresponding decrease in Triletes and Monocolpates. Characteristic species include: *Striatoabietites elongatus* (Luber & Valts) Hart, *Protohaploxypinus perfectus* (Naumova ex. Kara Myrza) Samoilovich, *Piceapollenites prolixus* (Luber & Valts) Hart, *Acanthotriletes rarospinosa* (Smirnov), *Zonotriletes pullatus* (Luber & Valts), *Cordaitina rotata* (Luber & Valts) Samoilovich, *Cordaitina ornata* Samoilovich, *Florinites? luberae* (Samoilovich), *Vittatina cincinnata* (Luber ex. manuscript Hart), *Vittatina vittifera* (Luber & Valts) Samoilovich, *Vittatina striata* (Luber & Valts) Samoilovich, *Cycapodites tunguskensis* (Luber & Valts) Hart, *Cycadopites glaber* (Luber & Valts) Hart, *Cycadopites caperatus* (Luber & Valts) Hart, *Acanthotriletes tenuis* (Luber & Valts), *A. levis* (Luber & Valts), and *A. spinosellus* (Luber & Valts).

Phase 4.—The Byzovian suite (upper part of Tatarian) represents the upper part of the Upper Permian deposits of the Pechora Basin. These deposits have a reduced number of Monosaccites and Triletes and an increased number of Disaccites, Aletes and Striatiti compared with arctic and subarctic palynofloras. Characteristic species include *Cordaitina rotata* (Luber & Valts) Samoilovich, *Cycadopites caperatus* (Luber & Valts) Hart, *Cycadopites cydadoformis* var. *Permica* (Kara-Myrza), *Cycadopites glaber* (Luber & Valts) Hart, *Leiotriletes rotundatus* (Naumova), *L. perpusilus* (Naumova), *A. tenuis* (Luber & Valts), *A. microdictyus* (Luber & Valts), and *Pityosporites alatus* (Luber & Valts) Hart.

Central Urals

Varlamov and Ozhiganova (1961) discussed miospores from the cold temperate palynofloral zone but gave no quantitative data. The palynofloral characteristics of their study, undertaken near the city of Magnitogorsk, appear similar to those of the Pechora Basin.

Northern Temperate to Warm Temperate Palynofloras

The temperate palynofloras are typically represented by the East European association. The central Asian Kazakhstan association probably also belongs to the temperate zone. Palynofloral work in this region was done by Zauer (1960, 1964), Samoilovich (1953), and Molin (1961). My examination of a large amount of material from the general Perm region indicates it is typical of the temperate palynoflora.

Phase 1.—The classical Orenburgian, Asselian

and Sakmarian Stages of Perm and the southern Urals represent the temperate to warm temperate palynoflora. These deposits have been described by Naoumova and Rauser-Chernousova (1964). Monosaccites, and disaccate Striatiti are dominant and Sporites are uncommon. Unfortunately no quantitative data are available on the assemblages.

Phase 2.—The Artinskian and Kungurian Stages represent the upper part of the Lower Permian deposits. Samoilovich's (1953) studies of the Artinskian present an assemblage similar to that of the Pechora area except she had more Monocolpites and less disaccate Striatiti. The characteristic Artinskian species are *Tuberculatosporites marattiformis* (Samoilovich) Hart, *Lycospora subdola* (Luber & Valts) Hart, *Granulatasporites irregularisplicatus* (Samoilovich) Hart, *G. subreticulatus* (Samoilovich) Hart, *G. pustillus* (Samoilovich) Hart, *Pilaspora bulbifera* (Luber & Valts) Hart, *Laricoidites levis* (Luber & Valts) Hart, *Cordaitina convallata* (Luber & Valts) Samoilovich, *Cycadopites erosus* (Luber & Valts) Hart, *C. glaber* (Luber & Valts) Hart, *Reticulatisporites compactus* (Luber & Valts) Hart, and some species of *Vittatina* and Disacciatrileti. Characteristic Kungurian species include *Cordaitina ornata* Samoilovich, *C. uralensis* (Luber & Valts) Samoilovich, *C. rotata* (Luber & Valts) Samoilovich, *Striatoabietites elongatus* (Luber & Valts) Samoilovich, *Vittatina vittifera* (Luber & Valts) Samilovich, *V. striata* (Luber & Valts) Samilovich, *V. subsaccata* Samilovich, *Piceapollenites prolixus* (Luber & Valts) Hart, *P. sublevis* (Luber & Valts) Hart, *Abiespollenites sylvestritypus* (Samilovich) Hart, *Jugasporites auritus* (Luber & Valts) Hart, *Potonieisporites turboeticulatus* (Samoilovich) Hart, *Cycadopites erosus* (Luber & Valts) Hart, *C. tunguskensis* (Luber & Valts) Hart, *Monosulcites subrotatus* (Luber & Valts) Hart, *Laricoidites levis* (Luber & Valts) Hart, *Granulatasporites indefinitus* (Samoilovich) Hart, *G. subreticulatus* (Samoilovich) Hart, *Reticulatasporites fabaginus* (Samoilovich) Hart, and *R. microdictyus* (Luber & Valts) Hart.

Phase 3.—The Kazanian and lower Tatarian miospore complexes represent the typical lower part of the Upper Permian assemblages. A major change is the increased number of disaccate Striatiti in the temperate to warm temperate zone compared with the cold temperate zone. Characteristic species include *Azonotriletes osmundae* (Samoilovich), *A. tenuis* (Luber & Valts), *Protodiploxypinus elongatus* (Luber &

Valts), *Hamiapollenites tractiferinus* (Samoilovich, Jansonius emend. Hart), *Densosporites graniferus* (Luber & Valts) Hart, *Protohaploxypinus perfectus* (Naumova ex Kara-Myrza) Hart, *Vittatina subsaccata* (Samoilovich), *Florinites luberae* (Samoilovich), *Potoniesporites turboreticulatus* Samoilovich) Hart, *Coniferites nudus* (Luber & Valts), *Vittatina vittifera* (Luber & Valts) Samoilovich, *Z. nigropunctatus* (Luber & Valts), *Acanthotriletes rectispinus* (Luber & Valts) forma *triangularis* (Andreyeva), *A. alligondontus* (Andreyeva), *A. decimaconfragosus* (Andreyeva), *A. osmundae* (Samoilovich), and *A. trimodius* (Andreyeva).

Phase 4.—The Tartarian deposits contain the upper part of the Upper Permian assemblages. The major characteristic is an increased number of Disaccites compared with the cold temperate palynoflora. Characteristic species include *Striatoabietites bricki* Sedova, *Protohaploxypinus latissimus* (Luber & Valts) Samoilovich, *P. perfectus* (Naumova ex. Kara Myrza) Samilovich, *Hamiapollenites bullaeformis* (Samoilovich) Jansonius, *Vittatina striata* (Luber & Valts) Samoilovich, *V. cincinnata* (Luber ex. manuscript) Hart, *V. subsaccata* Samoilovich, and *V. vittifera* (Luber & Valts) Samoilovich.

Northern Arid Palynoflora

During deposition of the Kungurian to Tatarian Stages the Atlantic association probably lay in the arid climatic zone. Surprisingly little information is available for this province, but the works of Visscher (1967, 1968), Klaus (1963) and Clarke (1965) are representative.

Phase 1.—The Autunian succession is equated with the Orenbergian, Asselian and Sakmarian Stages. The palynoflora shows an abundance of Triletes, Monoletes, and Monosaccites and appears palaeophytic as it contains many relic Carboniferous genera.

Phase 2.—The Saxonian (upper Rotliegendes) is poorly known palynologically but is very similar to the lower part of the Lower Permian containing mainly relic Carboniferous genera (e.g., Potoniesporites, Granulatisporites, Apiculatisporites) and only isolated disaccate Striatiti.

Phase 3.—There are few reports on the Kazanian miospores of Europe. Visscher's (1968) work on the Thuringian deposits of Esterel, Southern France, probably represents an assemblage from the lower part of the Upper Permian. The assemblage is dominated by Saccites

(disaccate Stratiti, Monosaccites and Disacciatriletes). Characteristic species include *Nuskoisporites dulhuntyi* Potonie & Klaus, cf. *Endosporites hexareticulatus* Klaus, cf. *Perisaccus granulatus* Klaus, *Jugasporites delsaucei* (Potonie & Klaus) Leschik, *Limitisporites granulatus* (Leschik) Hart, *Gigantosporites hallstattensis* Klaus, *Striatabietites richteri* (Klaus) Hart, *Strotersporites jansonni* Klaus, *Paravesicaspora splendens* (Leschik) Klaus, *Falcisporites zapfei* (Potonie & Klaus) Leschik, *Vesicaspora schaubergeri* (Potonie & Klaus) Jizba, *Pityosporites alatus* (Luber & Valts) Hart, *Platysaccus papilionis* (Potonie & Klaus), *Vittatina costabilis* Wilson, and *V. ovalis* Klaus.

Phase 4.—A considerable amount is known regarding the palynoflora of the Zechstein of Europe, assigned to the upper part of the Upper Permian. In general the assemblages show a dominance of disaccate Striatiti (50%), Monosaccites (35%) and Disacciatrietes (20%). Triletes, Zonales and Aletes are of minor importance. Characteristic species include *Lueckisporites virkkiae* Potonie & Klaus, *Vesicaspora schaubergeri* (Potonie & Klaus) Jizba, *Jugasporites delasaucei* Leschik, *Limitisporites granulatus* Leschik, *Falcisporites zapfei* (Potonie & Klaus) Leschik, *Nuskoisporites dulhuntyi* Potonie & Klaus, *Vittatina hiltonensis* Clarke & Chaloner, *Striatoabietites richteri* (Klaus) Hart, and *Taeniaesporites noviaulensis* Leschik.

Equatorial Palynoflora

The equatorial palynoflora is typically represented by the palynoflora of Turkey, Iraq and China (Singh 1964, Ouyang 1962, 1964, and Agrali and Akyol 1967). These palynoflora characterize the Cathaysian botanic province and were predominantly developed during the Early Permian. The Lower Permian of the Salt Range, described in part by Balme (1970), contains some elements of the Cathaysian palynoflora but is probably essentially Gondwanian. Hart (1969) pointed out the characteristics of these palynoflora as having an abundance of relic Carboniferous genera associated with some typical Lower Permian Saccites.

Phase 1.—The lower part of the Lower Permian palynoflora is known from the Kaiping Basin and includes *Pectosporites qualiformis* Imgrund, *Pericutosporites potoniei* Imgrund, *Tuberculatosporites ancystoides* Imgrund, *Specioiosporites specialis* (Imgrund) Potonie & Kremp, *Punctatosporites nanulus* (Imgrund) Potonie & Kremp, *Pityosporites tongshani* Imgrund, *Nuskoisporites coronatus* Imgrund, *Tri-*

quitrites rumulosus (Imgrund) Potonie & Kremp, *Raistrickia irregularis* Kosanke, *Gulisporites cochleatius* (Imgrund) Imgrund, *Verrucosisporites sinensis* (Imgrund) Imgrund, *V. ovimamnus* (Imgrund) Imgrund, *Converrucosisporites triquetrus* (Ibrahim) Potonie & Kremp, *C. variolaris* (Imgrund) Imgrund, *V. kaipingensis* (Imgrund) Imgrund, and *Latosporites ficoides* (Imgrund) Potonie & Kremp.

Phase 2.—Ouyang (1962) described material from the upper part of the Lower Permian of China. The palynoflora is somewhat similar in generic makeup to phase 1 but contains more saccate forms. The palynoflora includes *Gulisporites sp.* Ouyang, *Leiotriletes* cf. *L. adnatoides* Potonie and Kremp, *Pityosporites sp. B.* Ouyang, *Laevigatosporites desmoinensis* (Wilson & Coe), Schopf, Wilson & Bentall, *Verrucosisporites verrucosus* Ibrahim, *V. reticuloides* Ouyang, and *Triquitrites sp.* Ouyang.

Phase 3.—Ouyang (1964) described material from the lower part of the Upper Permian of China that shows a dominance of *Laevigatosporites, Latosporites* or *Punctatisporites.* Saccites form a small part of the palynoflora. Ouyang (1964) pointed out that the palynoflora includes *Leiotriletes ornatus* Ischenko, *L. adnatus* (Kosanke) Potonie & Kremp, *Punctatisporites minutus* Kosanke, *Calamospora platirugosus* (Luber & Valts) Ouyang 1964, *C. pedata* Kosanke, *C. cf. C. perrugosa* (Loose) Schopf, Wilson & Bentall, *Granulatisporites cf. piroformis* Loose, *Lophotriletes cf. L. pseudoculeatus* Potonie & Kremp, *Planoisporites cf. spinulistratus* Potonie & Kremp, *Knoxisporites instarrotulae* (Horst), Potonie & Kremp, *Triquetrites cf. T. exceptus* Potonie & Kremp, *T. tribullatus,* (Ibrahim) Potonie & Kremp *Lycospora cf. L. pseudoannulata* Kosanke, *Florinites*

cf. *F. elegans* Wilson & Kosanke, *F. uralensis* (Luber & Valts) Ouyang, *Laevigatosporites minimus* (Wilson & Coe) Schopf, Wilson, & Bentall, *L. vedius,* Kosanke, *L. desmoinensis* (Wilson & Coe) Schopf, Wilson & Bentall, and *Torispora cf. securis* Balme, which "are closely comparable to the forms of the Upper Carboniferous (Westphalian C-D, Stephanian) in Europe and North America" (Ouyang 1964). Only two species, *Cordaitina uralensis* and *Protohaploxypinus prolixus,* are found also in the flora of the Kuznets Basin.

SUMMARY AND CONCLUSIONS

An abundant literature exists about the occurrence and distribution of both miopsore and megaplant fossils in Permian rocks. When synthesized those data indicate the Permian flora was divisible into distinct floral provinces. The writer's hypothesis is that the floral provinces existing over Eurasia vary in a systematic fashion that may be related to a latitudinal climatic zonation during the Permian Period, and five latitudinally controlled palynofloral zones can be recognized in the Permian sediments for at least four time phases over the area of eastern Pangaea (Eurasia). Currently work is being undertaken to standardize the areal, temporal and taxonomic information available and subject it to a conventional hypothesis testing using statistical procedures. If temporal latitudinally related distributional patterns exist in eastern Pangaea then they should also exist in western Pangaea (North and South America). Although the information is scant from western Pangaea, it is evident from the view point of a designed experiment that the hypothesis of the existence of latitudinally oriented botanic provinces during the Permian Period in Eurasia may be tested using data yet to be gathered from the New World.

REFERENCES CITED

AGRALI, B., AND E. AKYOL. 1967. Etude palynologique de charbons de Hazro et considerations sur l'age des horizons lacustreals du Permo-Carbonifère. Bull. Miner. Res. Explor. Inst. Ankara, foreign ed. 68:1–27.

ANDREYEVA, E. M. 1956. Spore-pollen characteristics of the Balakhonsk and Erynakovsk suite of the Kuznets Basin. *In,* YAVORSK, V. I., Ed. Atlas of the leading forms of fossil flora and fauna of the Permian System of the Kuznets Basin. Trudy vses. nauchno-issled. geol. Inst. Moscow. p. 207–271.

BALME, B. E. 1970. Palynology of Permian and Triassic strata in the Salt Range and Surghar Range, West Pakistan. *In,* KUMMEL, B. AND C. TEICHERT, Eds. Stratigraphic boundary problems: Permian and Triassic of West Pakistan. Univ. Kansas Geol. Dept. Sp. pub. 4, Univ. Kansas Press. p. 305–453.

CHALISHEV, V. I., AND L. M. VARYUKHINA. 1960. The stratigraphy and spore-pollen complexes of the Upper Permian and Triassic deposits of the Perchora Urals and the Chernishev Range. Trudy Komi Fil. Akad. Nauk SSSR. 10:49–58.

CLARKE, R. F. A. 1965. British Permian saccate and monosulcate miospores. Palaeontology. 8(2):322–354.

DIBNER, A. F. 1958. Palynological complexes of the upper Paleozoic deposits of the northern Siberian Platform and their stratigraphic significance. Avtoreferat Diss. Kand. Nauk geol. gorn. vses. nauchno-issled. geol. Inst.

———. 1961. The separation of the upper Paleozoic deposits of the middle reaches of the River Anabara by spore-pollen analysis. Paleont. Biostrat. Sov. Arkt. Trudy nauchno-issled. Inst. Geol. Arkt. 124(2):66–69.

————. 1967. Permian complexes of spore and pollen of the Norilsk region and their significance for the purpose of comparing the deposits. Uchenye zapiski paleont. biostrat. Nauchno-issled. Inst. Geol. Arkt. 19:51–80.

HART, C. F. 1965. The systematics and distribution of Permian miospores. Univ. Witwatersrand Press. 1–252 p.

————. 1969. Palynology of the Permian Period. *In,* TSCHUDY, R. H. AND R. A. SCOTT, Eds. Aspects of Palynology. J. Wiley, New York. p. 271–289.

KLAUS, W. 1963. Sporen aus dem Sudalpinen Perm. Jb. geol. Bundesanst. (Austr). 106:229–316.

MEDVEDEVA, A. M. 1960. The stratigraphic separation of the lower horizons of the Tunguska Series by the method of spore-pollen analysis. Akad. Nauk. SSSR. Inst. Geol. Razrabot. Goryuch. Iskopaemyth, Moskva. 89 p.

MEYEN, S. V. 1970. Permian floras. *In,* VAKHRAMEYEV, V. A. AND OTHERS, Paleozoic and Mesozoic floras and phytogeography of Euroasia. Trudy Akad. Nauk SSSR. Geol. Inst. 208:111–157.

MOLIN, V. A. 1961. Spore pollen complexes of the Permian deposits of the Kanin Peninsula. *In,* Mater. Geol. Petrogr. Timana Polyostrova Kanin, Akad. Nauk. SSSR. p. 22–43.

NAOUMOVA [Naumova], S., AND D. RAUSER-CHERNOUSOVA. 1964. Sur La position stratigraphique de l'Autunien et de ses analogues. 5th Congr. Int. Strat. Geol. Carbonifère. 3:1215–1228.

OUYANG, S. 1962. The microspore assemblage from the Lungtan Series of Changshing, Chekiang. Acta Palaeont. sin. 10(1):76–119.

————. 1964. A preliminary report on sporae dispersae from the lower Shihhotze Series of Hokü District, northwest Shansi. Ibid. 12(3):486–519.

PACKHAM, G. H., AND D. A. FALVEY. 1971. An hypothesis for the formation of marginal seas in the western Pacific. Tectonophysics. 11:79–109.

PETRUSHEVSKY, B. A. 1971. On the problem of the horizontal heterogeneity of the earth's crust and uppermost mantle in southern Eurasia. Tectonophysics. 11:29–60.

PLUMSTEAD, E. P. 1973. The late Palaeozoic *Glossopteris* flora. *In,* HALLAM, A. Ed. Atlas of palaeobiogeography. Elsevier, Amsterdam. p. 187–205.

SAMOILOVICH, S. R. 1953. Pollen and spores from the Permian deposits of the Cherdynian and Aktyubinian Pre-Urals. Trudy vses. neft. nauchno-issled. geol.-razv. Inst. 75:1–51.

SEWARD, A. C. 1933. Plant life through the ages. 2nd ed. Cambridge Univ. Press. Cambridge. 603 p.

SINGH, H. P. 1964. A miospore assemblage from the Permian of Iraq. Palaeontology. 7(2):240–265.

TAMRAZYAN, G. P. 1971. Siberian continental drift. Tectonophysics. 11:433–460.

VARLAMOV, I. P., AND L. D. OZHIGANOVA. 1962. New data on the existence of continental Permian deposits on the eastern slope of the southern Urals. Dokl. Akad. Nauk SSSR. 147(4):893–895.

VISSCHER, H. 1967. Permian and Triassic Palynology and the concept of the Tethys twist. Palaeogeogr. Palaeoclimat. Palaeoecol. 3:151–1669.

————. 1968. On the Thuringian age of the upper Palaeozoic sedimentary and volcanic deposits of the Esterel (southern France). Rev. Palaeobot. Palynology. 6:71–83.

ZAUER, V. V. 1960. On the Late Permian flora in the Solikamsk region (according to spore pollen analysis). Paleont. Zh. 4:114–124.

————. 1964. The Permian flora of Solikamsk. Trudy vses. neft. nauchno-issled. Geol.-razv. Inst. 160–201.

SILURIAN AND DEVONIAN BIOGEOGRAPHY

ARTHUR J. BOUCOT

Department of Geology, Oregon State University, Corvallis, OR 97331

ABSTRACT—The interval from the Late Ordovician (Ashgill) through the Devonian (Famenne) includes the continuation of some provincialism in the Ashgill (which decreased steadily from an earlier Ordovician maximum) that gives way to fairly high cosmopolitanism in the Llandovery, followed by a gradual increase in provincialism that culminates in strongly developed provinces in the late Lower Devonian, and followed, in turn, by a return to conditions of high cosmopolitanism in the Late Devonian.

The factors influencing the levels of provincialism and cosmopolitanism are believed the result of climate (high and low thermal gradients), regression versus transgression, reef abundance or rarity, number of animal communities (essentially niche breadth plus reef abundance), distribution of marine currents, disposition of land masses and hypersaline water bodies on the continents that may influence any of the first cited factors, and possibly food supply (this last is very difficult to estimate from the geological record). All of these factors, acting together or separately, may serve to set up barriers to migration that influence level of provincialism.

INTRODUCTION

Boucot and Johnson (1972) have briefly summarized the data for Silurian biogeography, and Holland (1971) provides useful supplementary information. The most comprehensive summary of Devonian biogeography is given by Boucot and others (1969). Additional important information is provided by Johnson (1971) for the Middle Devonian, by House (1971) for ammonoids, by Oliver (1968; in press) for tetracorals, by Ormiston (1968; 1972) for trilobites, by Talent and others (1972) for trilobites, brachiopods and conodonts, by Wolfart and Voges (1968) for trilobites, and by Lesperance and Bourque (1971) for trilobites.

Most of this information concerning Silurian and Devonian biogeography considers brachiopods, the only group to have been analyzed on a worldwide basis. Conclusions based on brachiopod distribution patterns, however, do appear to be in accord with those for other groups. As more comprehensive, worldwide summaries are developed for nonbrachiopod groups we may expect some modifications of conclusions based on brachiopods alone, but present information strongly suggests that these will not be serious modifications.

Additional conclusions are presented in this paper and are a partial summary of a mass of data collected for a more extensive presentation by Boucot (in preparation). Middle Paleozoic biogeography is of great current interest, and numerous emendations and changes may occur in the near future. The important conclusion is that biogeographic units defined for the Silurian and Devonian appear to be comparable to those units employed in studying the distribution of Cenozoic shallow water marine invertebrates.

PRE-SILURIAN BACKGROUND

There is no comprehensive survey of Ordovician biogeography, although important contributions to the understanding of provincialism in certain regions have been made (Williams, 1969; Spjeldnaes, 1967; Whittington, 1973; Jaanusson, 1973; Skevington, 1973; Kaljo and Klaamann, 1973; Bergstrom, 1973). These studies show strong evidence for provincialism in the latest Ordovician. One of the chief problems encountered when trying to assess the Ordovician question is the lack of attention in distinguishing between faunal differences due to environment (communities within the same biogeographic unit) and faunal differences due to isolation produced by faunal barriers (biogeographic units proper).

Knowledge of the Late Ordovician is derived chiefly from consideration of Northern Hemisphere data. We know little about the Late Ordovician fauna, or its biogeographic affinities, of South America or Australia. Therefore, conclusions about the derivation of the lowest Silurian faunas and their biogeographic antecedents are restricted to consideration of Northern Hemisphere Ordovician. This defect in our knowledge may be serious, particularly because the Southern Hemisphere "Malvinokaffric" Silurian and Devonian faunas are highly provincial. The origins of the Silurian "Malvinokaffric" fauna in the Late Ordovician are poorly understood at present.

EARLY SILURIAN

Early Silurian biogeography is dominated by two major entities, the Northern Hemisphere North Silurian Realm and the Southern Hemisphere Malvinokaffric Realm. Also present in the Northern Hemisphere is the minor series of

localized faunas assigned to the Mongolo-Okhotsk Region. The Mongolo-Okhotsk Region is
a distinctive unit that may be either derived
from the North Silurian Realm during earliest
Silurian time, or derived independently from
pre-existing Ordovician ancestors in central
Asia.

The remarkably low taxonomic diversity of
the earlier Llandovery is probably the result of
the interaction of marked regression occurring
as a consequence of Late Ordovician and possibly early Llandovery continental glaciation in
the Southern Hemisphere and an intense climatic gradient, as well as the absence of widespread reef development. The latest Ordovician
is a time of very high extinction rate, apparently related to the same factors.

Malvinokaffric Realm.—The Malvinokaffric
Realm Silurian fauna is known from southern
Peru and the Amazon Basin region of Brazil,
south through Bolivia and west-central Argentina and South Africa and a portion of northwest Africa (fig. 1). It has been little studied.
However, a minimum of eight communities
have been recognized to date (Boucot, in preparation). Reef environments and carbonate
rocks in general are conspicuously absent from
the Malvinokaffric Silurian. The communities
of this realm, as known, are very low in taxonomic diversity, with one, two or three taxa
being the norm. The low taxonomic diversity,
absence of reefs and widespread limestone, plus
the occurrence of tillite beneath the Silurian of
both north Africa, south Africa and South
America from southern Peru to northern Argentina is consistent with a cold water environment. This Malvinokaffric group of communities with their low diversity faunas contrasts
markedly with the far richer Northern Hemisphere coeval North Silurian Realm faunas distributed in a far larger number of communities.
Available evidence also suggests that the Malvinokaffric Realm Silurian faunas did not extend as far offshore, that is, into as deep water
as did the North Silurian Realm faunas. Most
Silurian brachiopod genera that are endemic to
the Malvinokaffric Realm do belong to families
that either have or might have antecedents in
or far away from the Malvinokaffric Realm
region proper.

North Silurian Realm.—The North Silurian
Realm includes most of the Lower Silurian
fauna. It is the classic Lower Silurian fauna of
Europe and eastern North America, known
since the middle of the 18th Century. The level
bottom communities of this realm (reef envi-

ronments are very minor during the Llandovery, in number, area, and geographic extent)
are widespread and diversified. These communities occur from the shoreline region to relatively far offshore, deep water positions. The
term "deep water" for the Silurian and the
Devonian refers here to, in modern terms, the
edge of the Continental Shelf; we have no evidence during the Silurian and Devonian for the
existence of bathyal or abyssal benthic faunas.

The North Silurian Realm (fig. 1) extends
over most of North America (see Berry and
Boucot, 1970, for details), northern South
America (see Berry and Boucot, 1972, for details), the Caledonian Geosyncline region and
adjacent platforms (the small "platform" present in England and the large Fenno–Sarmatian
region) in Europe, portions of the Uralian
Geosyncline (particularly in southeast Kazakhstan), the Siberian Platform (defined as extending from the Chegitun area through
Kolyma, the Sette Daban to the Yenissei), the
Altai-Sayan, the western Himalaya, the Bos-
phoros region, and possibly portions of the Tasman Geosyncline region. On figure 1 the North
Silurian Realm includes the Late Silurian Uralian-Cordilleran and Circum-North Atlantic regions.

The faunal homogeneity of this vast provincial unit is most marked and striking. Collections from Utah, New York, Sweden and the
Yenissei are so similar that only a taxonomic
specialist can tell them apart; a situation completely different to that during most of the
early Paleozoic (except for the Late Devonian). One possible exception to this generalization is afforded by the ostracodes. Differing ostracode faunas, poorly known as they are for the
Lower Silurian, possibly may reflect provincialism in part rather than being completely environmental controlled.

Origins for the taxa of the varied communities included in the North Silurian Realm are
not hard to locate. Many of the taxa occur in
the northwestern part of the Old World, particularly in parts of the Caradoc and Ashgill
of the Baltic region. In fact, most of the earlier
Llandovery fauna appears to be merely a continuation of taxa existing in this part of the
world during the Late Ordovician. However,
near the beginning of the late Llandovery representatives of a number of families previously
absent from the Late Ordovician and earlier
Llandovery appear; they seem in large part to
have had earlier Llandovery, Ashgill and Caradoc antecedents in southeast Kazakhstan. The
reasons for the restriction of these taxa to such
a small enclave for such a long period followed

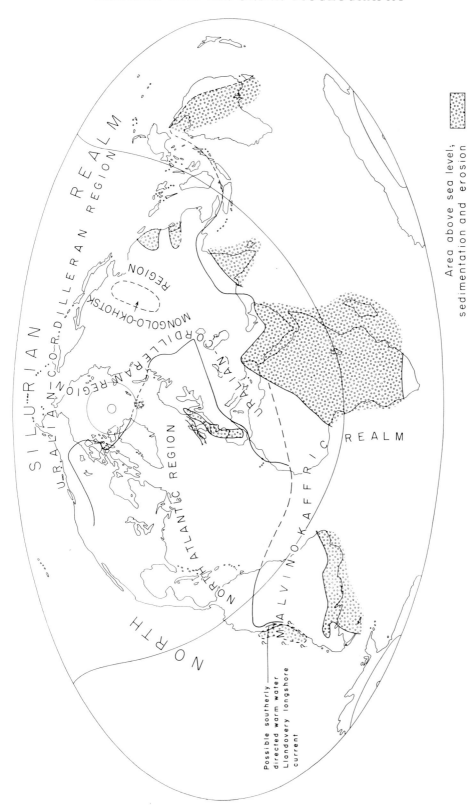

FIG. 1—Silurian biogeographic distributions (from Boucot, in prep.).

by their sudden migration over so large a part of the world is not known.

Mongolo-Okhotsk Region.—The Mongolo-Okhotsk region Lower Silurian has the least well known of the Early Silurian faunas. It might be argued that it represents merely a peculiar community existing under a special set of environmental conditions (unspecified and not obvious from what we know of the rocks or their distribution) rather than a separate set of faunas that developed under conditions of isolation from the adjacent North Silurian Realm. The oldest evidence for the existence of this region occurs in beds containing late Llandovery conodonts. Most of the rocks and fossils suggest a nearshore, shallow water environment. The absence of endemic taxa from similar environments elsewhere in the North Silurian Realm indicates that these faunas should be regarded as the products of evolution occurring under conditions of isolation rather than as products of a peculiar environment. In addition, the presence of similar faunas in the Late Silurian, also assigned to the Mongolo-Okhotsk region, and of provincial Devonian faunas in the same region suggests validity of the conclusion.

LATE SILURIAN

Late Silurian biogeography is dominated by three major entities, the Malvinokaffric Realm, a continuation from the Early Silurian, together with the two subdivisions of the North Silurian Realm, the Uralian-Cordilleran and circum-North Atlantic regions. Also present is the continuation of the localized Early Silurian Mongolo-Okhotsk region. The increasing degree of provincialism in the Late Silurian as contrasted with the Early Silurian correlates with several factors. Two factors, areally important reef developments and co-occurring, widespread regions of hypersaline water, that would favor the development of the faunal barriers necessary for isolation became increasingly widespread. All the great carbonate platforms of the Late Silurian apparently had associated hypersaline conditions in places (North American, Fenno–Sarmatian, Siberian and Australian).

During latest Silurian, Pridoli time, further provincialism is apparent with the recognition of precursors of the Devonian Eastern Americas Realm (the *Eccentricosta* faunas) in the central and northern Appalachians, and the Devonian Rhenish-Bohemian region with the *Quadrifarius* faunas occurring from Podolia through the Baltic region to Nova Scotia,

coastal New Brunswick, Maine and Massachusetts.

Malvinokaffric Realm.—The Malvinokaffric Realm (fig. 1) of the Late Silurian apparently occupied the same position as during the Early Silurian; however, shelly faunas of Late Silurian age within the geographic confines of this boundary have not been recognized yet in either north or south Africa. Also in South America this realm ceases to exist after the end of the Ludlow as Pridoli age marine faunas are unrecognized in that continent; beds of probable Pridoli age lack megafossils and possibly reflect either nonmarine, brackish or very nearshore conditions unfavorable for normal marine megafossils. Most taxa in the Late Silurian of the Malvinokaffric Realm have no readily apparent Devonian descendents. Devonian marine faunas of the Malvinokaffric Realm appear almost entirely derived from outside of this region; the few taxa with apparent Silurian antecedents within the area of the realm may have migrated back into it from regions elsewhere where they developed during the Pridoli as well as during the Gedinne and Siegen portions of the Early Devonian because marine megafossils in the Malvinokaffric region are thus far lacking.

North Atlantic Region.—The geographic limits of the North Atlantic region are outlined on figure 1. In the boundary regions with the Uralian-Cordilleran region in western North America, Arctic North America and the western Urals the transition occurs between moderate depth communities (included in Boucot, in preparation, Benthic Assemblages 1 through 3) belonging to the North Atlantic region and deeper water communities (included in Boucot, in preparation, Benthic Assemblages 4 through 6) belonging to the Uralian-Cordilleran region. Reef building became widespread during the later Wenlock and continued through the Ludlow, but fell off precipitously before the Pridoli, in this region as well as within the Uralian-Cordilleran region. The maximum marine transgression for the Silurian platforms (except for Africa) occurs during the Ludlow. Hypersaline conditions are widespread and important on the Silurian carbonate platforms during the Ludlow and Pridoli. Increasing provincialism manifested during the Late Silurian is a product of the interaction of many factors including reef buildup and hypersaline conditions. Marked decrease in taxonomic diversity characterizing the Pridoli is probably the combined result of the falloff in availability of the reef environment and evolution of many groups towards a condition of greater niche breadth that resulted in the extinction of many earlier Silurian forms.

Uralian-Cordilleran Region.—The position of the Uralian-Cordilleran region is indicated on figure 1. Reef-type developments are prominent in the region as are a variety of level bottom environments. Taxonomic diversity within this region is comparable to that found in the coeval North Atlantic region. Hypersaline conditions are widespread on the Siberian Platform during this time interval; as a result much of the platform has no well developed normal marine faunas during this time interval. This region also shows a marked decrease in taxonomic diversity during the Pridoli.

Mongolo-Okhotsk Region.—The geographically minor Mongolo-Okhotsk region, with its *Tuvaella* community, is still prominent in the Late Silurian. A possible extension of the region in the Late Silurian is found in the somewhat endemic Late Silurian shelly faunas of the Yangste Valley and Japan. These Chinese and Japanese faunas contain many endemic forms that may be interpreted either as a separate biogeographic entity, or alternatively as different communities that can be included within the Mongolo-Okhotsk region. Clearly the Late Silurian shelly fauna of this part of the world is endemic and distinctive.

EARLY DEVONIAN

The Early Devonian is the time of greatest provincialism for the Silurian-Devonian level bottom fauna; the height of provincialism for reef environment faunas is probably reached in the Eifel. Within the Early Devonian the Ems interval probably marks the height of provincialism for these level bottom faunas. The Gedinne faunas, particularly those of the early Gedinne are, as should be expected, transitional to those of the Late Silurian in all regards, including their lower level of provincialism. Provincialism increases from the Gedinne through the Ems. Factors leading to this greater provincialism are many. Regression of the Early Devonian seas on the platforms continues from Pridoli time in many parts of the world and favors conditions of provincialism. Existence of a climatic gradient north-south favors provincialism. This climatic gradient also is conducive to the existence of marine currents on the platforms which could provide water masses with different enough properties to encourage provincialism. Hypersaline water masses of the Early Devonian appear to have been more restricted than those of the Late Silurian, but

may have been comparable in their potential as faunal barriers conducive to provincialism by supplementing the land areas present on parts of the platforms and also by interacting with potential marine currents. The relative importance of any of these factors is not known, but their congruence would tend to produce a reinforcing effect with all of them working in the direction of higher provincialism and a resulting high production rate of taxa (there are more taxa of Ems age brachiopods than are present during any comparable interval of the Silurian or Devonian).

Our knowledge of Early Devonian provincialism is uneven geographically, particularly in regards to the faunas of Asia and of Australia to a lesser extent. The classic Lower Devonian faunas of Europe and eastern North America are the best known and the Southern Hemisphere Malvinokaffric and western North American faunas less known. When the faunas of Kazakhstan, the Amur River region, and Manchuria are better known we expect a significant increase in the number of endemic taxa described. Poor knowledge of animal communities for many regions of the world during this time interval handicaps a better understanding of provincialism during this time interval. Figure 2 outlines the biogeographic units currently employed for the Early Devonian, with the Ems as the actual example.

Comparison of figures 1 and 2 indicates that the northern boundary of the Malvinokaffric Realm in both northern South America and north Africa has moved a significant distance to the south. Malvinokaffric faunas are absent during the Devonian from the region to the north of the Amazon and from north Africa in strong contrast with the Silurian. This shift to the south with time is interpreted as a southerly shift of the isotherms during the two time intervals. Present evidence is consistent with the Malvinokaffric Devonian faunas having lived in an environment colder than that present to the north, but evidence for continental glaciation is absent, whereas during the Early Silurian the presence of continental glaciation within the Malvinokaffric region is readily inferred.

Conditions of marked provincialism reached in the early half of the Devonian are probably as intense as any known during the Phanerozoic. The faunal barriers, conditions of isolation for level bottom and reef communities, and climatic regimes involved, as well as our knowledge of the evolution and taxonomy of the organisms, are still fragmentary in comparison to what is known of that other major interval of great provincialism, the later Cenozoic. Wide-

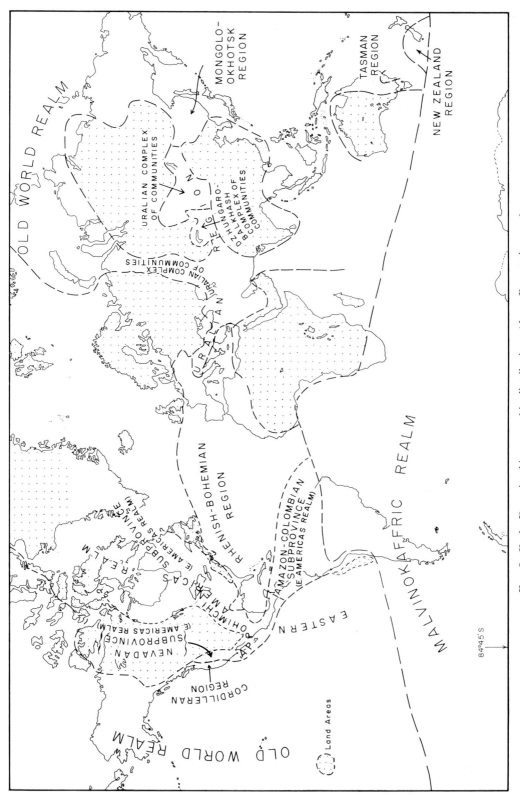

Fig. 2—Early Devonian biogeographic distributions (from Boucot, in prep.).

spread evidence for a land flora beginning near the base of the Devonian possibly correlates with the inception of well-defined provincialism but this coincidence is probably not causal. The definition of Devonian biogeographic units employed here, together with presentation of much of the evidence, is made by Boucot (in preparation).

Eastern Americas Realm.—Geographic limits of the Eastern Americas Realm are indicated on figure 2, for Ems time. The geographic limits during other intervals of Early Devonian and Middle Devonian time are similar, but not identical. The Eastern Americas Realm may now be broken down into three subprovinces which do not all co-occur in time. The main body of the Eastern Americas Realm, the Appohimchi Subprovince, is restricted to North America from central Chihuahua on the southwest to the Hudson Bay and Gaspé regions on the northeast. The boundaries of the Appohimchi Subprovince are not known to shift much in time. A minor shift is known south of the Saint Lawrence River in Quebec with the Appohimchi Subprovince boundary being situated to the northeast of Gaspé in the Early Devonian and shifting southwest to beyond the Lake Memphremagog region of Vermont and Quebec in the Eifel. Another minor shift is recorded in central Oklahoma where an Old World Realm fauna in the Turkey Creek Limestone, of probable late Siegen or early Ems age, occurs in the same area as younger and older Early Devonian Appohimchi Subprovince faunas. However, on a continental scale these minor shifts may be regarded as merely boundary oscillations or movements.

The fauna of the main body of the Eastern Americas Realm is highly endemic. It contains few genera that may be viewed as Silurian relicts, in strong contrast with the large number of such genera present in the Old World Realm. The boundaries of the Eastern Americas Realm are believed to be largely temperature controlled, possibly related to water currents sweeping over a part of the North American Platform. The presence on the western limits of the Appohimchi Subprovince of a land mass, which progressively diminished in size during the Devonian (virtually disappeared by the end of the Middle Devonian), and of large bodies of hypersaline water (evidenced by the existence of scattered evaporite deposits) that are more persistent in time than the land body (at best a causal factor only during a portion of the Early Devonian) may have been supplemental factors acting as partial faunal barriers to the

west. Although the presence in Gedinne time of the Nevadan Subprovince of the Eastern Americas Realm to the west of the land and hypersaline water area indicates that these two factors were no more than supplementary in their potential as faunal barriers.

The Eastern Americas Realm during the Early Devonian is dominated by level bottom communities, but in the Gedinne reef environments begin a gradual increase in abundance and distribution, although nothing like that which becomes present in the Middle Devonian.

The Amazon-Colombian Subprovince of the Eastern Americas Realm includes beds of Ems and possibly Eifel age, but none of pre-Ems Siegen or Gedinne age. Pre-Ems Lower Devonian marine megafossils have not been recognized with certainty in either the Amazon-Colombian Subprovince or the adjoining Malvinokaffric Realm of the Devonian in South America, South Africa or Antarctica. Most species in the Amazon-Colombia Subprovince are either identical or very similar to those occurring in the Appohimchi Subprovince. The distinctive feature of the Amazon-Colombian Subprovince is the co-existence of taxa that do not occur together in the Appohimchi Subprovince. For example, *Tropidoleptus,* a taxon unknown in the Appohimchi Subprovince until Givet (Hamilton) time, occurs with other taxa not known above the Onondaga and older (Eifel and older) Devonian. The faunas of the Amazon-Colombian Subprovince are "mixtures" of taxa that do not co-exist in the Appohimchi Subprovince; it is this characteristic that permits recognition of the different subprovinces. Also of interest, in view of the probability that most of the Malvinokaffric Realm brachiopods had Eastern Americas Realm antecedents, is the lack of transitional forms between the endemic, Appalachian-derived Malvinokaffric taxa and the adjacent Amazon-Colombian taxa. Clearly a significant faunal barrier, possibly a temperature gradient, occurred between these two biogeographic units. An understanding of the relations that existed between the faunas of the Appohimchi and the Amazon-Colombian Subprovinces is limited by an apparent lack of any Devonian fossils between Chihuahua in northern Mexico and the Perija Range bounding Colombia and Venezuela far to the south.

The Nevadan Subprovince of the Eastern Americas Realm emphasizes several Gedinne faunas (*Quadrithyris* zone and *Spinoplasia* zone) which contain a large number of Eastern Americas Realm genera. However, the species of these genera are much more different from those encountered either in the Appohimchi or in the Amazon-Colombian Subprovinces, thus indicating a greater degree of isolation. Eastern Americas type taxa occur sparingly adjacent to the Nevadan Subprovince indicating a still lower level of communication with the Appohimchi Subprovince in view of the increasing degree of endemism shown by the associated taxa.

Old World Realm.—The Old World Realm is the most widespread of the biogeographic units recognized in the Lower Devonian and occurs (fig. 2) from New Zealand to Britain, from Mexico to the Canadian Arctic, from Malaya to the Arctic reaches of the Soviet Union, from north Africa to the Rhineland, and, not surprisingly, shows evidence for the greatest amount of division into regions. The division into these regions is probably the result of a combination of various faunal barriers operating over vast distances that set up faunal gradients (clines) that resulted ultimately in a high degree of geographic speciation near the various limits of the realm.

The Old World Realm shares with the Eastern Americas Realm a gradual increase in the abundance and distribution of reefs from a Gedinne low to an Eifel through Frasne high. Post-Lower Devonian evaporite deposits are a prominent feature of the Old World Realm that may have acted as supplementary causes of provincialism as is inferred for the western limit of the Eastern Americas Realm. Land areas are prominent during the Lower Devonian in the Old World Realm region, and as with the Eastern Americas Realm, these land areas decline significantly in extent, beginning in Ems time and reaching a minimum in the Late Devonian.

One of the prime characteristics of the Old World Realm is the presence of a far greater number of genera that also were present in the Silurian; this contrasts strongly with both the Eastern Americas and Malvinokaffric Realms where Silurian genera are either absent or very low in number. Thus, the Old World Realm fauna did not depart as rapidly from that of the Silurian, possibly because of the presence of larger populations that evolved far more slowly from Silurian antecedents than those present in the other two realms.

The presence of both North Atlantic and Uralian-Cordilleran region Late Silurian faunas beneath portions of the Old World Realm suggests derivation from elements of both.

The Rhenish-Bohemian Region is the best known subdivision of the Old World Realm. This region, established by Boucot and others (1969), contains the widely differing Rhenish and Bohemian faunas of Europe, which apparently are best explained in terms of differing environments resulting in different community complexes (Rhenish and Bohemian) rather than as the result of faunal barriers.

The Rhenish-Bohemian region had gradational relations with the Uralian region, sharing a large number of common taxa, and shared very few taxa with the Eastern Americas Realm, except in southern Quebec where a limited number of Old World taxa include some Rhenish-Bohemian region taxa.

The Rhenish-Bohemian region is unique during the Early Devonian for the wide extent of the graptolitic facies (pelagic community) known from Thuringia in the north into Algeria in the south. Although Lower Devonian graptolites do occur in the pelagic community of the Eastern Americas Realm and many other regions of the Old World Realm they did not cover so large a region; a black sea literally extended from North Africa through much of central and northern Europe west of the Russian Platform. Formerly these black shales with their pelagic community fauna, rich in graptolites, were mistakenly assigned to the Silurian. Elsewhere the only wide development of this sort is to be found in the Road River Formation of the Yukon and portions of British Columbia. Our knowledge of Rhenish-Bohemian region communities is not as well organized as that for the Eastern Americas Realm Lower Devonian or for the Silurian.

The Uralian region was first defined and discussed by Boucot and others (1969). Definition of the unit here is considerably extended to cover the shelly faunas of the clastic facies that occur so abundantly in southeast Kazakhstan where they are bounded on at least three sides (northwest, northeast and southwest) by carbonate facies containing the typical Uralian faunas discussed by Boucot and others (1969). These Kazakhstan faunas apparently represent a complex of communities analogous in many ways to the Rhenish complex of communities just as the carbonate rich Uralian complex of communities is analogous to the Bohemian complex of communities. Soviet workers have designated this Kazakhstan clastic development as a separate biogeographic entity, the Dzhungaro-Balkhash Province, but it appears better understood as an additional complex of communities within the Uralian region that is the result of differing environmental factors rather than isolating, faunal barrier factors. Although many endemic taxa from the Kazakhstan fauna have not yet been described, the fauna is distinctive because of the disjunct occurrence of certain Eastern Americas Realm and Tasman region taxa. These disjunct occurrences may be better understood in terms of similar occurrences of Eastern Americas and Tasman taxa far to the east in the Mongolo-Okhotsk region, the latter being far closer to a circum-Pacific migration route. This dispersal route is chosen rather than a western connection through the Rhenish-Bohemian region because of the near absence of Eastern Americas, as well as Tasman taxa, in the Rhenish-Bohemian region. Our knowledge of communities within the Uralian region is still very fragmentary and inadequate.

The Mongolo-Okhotsk region (Boucot, in preparation) was established to explain endemic taxa in the Lower Devonian of the Upper Amur region and Manchuria that occur with disjunct Appalachian and Tasman elements and also *Tuvaella* community faunas. The fauna of the Mongolo-Okhotsk region is very poorly known but is distinctive enough to suggest that the differences are due to faunal barriers and not to peculiar or specialized environmental conditions. At present we only have information about clastic facies faunas in this region, although it is to be expected that carbonate rock faunas will eventually be found in eastern Asia that belong to the unit.

The Tasman region, defined by Boucot and others (1969), has been more recently considered by Talent and others (1972). It contains a variety of highly endemic taxa occurring from Tasmania through New South Wales and also in New Zealand. The reef environment is largely absent within the region near the beginning of the Devonian but increases in importance near the end of the Early Devonian. The presence of a single Malvinokaffric taxon in Tasmania for the Tasman region suggests affinities with that realm.

The New Zealand region was defined by Boucot and others (1969). Unfortunately, knowledge of it is still confined to a restricted area near Reefton, New Zealand. The presence of a few taxa with Malvinokaffric Realm affinities suggests proximity to that realm.

The Cordilleran region was defined by Boucot and others (1969) for faunas from western North America that had Old World Realm affinities and also enough endemic character to justify seting up an additional biogeographic unit.

Our present knowledge of other Old World Asiatic and Arctic regional faunas is very limited compared to those known from Europe, Africa, the Malvinokaffric regions, most of North America and Australia. More lower rank units are expected to be defined as this gap in our knowledge is filled.

Malvinokaffric Realm.—The Malvinokaffric Realm of the Devonian (Ems-Eifel) was thoroughly considered by Boucot and others (1969). Most of level bottom taxa (reefs are unknown in the region) have Eastern Americas Realm antecedents, although the transitional taxa are not known and the place where the transition took place is not obvious. The faunas are interpreted to have been affected by a cooler water environment than those known elsewhere.

MIDDLE DEVONIAN

The Middle Devonian is a time of decreasing provincialism for level bottom communities. Devonian reef communities reach a peak in the Middle Devonian that continues through the Frasne before terminating abruptly prior to the Famenne. A high degree of provincialism is shown by the reef faunas of Eifel age and to a lesser degree by those of Givet age. A study of provincialism that combines reef and level bottom communities would suggest that provincialism in both the Ems and the Eifel is about at the same level, but such is not the case if reef endemics are separated out. The high degree of Eifel reef endemism is apparently related to the relative sparsity of reef environments in the Ems.

Middle Devonian marine deposits cover more of the cratonic platforms than do Early Devonian ones except in the Malvinokaffric region where post-Eifel marine sediments have not been clearly shown to exist. A few Andean goniatites of Late Devonian age may herald the onset of another cycle of marine sedimentation in the Late Devonian-Lower Carboniferous that is unrelated to that of the earlier Middle Devonian cycle and separated from it by a considerable interval of non-marine conditions. The more widespread, transgressive nature of the Middle Devonian is conducive to lowered provincialism, although the importance and wide distribution of hypersaline water masses on the continents replaces the more widespread Lower Devonian land areas as a possible factor encouraging provincialism. The climate of the Middle Devonian was probably strongly differentiated into a cool Southern Hemisphere region and a tropical to subtropical northern region compatible with lateritic processes (formation of bauxites), all of this being consistent with a tendency favoring provincialism. Thus the Middle Devonian decline in level of provincialism is the resultant of a number of factors of varying magnitude that includes the removal or diminution of faunal barriers of one sort or another.

The provincial units of the Middle Devonian are continuations of the Early Devonian units or the merging of some Early Devonian units. The Middle Devonian does not see the production of any newly organized biogeographic units.

Eastern Americas Realm.—The faunas of Eifel age in the Eastern Americas Realm are continuations in almost every aspect of those present in the underlying Ems age strata; in fact distinguishing between the Ems and Eifel is not always easy in the absence of a rich fauna. However, the marked environmental change encountered in the late Eifel (Onondaga to Marcellus) is accompanied by the appearance of a number of elements, or their close relatives, known elsewhere chiefly in the Rhenish-Bohemian region during Early Devonian and to a lesser extent in the Malvinokaffric Realm and Amazon-Colombia region during Early Devonian or Eifelian. Later Hamilton and terminal Givet age Tully faunas are largely a continuation of this mixture of taxa derived from Eastern Americas and Rhenish-Bohemian faunas. It is unclear what environmental or other factors were conducive to the mingling of elements from what had been earlier strongly disparate units.

The geographic limits of the Eastern Americas Realm during the Middle Devonian remain about the same as during the latter part of the Lower Devonian, except that marine conditions ceased in the Amazon-Colombia region area well before Givet time.

Old World Realm.—The Middle Devonian biogeography of the Old World Realm is not thoroughly studied. However, a number of provincial units still remain from the Early Devonian, although an overall trend is clearly seen by Givet time for a marked decrease in the level of provincialism of level bottom communities and a less marked decrease in reef and reef-related communities.

During Eifel time Boucot (in preparation) recognizes the following regions in the Old World Realm: Cordilleran, Rhenish-Bohemian, and Tasman. During the Givet only a Cordilleran and an undifferentiated Old World Realm are recognized. A better acquaintance with Eifel and Givet faunas of Asia may demonstrate a more detailed series of subdivisions for the Givet and possibly additional units for the Eifel.

Notable in both Eifel and Givet time is the higher degree of provincialism shown, on the average, by reef and reef-related fossils than by those occurring in level bottom communities. Even for the genera belonging to a single family, for example, level bottom genera may be highly cosmopolitan whereas reef and reef-related ones may be highly provincial. This behavior reflects the fact that reef communities contain much smaller populations that may exist easily in relative isolation as contrasted with level bottom populations.

LATE DEVONIAN

Late Devonian biogeography is of interest chiefly because there does not appear to be a firm basis for recognizing any biogeographic subdivisions and one must conclude that the shelly marine invertebrates of both the Frasne and the Famenne are completely cosmopolitan. This conclusion is reached despite the fact that at the end of the Frasne most of the Silurian-Devonian taxa at every level from superfamily on down become extinct. This terminal Frasne extinction is one of the most marked mass extinction records in the Phanerozoic. It takes second place to the classical Permo-Triassic extinction event, but not by as much as many would suspect. In any event the faunas are cosmopolitan for both reef and level bottom taxa in the Frasne, and for level bottom taxa in the Famenne when reef environments were virtually absent.

SUMMARY OF SILURIAN AND DEVONIAN PROVINCIALISM

The development of provincialism during the Silurian and Devonian, an interval of possibly 100 million years, is a complete cycle. Following the development of marked provincialism in the Late Ordovician (the earlier Ordovician appears to be even more provincial than the Late Ordovician) and subsequent massive extinctions, the Llandovery is a time of widespread cosmopolitanism except for the temperature controlled cold water faunas of the Malvinokaffric Realm. This cosmopolitan time interval is followed by an interval of increasing provincialism that begins at a very low level in the Wenlock and reaches a maximum in the Ems (late Early Devonian) for level bottom community taxa provincialism and slightly later in the succeeding Eifel (Middle Devonian) for reef and reef-related taxa. This is followed by a rapid decrease in provincialism into the worldwide cosmopolitan fauna of the Frasne and Famenne. The absence of marine faunas of Frasne and Famenne age in most of the area formerly occupied by the Malvinokaffric fauna (except for two or three possible occurrences of goniatites) leaves doubt as to the nature of the climate in that region during the Late Devonian. The high cosmopolitanism of the Late Devonian is probably equal to that of any other interval of Phanerozoic time including times like the Early Triassic.

The bulk of these conclusions regarding Silurian and Devonian provincialism are based on the study of brachiopods because other groups are not known in the same detail worldwide. However, information about provincialism and cosmopolitanism in other groups during this time interval is highly consistent with the conclusions based on brachiopods alone.

CAUSES OF PROVINCIALISM

Provincialism and cosmopolitanism are clearly cyclic phenomena in the evolution of the biota during the Phanerozoic. Boucot (in preparation) emphasizes that the levels of both provincialism and cosmopolitanism reached at any one time, and the rate at which they have been reached, are the resultant of a number of causal factors. The factors that govern the levels of provincialism and cosmopolitanism also are considered to be strongly involved in determining the rate at which evolution proceeds. However, it is important to understand that rate of evolution is not necessarily related to level of provincialism or cosmopolitanism except in a general, statistical manner. High and low rates of evolution are encountered for specific groups under conditions of both provincialism and cosmopolitanism, although it is true that rates of evolution overall tend to be significantly higher during intervals of provincialism.

The factors involved here are those tending to set up faunal barriers which permit the elements of a formerly cosmopolitan population to evolve in isolation. The factors recognizable in the geologic record of importance in this regard are: highly differentiated climatic regimes (glacial to tropical as opposed to equable climates); conditions of marine regression (tending to diminish the size of populations and to keep them separate from each other) as opposed to transgression; increased number of communities (tending to keep individual, interbreeding populations smaller) as opposed to a decreased number of communities; abundance and scatter of reef environments as opposed to the absence of reef environments; presence of ocean currents with water masses possessing different properties (particularly temperature) than water to either side; presence of significantly large land masses that are crossed by marine isotherms in such a manner as to set up thermal barriers (the situation for the New World today from the Arctic to the Straits of Magellan); and the presence of very extensive bodies of hypersaline water on the continents. Undoubtedly, many other important factors are involved in producing conditions of provincialism or cosmopolitanism, but at present we have difficulty in evaluating them from the geologic record. For example, the distribution of the food supply should exercise a very important effect.

REFERENCES CITED

BERGSTROM, S. M. 1973. Ordovician conodonts. *In,* HALLAM, A., Ed. Atlas of palaeobiogeography. Elsevier, Amsterdam. p. 47–58.

BERRY, W. B. N., AND A. J. BOUCOT. 1970. Correlation of the North American Silurian rocks. Spec. Pap. geol. Soc. Am. 102:1–289

———— AND ————. 1972. Correlation of the South American Silurian rocks. Ibid. 133:1–59.

BOUCOT, A. J. In prep. Evolution and extinction rate controls. Elsevier.

BOUCOT, A. J., AND J. G. JOHNSON. 1972. *Callicalyptella,* a new genus of notanopliid brachiopd from the Devonian of Nevada. J. Paleont. 46:299–302.

————, ————, AND J. A. TALENT. 1969. Early Devonian brachiopod zoogeography. Spec. Pap. geol. Soc. Am. 119:1–113.

HOLLAND, C. H. 1971. Silurian faunal provinces? *In,* MIDDLEMISS, F. A., P. F. RAWSON, AND G. NEWALL, Eds. Faunal provinces in space and time. Geol. J. Spec. Issue. 4:61–76.

HOUSE, M. R. 1971. Devonian faunal distributions. *In* MIDDLEMISS, F. A., P. F. RAWSON, AND G. NEWALL, Eds. Faunal provinces in space and time. Ibid. 4:77–94.

JAANUSSON, V. 1973. Ordovician articulate brachiopods: *In,* HALLAM, A., Ed. Atlas of palaeobiogeography. Elsevier, Amsterdam. p. 19–26.

JOHNSON, J. G. 1971. A quantitative approach to faunal province analysis. Am. J. Sci. 270:257–280.

KALJO, D., AND E. KLAAMANN. 1973. Ordovician and Silurian corals. *In,* HALLAM, A., Ed. Atlas of palaeobiogeography. Elsevier, Amsterdam. p. 37–46.

LESPERANCE, P. J., AND P. A. BOURQUE. 1971. The Synphoriinae: An evolutionary pattern of Lower and Middle Devonian trilobites. J. Paleont. 45:182–208.

OLIVER, W. A., JR. 1968. Succession of rugose coral faunas in the Lower and Middle Devonian of eastern North America. *In,* OSWALD, D. H., Ed. Int. Symp. Devonian Syst. Calgary, Alberta Soc. Petrol. Geol. 2:733–744.

————. In press. Endemism and evolution of Late Silurian to Middle Devonian rugose corals in eastern North America.

ORMISTON, A. R. 1968. Lower Devonian trilobites of Hercynian type from the Turkey Creek inlier, Marshall County, south-central Oklahoma. J. Paleont. 42:1186–1199.

———. 1972. Lower and Middle Devonian trilobite zoogeography in northern North America. 24th Int. geol. Congr. Montreal, Sec. 7, p. 594–604.

SKEVINGTON, D. 1973. Ordovician graptolites: *In,* HALLAM, A., Ed. Atlas of palaeobiogeography. Elsevier, Amsterdam. p. 27–36.

SPJELDNAES, N. 1967. The palaeogeography of the Tethyan region during the Ordovician. *In,* ADAMS, C. G. AND D. V. AGER, Eds. Aspects of Tethyan biogeography. Systematics Ass., New York. p. 45–57.

TALENT, J. A., K. S. W. CAMPBELL, P. J. DAVOREN, J. W. PICKETT, AND P. G. TELFORD. 1972. Provincialism and Australian Early Devonian faunas J. geol. Soc. Aust. 19:81–97.

WHITTINGTON, H. B. 1973. Ordovician trilobites. *In,* HALLAM, A., Ed. Atlas of palaeobiogeography. Elsevier, Amsterdam. p. 13–18.

WILLIAMS, A. 1969. Ordovician faunal provinces with reference of brachiopod distribution. *In,* WOOD, A., Ed. The Pre-Cambrian and lower Paleozoic rocks of Wales. Univ. of Wales Press, Cardiff. p. 117–154.

WOLFART, R., AND A. VOGES. 1968. Beiträge zur Kenntnis des Devons von Bolivien. Beih. geol. Jb. 74:1–241.

EARLY PALEOZOIC PALYNOMORPH PROVINCES AND PALEOCLIMATE

FRITZ H. CRAMER and MARÍA DEL CARMEN R. DÍEZ

Department of Geology, Florida State University, Tallahassee, FL 32306

ABSTRACT—Lower Paleozoic palynomorphs show large morphologic diversity and are generally extremely abundant in unmetamorphosed marine sediments although the stratigraphic ranges and regional distribution of most taxa are still poorly known. Sufficient data are now becoming available to determine the distribution of palynomorphs in the Silurian System, and, to a lesser extent, in the Upper Ordovician and Lower Devonian.

A number of contrasting, worldwide, acritarch biofacies existed in the regions bordering the Atlantic, in Arctic Canada, and in Siberia during the Silurian. Megafossil evidence indicates that these biofacies were contemporaneous and are regularly and predictably time-transgressive. Regionally the biofacies are not significantly correlative with local lithofacies. However, the lineations based on differences in acritarch assemblages approximately parallel lithotope boundaries and a causal relationship between them is suspected.

On a Wegnerian palinspastic reconstruction of Atlantic Pangaea, the parallelism of biofacies lineations, lithotopes, and perhaps even paleomagnetic latitudes is conspicuous. We interpret this as reflecting regional paleotemperature differences.

In order to account for the regional distribution of palynomorph biofacies in the lower Paleozoic, we propose a model that has mobile crustal blocks and essentially stable climatic conditions from Late Ordovician into Early Devonian time. Therefore, we interpret shifts in biofacies to be correlative with amount and rate of crustal movements. Because Silurian acritarch biofacies boundaries parallel paleoisotherms, they also parallel paleolatitudes. Supporting evidence includes: (1) the epeiric sea on Atlantic Pangaea had a minimum width of at least 45 degrees and probably had a pronounced latitudinal temperature gradient, (2) regionally continuous biofacies have a simple and regular geometry, (3) lithotopes and biofacies are parallel and their boundaries follow small circles, (4) regional biofacies are independent of such ephemeral factors as islands, troughs, and local sediment source changes, (5) biofacies form a transcontinental chronological and regional homotactic arrangement, (6) the biofacies are time-transgressive and follow a polar trajectory from Ordovician to Devonian pole positions.

INTRODUCTION

This paper contains a summary of ideas published by Cramer (1970, 1971a, 1971b, 1973), and Cramer & Díez (1972) on Silurian phytoplanktonic palynology. It also includes conclusions inferred from these data; some of these conclusions are well founded, and others are speculative.

In an area exceeding 60 by 60 degrees on a reassembled Pangaea, Silurian phytoplankton and chitinozoan assemblages show regular, predictable biofacies. These biofacies and their predictability appear to be best explained by rotational paleolatitude-related thermal stratification of the Silurian Pangaean Epeiric Sea.

Silurian palynological data are projected on a Wenlockian isochronal surface, (fig. 1) that is used in a paleoclimatological interpretation of the planktonic palynomorph biofacies. All plotted palynological data points are statistically relevant, objective and reproducible observations that are independent of taxonomic treatment, or preservational bias within the assemblages, and they are almost without exception based on very large, well preserved assemblages that are either dated by megafossil content or the geologic age, as in Spain, has been determined during many years of fieldwork by the authors.

Six acritarch biofacies (Cramer, 1970, 1971b; Cramer & Díez, 1972) are distinguished: (i) the Baltic palynofacies, (ii) the *Gloeocapsamorpha prisca* facies, (iii) the *Deunffia-Domasia* facies, (iv) the *Neoveryhachium carminae* facies, (v) the *Pulvinosphaeridium-Estiastra* facies, and (vi) the *Deunffia eisenackii* facies. The *Neoveryhachium carminae* facies is further subdivided into (a) the Iberian, (b) the Transitional, and (c) the Brazilian-Libyan regions. The localities where selected taxa reach statistically relevant dominance are also shown.

PALYNOLOGICAL CONTROL POINTS

The palynological control points vary in geographical and chronological precision. Where the post-Silurian tectonic history is imprecisely known, a few palynological data point locations on the palinspastic reconstruction may err by hundreds of kilometers, particularly the lowermost Devonian of Oklahoma, (Loeblich & Drugg, 1968; Loeblich & Tappan, 1970; Cramer & Díez, *in* ms), the Middle Silurian of Tennessee (Cramer & Díez, *in* ms), and the Silurian sections of Anticosti Island (Cramer, 1970; Cramer & Díez, 1972).

The palynological trends in Oklahoma and Tennessee show paleolatitudes which appear too low for their palynomorph composition and may

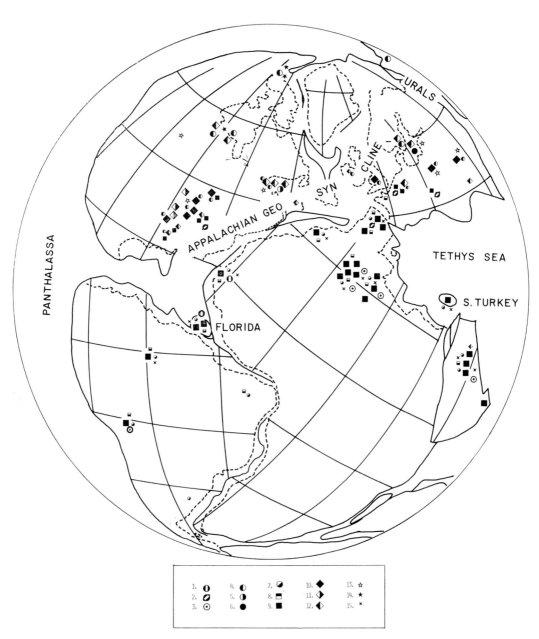

Fig. 1—Selected Silurian palynomorph data. 1. *Angochitina eisenacki* abundant in the Wenlockian; 2. *Cyathochitina campanulaeformis* abundant in the Llandoverian; 3. *Angochitina* cf. *eisenacki* (sculptural elements shorter than those of *A. e.*) abundant in the Wenlockian or Ludlovian; 4. Silurian forms of *Baltisphaeridium digitatum*-complex; 5. *Pulvinosphaeridium/Estiastra*-facies (1); 6. Combination of symbols 4 and 5; 7. *Leiosphaeridium* and *Protoleiosphaeridium* abundant to dominant in the Silurian; 8. *Neoveryhachium carminae* facies; 9. *Linochitina erratica* and/or *L. cingulata* abundant in the Wenlockian and/or Ludlovian; 10. *Deunffia/Domasia*-facies (1); 12. *Domasia* spp. (1); 13. Upper Ordovician occurrences of abundant to dominant *Gloeocapsamorpha prisca*; 14. Silurian occurrences of *Gloeocapsamorpha prisca*; 15. Forms belonging to the *Ancyrochitina ancyrea*-complex characterized by crab-clawlike processal terminations.

result from the post-Silurian opening of the Gulf of Mexico. Anticosti Island, on the other hand, appears to be located at paleolatitudes that are too high because a portion of the *Deunffia-Domasia* facies seems to be missing. Although the paleocoordinates of these points are not accurately located, this is negligible for all practical purposes as the true width of the Appalachian region in the Silurian is not known, and the fit of the continental borders also shows considerable errors.

Independent megafossil age control is available for the vast majority of the Silurian palynological data points. Admittedly, control is not good at a number of points and several points may be chronologically misplaced by up to one epoch, but errors of this magnitude are rare. Cramer & Díez (1972) have discussed the age control for most of the North American palynological localities shown here and the precision of localities on other continental blocks is comparable with that of the North American localities. However, an error of even ten million years cannot change the model *significantly* because the Silurian data was averaged over an interval of thirty or forty million years to delineate the basic palynological trends.

In three localities, ages based on palynological fossils were selected over ages based on megafossils. This is justified where the palynological data provides more precise ages, for example in Florida where Middle and Late Silurian ages are determined instead of Silurian (Cramer, 1973). Also, some ages involve no more than a change at most of ten million years, for example, in the Neahga and Maplewood Formations where a downward shift of five or six Llandoverian graptolite zone time-equivalents is suggested (Cramer & Díez, 1970). One palynological data point without independent megafossil control is the basal Lower Silurian or uppermost Upper Ordovician of South Africa where the age of the formation was determined from chitinozoans and, therefore, cannot be used for the determination of the palynological trend.

PRIMARY PALEOGEOGRAPHICAL PARAMETERS

The worldwide paleogeographical maps of the Atlantic continents by Termier & Termier (1964) show that the distribution of Upper Ordovician, Silurian, and Lower Devonian epeiric Pangaean seas were essentially continuous. Within the limits set by shifting climatic belts caused by the movement of Pangaea over the rotational geographic grid, lithotopes must have had a stable configuration. The distribution of coral reefs, however, is not continuous throughout this interval. As shown by Hill (1958) coral reefs became abundant for the first time on a world wide basis in the Silurian. The African glaciation seems to have left sediments only of Late Ordovician age or older and of Early Devonian age or younger. This does not necessarily prove a climatic amelioration during the Silurian because calcareous bioherms range throughout the area of coral reef coverage during the entire interval considered here, and the Ordovician glaciation is followed by an Early Devonian one. These glaciations occur precisely where a Silurian glaciation would have most likely occurred, hence, the apparent absence of Silurian glacially derived sediments may well be the result of post-Silurian erosion, of non-deposition (perhaps because of glacial desert conditions), or a spotty record. Therefore, possible lithological control on the distribution of palynomorphs, except where induced by tectonic or by primary climatic factors, was similar throughout the Late Ordovician to Early Devonian interval.

Distributional patterns of Recent phytoplankton approximate latitudinal boundaries and relate to either temperature or availability of light. Acritarchs were probably autotrophs and their distribution should be controlled by both factors, but the effect of each of the controls was not equal. Furthermore, both factors are interdependent, but because global distribution of light changes much more uniformly by latitude that does temperature, the discussion of the controls and their effect may be restricted to the tolerance of acritarchs to differences of temperature which is the most clearly and strongly latitude-related factor.

Morphologic changes in phytoplankton may reflect genetic response to environmental changes. Hence, if a given taxon is nonvariable and remains in essentially the same lithotope during a length of time, it probably indicates a nonchanging set of environmental factors. This justifies extrapolations into the Silurian of any palynological data sequences which can be derived from chronologically long ranging and geographically adjacent occurrences.

Figure 2 shows data points derived from Ordovician palynomorph assemblages (Górka, 1969; Kjellström, 1971a, 1971b; Eisenack, 1931–1969; Martin, 1965, 1968a, 1968b). These points must agree with the Silurian trend if the model is to be acceptable.

Independent lithological, paleoclimatological, and paleomagnetic information sets topologic constraints to palynological interpretations. Figure 3 shows data from Lotze (1964), Fair-

Fig. 2—Selected Upper Ordovician palynomorph data. 1. *Cyathochitina campanulaeformis, Hercochitina,* and related forms abundant; 2. Assemblages with *Cyathochitina campanulaeformis;* Baltic aspect of assemblages; 3. Assemblages with few or no *Cyathochitina campanulaeformis;* 4. Abundant micrhystridid acritarchs of bilateral symmetry; 5. Assemblages with few or no bilaterally symmetrical micrhystridid acritarchs; 6. Abundant to dominant *Protoleiosphaeridium* and/or *Tasmanites;* 7. Abundant to dominant *Gloeocapsamorpha prisca.*

bridge (1964), Berry & Boucot (1967, 1970), Maack (1960, 1964), Termier & Termier (1964), and Beuf and others (1966).

During the Late Ordovician, Silurian, and probably also Early Devonian, extensive areas were covered by an epeiric sea *sensu* Shaw (1964). Comparison of megafossil lists from palynological localities shows that exchange of faunal elements was common between time-equivalent, adjacent sections and that all our palynological sites fall within one contiguous sea, the Pangaean Epeiric Sea.

Only shallow water sediments have yielded palynomorphs thus far; they represent reefs (e.g., the Silurian sections of Gotland and Ekwan Formation of Hudson Bay area); lagoons (e.g., the Kuckers' Shale of the Baltic and its equivalent in Hudson Bay, many levels in strata of Black Riverian age in Michigan, and the *Lecthyalus* Shale of Illinois); probable tidal flats (e.g., San Pedro Formation and facies in northwestern Spain and Red Mountain Formation in Alabama and Georgia); and even the melting zone fringing an ice-covered flat land-

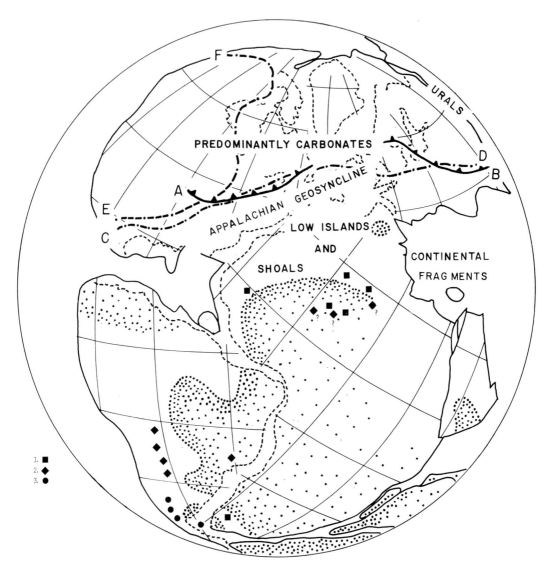

Fig. 3—Silurian lithotopes. Stippled areas represent approximate, average extension of Silurian land; A-B: southernmost extension of Silurian evaporite facies; C-D: Approximate, averaged southern boundary of lithotope characterized by predominantly carbonates; E-F: Approximate, averaged eastern boundary of lithotope characterized by predominance of dolomite; 1 to 3: Representative plots of evidence of continental glaciation. 1. Upper Ordovician; 2. Middle Silurian; 3. Lower Devonian.

mass (Beuf and others, 1966). No palynomorphs have been obtained from unmetamorphosed sediments deposited in deep troughs (e.g., Wales, Newfoundland).

To the south of the Pangaean Epeiric Sea was a large landmass, Southland (fig. 3). The approximate position was obtained from published paleogeographic compilations (Harrington, 1962; Termier & Termier, 1964; Beuf and others, 1966, and Rust, 1969). Its topographic relief was inconsequential because no, or very few, coarse turbidites, conglomerates, or other

high energy sediments were deposited over more than small local areas fringing Southland. Although the outline and size of this landmass may have changed slightly during the hundred million years discussed herein, the Wenlockian geography seems representative of the entire period. Thus, Southland is just as stable a feature in our palynologic model as the Pangaean Epeiric Sea.

The Appalachian, Arctic, and Uralian Geosynclines were mostly shallow. Compared with the size of the Pangaean Epeiric Sea, these trenches may have been narrow and much smaller than the Tethys Sea and the Pacific part of Panthalassa (names from Dietz & Holden, 1970) (fig. 1). It seems unlikely that a major water current system would develop in the Appalachian Geosyncline where the troughs were discontinuous in space and time and where many short-lived, small and steep islands were present (for example, the paleogeographic maps and p. 64f in Berry & Boucot, 1970, and, for the Welsh Borderland, Jones, 1925, White, 1950, and Williams, 1951).

These discontinuous islands in the Appalachian Geosyncline were ineffective as barriers and had no apparent influence on the regional dispersal of palynomorphs. Whether the Appalachian Geosyncline continued south of the Gulf of Mexico area of Pangaea is not known, but the Silurian palynomorph distribution seems to be unaffected in the South American-African portion of Pangaea.

Palynological data are insufficient to conclude if the Protoatlantic Basin was wide in the Ordovician as Bird & Dewey (1970) suggested, however the Ordovician Protoatlantic cannot have been more than a fraction the width of the present North Atlantic, if the palynological control points are to fall into a logical homotactic arrangement.

The Pangaean Epeiric Sea was in contact with Panthalassa at the eastern borders of the Americas, through the Tethys Sea, and possibly also through the Arctic. Freshening (Shaw, 1964) of the Pangaean Epeiric Sea could have come from adjacent oceans and from the runoff from Southland. The influence of the Appalachians should have been much less than that of oceanic and runoff freshening. The freshening through the Uralian Gap was negligible inasmuch as the European Silurian limestone belt is continuous with the Transuralian. Neither magnetic lineations nor coral and evaporite lithotopes fix longitudes, but if parallel bands of lithofacies inevitably were produced by salinity gradients in epeiric seas (Shaw, 1964), then the Uralian Gap was probably narrow or not open during the Silurian to earliest Devonian interval.

FACTORS CONTROLLING PALYNOMORPH DISPERSION

Only salinity, turbulence, and temperature appear significant in limiting the dispersal of palynomorphs living in Recent epeiric seas, and Silurian phytoplankton distribution in the large, regular Pangaean Epeiric Sea appears to respond to certain, but not all, of these factors.

Salinity gradients in the Pangaean Epeiric Sea were not a major controlling factor for the following reasons. Assemblages from the brackish fringe of Southland and the holomarine Iberian tidal flats show no significant difference. Assemblages from the green shales of the Osgood Formation in Ohio and Indiana (Cramer & Díez, 1972) and reef-limestones above and below the Wenlock Shale of England (Downie, 1959, 1960, 1963; Lister, 1970; Cramer, 1970) show no relevant differences. A salinity gradient presumably existed across these areas as they are at increasing distances from possible oceanic freshening. No sharp changes in palynomorph assemblages occur from the uppermost portion of the Visby Marl and Hoegklint Formation in Gotland (section described by Regnell & Hede, 1960; palynology by Eisenack, 1931–1971). The Visby Marl is much less of a reef facies than the Hoegklint and it must represent a different salinity (Shaw, 1964). Therefore, salinity gradient is not a prime factor in determining palynomorph distribution.

The palynological record also suggests that turbulence was not a major influence on the composition of the assemblage because palynofacies are not clearly dependent on lithology. Palynomorph assemblages from the siltstones and the shales from the Red Mountain Formation in Alabama and Georgia show no sharp differences. No compositional variations occur among assemblages from siltstones, sandstones, pure shales, alternations of sandstones with trace fossils and shales and siltstones of the San Pedro Formation in the northern part of northwestern Spain. No relevant changes occur in palynomorph assemblages from calcareous, marly, and shaly beds of the Rochester Formation of the Niagara Escarpment. Lithologically similar units, on the other hand, may contain different assemblages. The Rochester Formation is characterized by two different contemporaneous palynofacies in the Niagara Escarpment and in Pennsylvania. In addition to geographical differences, chronological variation is also identifiable. The Red Mountain Formation of Georgia shows vertical alternations of two fairly contrasting palynological associations. A less pronounced, but quite similar situation exists in approximately contemporaneous sections of Belgium (Martin, 1968a, 1968b; Cramer & Díez, 1972), and in central Alabama. There are few lithologic differences between the Ross Brook Formation of Nova Scotia, the central portion of the Rose Hill Formation of Pennsylvania, and selected localities in the lowermost portion of the San Pedro Formation in Spain, however, the palynomorph assemblages are, respectively, the *De-*

unffia-Domasia facies, a vertical alternation of the *Deunffia-Domasia* facies and the *Neovery-hachium carminae* facies, and a pure *Neovery-hachium carminae* facies.

Differences in phytoplankton distribution is unlikely to be due to salinity gradients or sedimentary environment. One plausible parameter remains that has dimensions comparable in size with the sample area: a temperature gradient induced by paleoclimate. Such a paleo-temperature gradient could have existed in the central portion of the Pangaean Epeiric Sea.

Effective mixing of bodies of water having different temperatures becomes increasingly difficult with decreasing water depths and with an increasing longitudinal dimension of the sea. The Epeiric Sea was very large and very shallow. As pointed out by Shaw (1964) water currents created by density differentials which could significantly modify the salinity regime were unlikely. Salinity gradients produce differences in density and are, for practical purposes, directly comparable with temperature gradients. If currents could not modify salinity gradients, they also could not modify temperature gradients. Wind-driven currents will have essentially paralleled latitude and could only accentuate a temperature gradient.

Silurian rotational latitudes and major climatic belts were apparently parallel, closely similar to the present pattern, and did not intersect rotational latitudes at high angles. Although the widths of Silurian climatic belts may have differed from those of the present day, the equatorial region was probably warm and the poles cold. In the absence of factors which may have modified the climatic zonation (e.g., mixing at the ocean-epeiric sea interfaces, rain-catching mountain belts), the progression from cold to warm could only be regular and normal to rotational latitudes. Thus, in the Pangaean Epeiric Sea, isotherms ran approximately as small-circles centered around the rotational poles.

Existing data favor the existence of Silurian planktonic palynomorph provinces. It is possible to place a series of mutually isospectral, contemporaneous assemblages in a set of concentric circles so that each small-circle characterizes one kind of isospectral assemblage and successive circles differ in assemblage composition. A rather gradual but regular and predictable assemblage differentiation occurs across the set of concentric circles.

These Silurian isospectral palynomorph assemblages lie in concentric circles that are closely parallel to paleoclimatic latitudes derived from lithological data (fig. 4). The circles are compatible with magnetic latitudinal directions and these are indicative of Silurian isotherms. These Silurian phytoplankton provinces may be used to reconstruct paleolatitudes in the Pangaean Epeiric Sea at a reasonable distance from Panthalassa. Chitinozoans, if they grazed directly or indirectly on phytoplankton, show a regional differentiation that may also be used as paleogeographical indicators because their food would be ultimately controlled also by paleotemperatures. Where palynological lineations do not conform with the predicted trend, secondary factors, such as irregularities in the thermal regime or post-Silurian tectonic deformation, may have disturbed the parallelism.

IRREGULARITIES IN THE PALYNOFACIES ARRANGEMENT

Horizontal displacements in age-equivalent sections can cause deflections in the palynological trends. Sections having independent age dating may be moved back to a logical position in the palynological trend. Lithologies of the repositioned crustal fragment and its surroundings must be compatible. An example is the transposition of the north Florida lower Paleozoic block back to north Africa placing it into palynological and lithological compatibility with Brazil and Portuguese Guinea and removing it from the Appalachian facies with which the block is incompatible. A similar transposition (Cramer, 1971a) is necessary for the lower Paleozoic block of Silifke in southern Turkey.

In contemporaneous sections, an irregular arrangement of palynological assemblages may exist if one section lies in a temperature sink, such as an ocean or another large, deep body of water. Obviously, as an open ocean, such as the Tethys Sea, is approached, an epeiric sea loses its thermal stratification and develops irregularities.

No large deviations have been found from the predicted trends close to the present coasts of Tunisia, Libya, and eastern Algeria. This suggests that the climate regime of glaciated Southland extended into the Tethys Sea, (similar to the present influence of the antarctic climate on the southern oceans), or that the Tethys Sea was as shallow as the Tunisian basin. Another explanation is that a number of Madagascar-type islands or continental fragments were present between Tunisia and the Tethys Sea proper and later split off from Africa and moved away from it. The portion of the Tethys Sea close to Tunisia may have contained a series of small, deep holes which were ineffective as temperature sinks. The tectonic

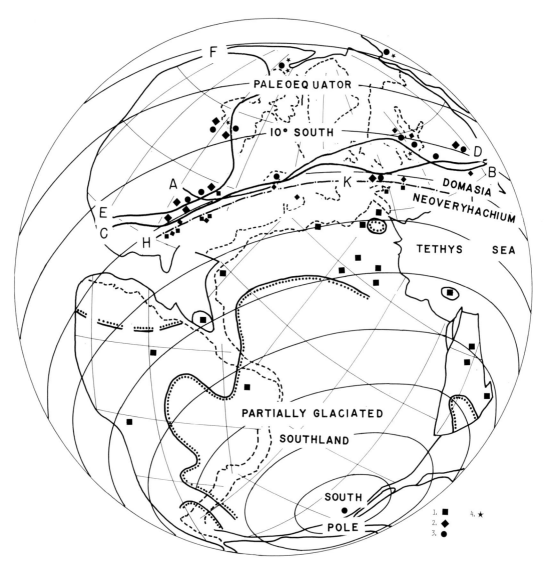

Fig. 4—Composite of lithotope and palynological data A-B, C-D, E-F: see explanation of figure 3.
1. *Neoveryhachium carminae* facies; 2. *Domasia* facies; 3. *Baltisphaeridium digitatum* and/or *Pulvinosphae-
ridium;* 4. Silurian occurrences of *Gloeocapsamorpha prisca.* HK: southernmost boundary of *Domasia* spp.
Paleolatitudes shown are 10 degrees apart, they are the topologically most plausible ones.

pattern suggests that one such fragment might
be the Silifke Block, which is part of southern
Turkey.

Sporadic warm elements (e.g., *Domasia* spp.;
similar to, but not identical with, the "Baltic"
variety of *D. elongata*) are clearly out of place
in the otherwise moderate temperature assemblages of the Silurian section from northern-
most Saudi Arabia and might indicate the
warming influence of the Tethys Sea on an essentially cold to moderate portion of the
Pangaean Epeiric Sea at the edge of glaciated
Southland. If the Protoatlantic did open to

form a wide, deep inter-ocean connection, the
heat-sink caused by this watermass would gradually disturb the original regular palynofacies
trends at both sides of the gap. Hence, blurred,
irregular palynofacies along the Protoatlantic
point to an open ocean, while palynofacies that
are intercontinentally continuous indicate a
closed ocean.

The position of the rotational pole for the
Silurian, plotted on the isochronal surface of
the Wenlockian (fig. 4), can be determined
from the arrangement of the palynofacies lineations (Cramer, 1971b). The position of the ro-

tational pole controls the position of the climatic belts. These will shift over a drifting continent, causing a maximum time-transgression of palynofacies boundaries along the polar trajectory, but no time-transgression at all normal to the trajectory. Thus, a simple relationship exists between geographic location, absolute amount of time-transgression of the facies boundaries, the direction of the polar trajectory, and the rate of drift. Cramer (1970; revised by Cramer & Díez, 1972) estimated the rate of drift along the polar trajectory to be two or three centimeters per year during the Wenlockian; approximately the same rate as present. A number of assumptions (discussed in some detail by Cramer, 1970, 1971a, 1971b, and by Cramer & Díez, 1972) were made: (1) graptolite stratigraphy is chronologically perfect in the twenty to sixty degree paleolatitudinal area around the Atlantic; by consequence, tops and bottoms of graptolite zones are time-flat; (2) the Wenlockian had a duration of six to ten million years; (3) no significant global cooling or amelioration of the Wenlockian climate occurred; (4) the precision with which the (palynological) rotational pole can be located falls within a circle of a radius of no more than five degrees.

ORDOVICIAN TRENDS

All organisms, including the palynomorphs that floated in the early Paleozoic Epeiric Sea, have optimum, minimum, and maximum temperature requirements for their survival. Thus phytoplankton and their selective grazers are susceptible to climatic zoning. If their tolerances are broad, the plankton may be cosmopolitan, however, it is unlikely that only acritarchs among planktonic organisms had sufficiently narrow tolerances to have a temperature-controlled distribution. Certainly some, but not all, chitinozoans show paleolatitudinal limits in their distribution. To our knowledge no one has processed all the graptolite data to find out if they are really cosmopolitan.

Tappan (1970, 1971) and Tappan & Loeblich (1971) have presented data indicating that the variety, but not necessarily the abundance, of Paleozoic phytoplankton species increased from the Cambrian onward. The Late Precambrian has a quite undiversified flora, made up of morphologically quite invariable simple, spherical, unsculptured taxa. From this it might be inferred that no climatic zonation will be detectable in the Late Upper Precambrian, but was there a Cambrian or an Ordovician climate zonation? That such climatic zonations are unreported may be the result of the paucity of

recorded assemblages and the lack of knowledge of the tectonic history of the continents. Continental scattering makes it inherently difficult to recognize trends unless one first knows how to fit the continental fragments together. Except for work by Timofeev (1959, 1966), some data by Downie (1958, 1967), Vanguestaine (1967, 1968, 1970) and Combaz (1967a, 1967b) little has been published on pre-Lower Ordovician phytoplankton. Most of this literature refers to small, local assemblages. Our unpublished data based on many localities over four continents, generally with very large assemblages, show the existence of many co-existing phytoplankton taxa from at least the late Middle Cambrian onward. Allowing for the differences in length of time intervals, the specific diversity of Middle Cambrian acritarchs is estimated as at least one-third that of Middle Silurian acritarchs. Lower Ordovician and Silurian diversities are of comparable magnitudes.

If the five hundred Silurian "species" have numerous noncosmopolitan taxa, then the Ordovician "species" might include several noncosmopolitan taxa as well inasmuch as the climatic setting of the Late Ordovician, and probably back as early as the Middle Cambrian, did not significantly differ from that of the Silurian. All of these sediments contain belts of tillites, reefs and evaporites.

In principle, it should be feasible to determine whether the greater abundance of corals in the Wenlockian, as compared to the immediately preceding and following stages, was caused by an amelioration of worldwide climate, or whether a shift in the ocean currents simply caused a better heat distribution over a larger area, thereby creating successively more suitable habitats for corals on the Pangaean Epeiric Sea. Climate amelioration would raise the equatorial temperature, if not in the ocean, then at least in the Epeiric Sea. A change in the atmospheric circulation (which is unlikely because no major, high, wide, and long mountain belts arose or disappeared in the late Llandoverian or early Wenlockian), or a change in oceanic circulation (which is likely because water currents are modified easily by rapidly drifting continental fragments in their path), would cause a widening of the tropical and moderate temperature bands on Pangaea. Climate amelioration would result in the emplacement of an equatorial heat barrier for taxa whose maximum temperature tolerance was just below the equatorial temperatures prevailing in late Llandoverian time. Even though no evidence is available yet, it is postulated that the bipartition of the gene pool of these taxa should result, provided their morphologic evolution was rapid enough, in disjunct and increasingly different, palynological biofacies. A comparison of the Ordovician through Upper Silurian strata of Gotland with a section of similar age in the northwest part of Transuralic Siberia is needed to demonstrate these biofacies. In the Wenlockian, both sections were about equidistant to the equator, but on opposite paleohemispheres.

CONCLUSIONS

1. In the Silurian Pangaean Epeiric Sea, palynofacies boundaries lie on small-circles.

2. These palynofacies boundaries and Silurian isotherms paralleled rotational latitudes.

3. Where palynofacies boundaries do not follow small-circles, their deviation reflects either a change in thermal regime or results from tectonic deformation of originally regular boundaries.

4. Major abrupt deviations or irregularities in otherwise regularly arranged palynofacies in adjacent and contemporaneous sections located on the same paleolatitude indicate crustal movement normal or oblique to the paleolatitude.

5. Encroachment of an oceanic thermal regime into an epeiric sea will progressively blur palynofacies trends.

6. Since Silurian palynofacies along the Protoatlantic are sharply defined, the ocean was probably narrow, or did not exist, during most or all of the Silurian.

7. Because of movement of crustal blocks, biofacies are time-transgressive along the component of motion that is directed toward the climatic pole.

8. The rate of Pangaean drift in the Wenlockian, measured along its polar vector, was a few centimeters per year.

ACKNOWLEDGMENTS

The authors gratefully acknowledge the support of the National Science Foundation through Grants GA-19419 and GA-30879. The Research Council, Florida State University, has provided us with indispensable financial aid in the early days of our research program.

We wish to thank our colleague Steven Schamel, Department of Geology, Florida State University, for his help with the preparation of the original draft of the manuscript. It is a pleasure to acknowledge with much appreciation the time-devouring and undoubtedly difficult job of editing the original and the second drafts of the manuscript by two referees, and by Charles A. Ross, Department of Geology, Western Washington State College. Many improvements were made thanks to their helpful criticism.

REFERENCES CITED

BERRY, W. B. N., AND A. J. BOUCOT. 1967. Continental stability. A Silurian point of view. J. geophys. Res. 77:2254–2256.

——, AND ——. 1970. Correlation of the North American Silurian rocks. Spec. Pap. geol. Soc. Am. 102:1–289.

BEUF, S., B. BIJU-DUVAL, J. STÉVAUX, AND G. KULBICKI. 1966. Ampleur des glaciations siluriennes au Sahara. Leurs influences et leurs conséquences sur la sédimentation. Revue Inst. fr. Pétrole. 21:363–381.

BIRD, J. M., AND J. F. DEWEY. 1970. Lithosphere plate-continental margin tectonics and the evolution of the Appalachian orogen. Bull. geol. Soc. Am. 81:1031–1060.

COMBAZ, A. 1967a. Un microbios du Trémadocien dans un sondage d'Hassi-Messaoud. Act. Soc. linn. Bordeaux. ser. B. 104(29):1–26.

——. 1967b. Sur un microbios d'âge Trémadocien à Hassi-Messaoud. Act. Soc. linn. Bordeaux Spéc. vol. Congr. A.F.A.S. 1967, p. 115–119

CRAMER, F. H. 1970. Distribution of selected Silurian acritarchs. Revta Española Micropaleont. Num. Extraord. 1, 203 p.

——. 1971a. Position of the north Florida lower Paleozoic block in Silurian time. J. geophys. Res. 76: 4754–4757.

——. 1971b. A palynostratigraphic model of Pangaea during Silurian time. Colloque Ordovicien-Silurien, Brest. Mém. Bur. Rech. Géol. Min. 73:229–235.

——. 1973. Middle and Upper Silurian chitinozoan succession in Florida subsurface. J. Paleont. 46:279–288.

——, AND M. D. C. R. DÍEZ DE CRAMER. 1970. Acritarchs from the Lower Silurian Neahga Formation, Niagara Peninsula, North America. Can. J. Earth Sci. 7:1077–1085.

——, AND ——. 1972. North American Silurian palynofacies and their spatial arrangement: acritarchs. Palaeontographica, Abt. B. 138:107–180.

DIETZ, R. S., AND J. C. HOLDEN. 1970. Reconstruction of Pangaea: breakup and dispersion of continents, Permian to present. J. geophys. Res. 75:4939–4956.

DOWNIE, C. 1958. An assemblage of microplankton from the Shineton Shales (Tremadocian). Proc. Yorks. geol. Soc. 31:331–350.

——. 1959. Hystrichospheres from the Silurian Wenlock Shale of England. Palaeontology. 2:56–71.

——. 1960. Deunffia and Domasia, new genera of hystrichospheres. Micropaleontology. 6:197–202.

————. 1963. "Hystrichospheres" (acritarchs) and spores of the Wenlock Shales (Silurian) of Wenlock, England. Palaeontology. 6:625–652.

————. 1967. The geological history of the microplankton. Revue Paleobot. Polynal. 1:269–281.

EISENACK, A. 1931. Neue Mikrofossilien des baltischen Silurs. 1. Paläont. Z. 13:74–118.

————. 1932. Neues Mikrofossilien des baltischen Silurs. II. Ibid. 14:257–277.

————. Neue Mikrofossilien des baltischen Silurs. III. und neue Mikrofossilien des böhmischen Silurs. I. Ibid. 16:52–76.

————. 1937. Neue Mikrofossilien des baltischen Silurs. IV. Ibid. 19:217–243.

————. 1938. Hystricosphaerideen und verwandte Formen im baltischen Silur. Z. Geschiebeforsch. Flachldgeol. 14:1–30.

————. 1939. Chitinozoen und Hystrichosphaerideen im Ordovizium des Rheinischen Schiefergebirges. Senckenbergiana. 21:135–152.

————. 1951. Über Hystrichosphaerideen und andere Kleinformen aus baltischem Silur und Kambrium. Ibid. 32:187–204.

————. 1954. Hystrichosphären aus dem baltischen Gotlandium. Ibid. 34:205–211.

————. 1955. Chitinozoen, Hystrichosphären und andere Mikrofossilien aus dem Beyrichia-Kalk. Senckenberg. leth. 36:157–188.

————. 1958a. Mikrofossilien aus dem Ordovizium des Baltikums. Ibid. 39:389–405.

————. 1958b. Tasmanites Newton 1875 und Leiosphaeridia n. g. als Gattungen der Hystrichosphaeridea. Palaeontographica, Abt. A. 110:1–19.

————. 1959a. Neotypen baltischer Silur-Hystrichosphären und neue Arten. Ibid. 112:193–211.

————. 1959b. Neotypen baltischer Silur-Chitinozoen und neue Arten. Neues Jb. Geol. Paläont. Abh. 1:1–20.

————. 1960. Über einige niedere Algen aus dem baltischen Silur. Senckenberg. leth. 41:13–26.

————. 1962a. Mitteilungen über Leiosphären und über das Pylom bei Hystrichosphären. Neues Jb. Geol. Paläont. Abh. 114:58–80.

————. 1962b. Mikrofossilien aus dem Ordovizium des Baltikums. 2. Vaginatenkalk bis Lyckholmer Stufe. Senckenberg. leth. 43:349–366.

————. 1963. Mitteilungen zur Biologie der Hystrichosphären und über neue Arten. Neues Jb. Geol. Paläont. Abh. 118:207–216.

————. 1965a. Mikrofossilien aus dem Silur Gotlands Hystrichosphären, Problematika. Ibid. 122:257–274.

————. 1965b. Die Mikrofauna der Ostseekalke. (1) Chitinozoen, Hystrichosphären. Ibid. 123:115–148.

————. 1968a. Mikrofossilien eines Geschiebes der Borkholmer Stufe, baltisches Ordovizium, F₂. Mitt. geol. St. Inst. Hamb. 37:81–94.

————. 1968b. Über die Fortpflanzung paläozoischer Hystrichosphären. Neues Jb. Geol. Paläont. Abh. 131:1–22.

————. 1968c. Über Chitinozoen des baltischen Gebietes. Palaeontographica, Abt. A. 131:137–198.

————. 1969. Zur Systematik einiger paläozoischer Hystrichosphären (Acritarcha) des baltischen Gebietes. Neues Jb. Geol. Paläont. Abh. 133:245–266.

————. 1970. Mikrofossilien aus dem Silur Estlands und der Insel Ösel. Geol. För. Stockh. Förh. 92:302–322.

————. 1971. Weitere Mikrofossilien aus dem Beyrichienkalk (Silur). Neues Jb. Geol. Paläont. Mh. 8:449–460.

FAIRBRIDGE, R. W. 1964. The importance of limestone and its Ca/Mg content to palaeoclimatology. In, NAIRN, A. E. M., Ed. Problems in palaeoclimatology. Proc. NATO Palaeoclimat. Conf. Newcastle-on-Tyne, 1963. Interscience, New York, London, Sydney. p. 431–478.

GÓRKA, H. 1969. Microorganisms de l'Ordovicien de Pologne. Palaeont. Pol. 22:1–102.

HARRINGTON, H. J. 1962. Palaeogeographic development of South America. Bull. geol. Soc. Am. 46:1773–1814.

HILL, D. 1958. Distribution and sequence of Silurian coral faunas. J. Proc. R. Soc. N.S.W. 92:151–171.

JONES, O. T 1925 On the geology of the Llandovery district, pt 1. Quart. J. geol. Soc. Lond. 81:344–388.

KJELLSTRÖM, G. 1971a. Ordovician microplankton (baltisphaerids) from the Grötlingbo borehole No. 1 in Gotland, Sweden. Sver. geol. Unders. Afh. ser. C. 65(655):1–75.

————. 1971b. Middle Ordovician microplankton from the Grötlingbo borehole No. 1 in Gotland, Sweden. Ibid. ser. C. 65(669):1–35.

LISTER, T. R. 1970. A monograph of the acritarchs and Chitinozoa from the Wenlock and Ludlow Series of the Ludlow and Millichope areas, Shropshire. Palaeontogr. Soc. (Monogr.) 1:1–100.

LOEBLICH, A. R., AND W. S. DRUGG. 1968. New acritarchs from the Early Devonian (late Gedinnian) Haragan Formation of Oklahoma, U.S.A. Tulane Stu. Geol. 6:129–137

————, AND H. TAPPAN. 1970. Thysanoprobolus, a new acritarch genus from the Early Devonian (late Gedinnian) Haragan Formation of Oklahoma. Proc. biol. Soc. Wash. 83:261–266.

LOTZE, F. 1964. The distribution of evaporites in space and time. In, NAIRN, A. E. M., Ed. Problems in palaeoclimatology. Proc. NATO Palaeoclimat. Conf. Newcastle-on-Tyne, 1963. Interscience, New York, London, Sydney. p. 491–509.

MAACK, R. 1960. Zur Palaeogeographie des Gondwanalandes. 21st. Int. Geol. Congr. Copenhagen, Pt. 12, p. 35–55.

————. 1964. Characteristic features of the palaeogeography and stratigraphy of the Devonian of Brazil and South Africa. In, NAIRN, A. E. M., Ed. Problems in palaeoclimatology. Proc. NATO Palaeoclimat. Conf. Newcastle-on-Tyne, 1963. Interscience, New York, London, Sydney. p. 285–293.

MARTIN, F. 1965. Les Acritarches de Sart-Bernard (Ordovicien belge). Bull Soc. Belge Géol. 74:1–22.

————. 1968a. Les Acritarches de l'Ordovicien et du Silurien belges. Inst. Roy. Soc. Nat. Belg. Mém. 160:1–175.

————. 1968b. Ordovicien et Silurien belges; données nouvelles apportées par l'étude des Acritarches. Bull. Soc. belge Géol. Paleont. Hydrol. 1969. 77:175–181.

REGNÉLL, G., AND J. E. HEDE. 1960. The lower Paleozoic of Scania. The Silurian of Gotland. 21st Int. Geol. Congr. Copenhagen. Fieldbook, p. 4–87.

RUST, I. C. 1969. The Western Cape some 450 million years ago. S. Afr. J. Geog. 3:346–353.

SHAW, A. B. 1964. Time in stratigraphy. McGraw-Hill, New York, 365 p.

TAPPAN. H. 1970. Phytoplankton abundance and the late Paleozoic wave of extinctions. Palaeogeogr., Palaeoclimat., Palaeoecol. 8:56–66.

———. 1971. Microplankton, ecological succession and evolution. Proc. North Am. Paleont. Conv. 1969, pt. H, p. 1058–1103.

———, AND A. R. LOEBLICH. 1971. Geobiologic implications of fossil phytoplankton evolution and time-space distribution. Spec. Pap. geol. Soc. Am. 127:247–340

TERMIER, H., AND G. TERMIER. 1964. Les temps fossilifères 1. Paléozoique inférieur. Masson, Paris. 689 p.

TIMOFEEV., B. V. 1959. The ancient flora of the Baltic region and its stratigraphic significance. Trudy vses. neft. nauchno-issled. geol. razv. Inst. 129:1–320.

———. 1966. Mikropaleontologiceskoe issledovanie drevnich svit. Akad. Nauk SSSR, Moscow p. 1–147.

VANGUESTAINE, M. 1967. Decouverte d'Acritarches dans le Révinien Supérieur du Massif de Stavelot. Annls. Soc. géol. Belge. 90: 1966–1967:B585–B600.

———. 1968. Les Acritarches du sondage de Grand Halleux (Note préliminaire). Ibid. 91:361–375.

———. 1970. L'appartenance au Révinien inférieur et moyen des roches noires de la partie profonde du sondage Grand-Halleux et leur disposition en un pil couché. Ibid. 93:591–600.

WHITE, E. I. 1950. The vertebrate faunas of the Lower Old Red Sandstone of the Welsh Border. Bull. Brit. Mus. (Nat. Hist.) Geol. 1:51–67.

WILLIAMS, A. 1951. Llandovery brachiopods from Wales with special reference to the Llandovery district. Quart. J. geol. Soc. Lond. 107:85–136.

PROVINCIALISM EXHIBITED BY ORDOVICIAN CONODONT FAUNAS

WALTER C. SWEET AND STIG M. BERGSTRÖM

Department of Geology and Mineralogy, The Ohio State University, Columbus, OH 43210

ABSTRACT—Throughout the Ordovician, two well-distinguished provinces were delineated by distribution of conodonts in the northern hemisphere. One, the North Atlantic Province, includes all of northwest Europe, much of the British Isles, and a tract in the eastern Appalachians that stretches from Newfoundland on the north to Georgia and Alabama on the south. A second, the North American Midcontinent Province, embraces all of interior North America, the western belts of the Appalachians, and at least part of the Canadian Arctic Archipelago. Although there was limited and episodic exchange between North Atlantic and North American Midcontinent conodont faunas, and vicarism is evident between some elements, the two were strikingly different and apparently largely unrelated through the Ordovician. Limited information suggests that Midcontinent faunas were also characteristic of at least part of the Siberian Platform and elements of these faunas are also known from the Ordovician of New Zealand, Australia, and probably South Korea. Elements of North Atlantic type have been recorded from western Nevada, the Yukon, east-central Alaska, and northwest Argentina. Lithologic associates of Midcontinent conodonts suggest that the Midcontinent fauna developed at low latitudes, perhaps astride the Ordovician equator, and that the North Atlantic fauna was characteristic of higher latitudes. Water temperature was probably the most important factor in defining boundaries between the two conodont provinces.

INTRODUCTION

For more than 100 years after the initial discovery of conodonts (Pander, 1856), writers who considered the subject at all seem to have held the view that, unlike most other organisms, taxa of these zoologically enigmatic animals were remarkably cosmopolitan in distribution in Paleozoic and Triassic seas. Such a view lingers even today and may be tenable for faunal complexes of certain ages (e.g., Late Devonian), but it must be emphatically abandoned in interpreting those characteristic of the Ordovician. Within the last 20 years it has become increasingly clear that Ordovician conodonts of the present northern hemisphere developed in at least two sharply distinct faunal realms, between which there was only limited and episodic exchange. Our purpose in this short contribution is to review the evidence for recognizing these faunal realms, or provinces; chart their known distribution; speculate on reasons for their long-term separation; and comment on special aspects of the faunas themselves that may bear on subsequent interpretations of conodont phylogeny and distribution. We concentrate on Ordovician faunal differentiation in the present-day northern hemisphere because Ordovician conodonts from southern continents are still very incompletely known and difficult to interpret biogeographically.

ORDOVICIAN CONODONT PROVINCES

The known geographic distribution of taxa represented in large collections of conodonts from Edenian (Late Ordovician) strata in the Cincinnati region of Ohio, Kentucky, and Indiana, led Sweet and others (1959) to postulate the existence of two major conodont provinces in the Late Ordovician. One, characterized by faunas that are distinctive of Middle and Upper Ordovician rocks in much of extra-Appalachian North America, was termed the *North American Midcontinent Province*. The other, distinguished by faunas known in 1959 primarily from scattered localities in Great Britain, Scandinavia, Estonia, Germany, and the Appalachians, was named the *Anglo-Scandinavian-Appalachian Province*. The occasional presence of a few elements typical of one fauna in collections dominated by representatives of the other was taken to indicate limited periodic exchange between the two, but too little was known in 1959 of the stratigraphic and geographic distribution of the components of either fauna to evaluate the significance of those exchanges or use them biostratigraphically.

Studies during the 1960's (Pulse and Sweet, 1960; Sweet and Bergström, 1962; Bergström and Sweet, 1966; Sweet and Bergström, 1966; Schopf, 1966, Kohut and Sweet, 1968; Lindström, 1969) affirmed the reality of the provincial faunas postulated in 1959 and provided further evidence for their geographic distribution in Middle and Late Ordovician times. This evidence, combined with additional data, is summarized in four recently published reports (Bergström, 1971; Sweet and others, 1971; Bergström, 1973; Barnes and others, 1973). In those summaries the term North American Midcontinent Province is used, but the Anglo-Scandina-

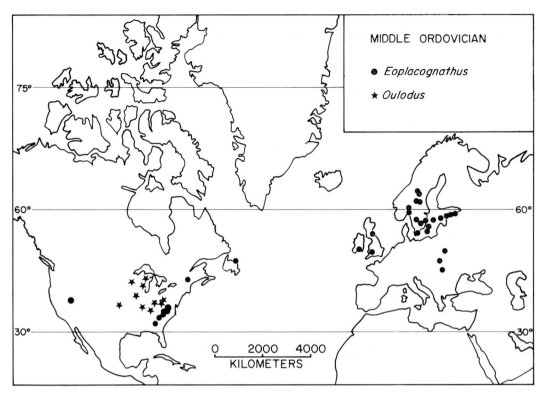

Fig. 1—Distribution of *Oulodus* (stars), a typical Midcontinent conodont genus, and *Eoplacognathus* (dots),
a genus characteristic of the North Atlantic conodont province.

vian-Appalachian Province of Sweet and others
(1959) (=European Province of Bergström and
Sweet, 1966, and Seddon and Sweet, 1971) has
been re-named *North Atlantic Province* in
Bergström's recent papers and we use this des-
ignation with unvarnished relief in the following pages.

In figures 1 through 4 we plot the known
distribution of *Oulodus, Plectodina, Phragmodus,* and *Belodina,* which we regard as typical
of the North American Midcontinent Province,
and that of *Eoplacognathus, Pygodus, Prioniodus,* and *Periodon,* which were common constituents of North Atlantic faunas in the Ordovician. *Oulodus* is represented in most collections from the Middle and Upper Ordovician
of the North American Midcontinent, but it
has never been reported from samples dominated by North Atlantic faunal elements. *Plectodina* is even more widespread than *Oulodus*
in the Midcontinent, where it is represented by
several species. Elements referable to *Plectodina* are known from Wales and Ireland, but
the genus is otherwise known in Middle Ordovician rocks of northwestern Europe only in
the Mjøsa Limestone of Norway and equivalent
Oandu strata in Estonia. We should point out,

however, that both the Mjøsa and Oandu yield
numerous megafossils of North American type
(Rõõmusoks, 1968) that are not found elsewhere in the Balto-Scandic area. This suggests
that there was a brief invasion of forms from
the Midcontinent faunal area in late Middle
Ordovician time.

Phragmodus is commonly represented in Middle and Upper Ordovician faunas of the Midcontinent Province, but the only representatives
of this genus known to us in the Middle Ordovician of Europe are from the Mjøsa Limestone of Norway and the Castell Limestone of
Wales (Webers, 1966). *Belodina,* which is commonly represented in Middle and Upper Ordovician Midcontinent faunas, is known with certainty in the Middle Ordovician of northwest
Europe only in a few collections from the
Southern Uplands of Scotland (Bergström,
1971).

Most of the compound-element conodont
species of the Middle and Upper Ordovician
in the North Atlantic Province are referable
to the genera *Eoplacognathus, Prioniodus,* and
Pygodus. Specimens assignable to species of
any of these genera have yet to be found in
the interior of the Midcontinent Province (figs.

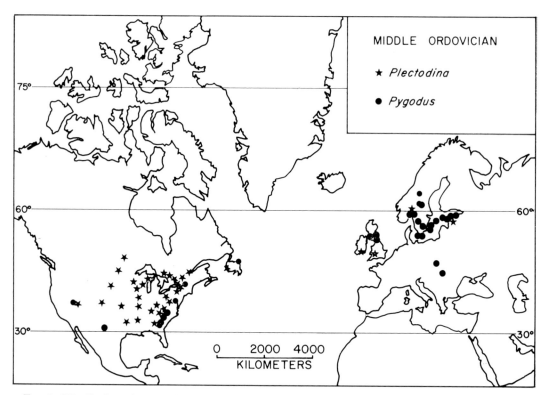

FIG. 2—Distribution of *Plectodina* (stars), a typical Midcontinent conodont genus, and *Pygodus* (dots), a genus characteristic of the North Atlantic conodont province.

1–3), although such specimens occur with some Midcontinent species in the Appalachians and in central Nevada. *Periodon,* on the other hand, includes distinctive North Atlantic Province species but is also represented in some collections from the interior of the North American Midcontinent Province. In the latter collections, however, *Periodon* is customarily represented by only a few specimens and the distribution of such specimens in most sections is erratic. This suggests that *Periodon* was not indigenous to the Midcontinent, but was an occasional immigrant into that province.

The genera whose distribution is mapped in figures 1–4 are just a few of the ones whose distribution provides the basic framework for our concept of the North American Midcontinent and North Atlantic faunal provinces. Additional data on these faunas have recently been published by Bergström (1973).

Figure 5 tabulates and contrasts the numbers of conodont species we now recognize in successive and broadly equivalent biostratigraphic units of the Middle and Upper Ordovician in the North American Midcontinent and North Atlantic Provinces. Figure 5 also indicates cosmopolitan species separately and the numbers

of "exotic" species identified in each of the tabulated intervals. To those who turn to the literature to verify our tabulations, the species recognized are, for the most part, multielement species, and a number of the ones we include have not been described, revised, or named in print. Also, our current concept of conodont species is relatively broad and, because we include only forms that appear distinct to us now, the numbers given may have to be adjusted upward when North Atlantic and Midcontinent faunas have been fully described. In all probability this will not change to any notable degree the relative relations between the North Atlantic and Midcontinent faunas suggested in figure 5.

A very large part of the Ordovician is unrepresented in figure 5 primarily for two reasons. First, Lower Ordovician conodonts have received much attention in the North Atlantic Province, but relatively little in the North American Midcontinent; and second, there are few rocks of pre-Black River Middle Ordovician age in the interior of North America from which to derive distributional data that might be compared with those from the equivalent interval in the North Atlantic Province.

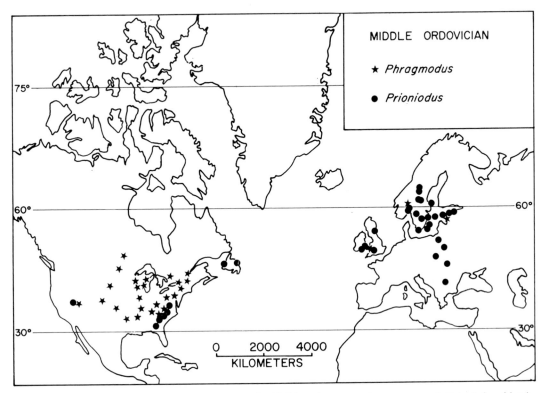

Fig. 3—Distribution of *Phragmodus* (stars), a typical Midcontinent conodont genus, and *Prioniodus* (dots), a genus characteristic of the North Atlantic conodont province.

Thus our comparisons in figure 5 deal with conodonts of "Black River" and younger Ordovician age exclusively.

Despite these limitations and reservations, figure 5 displays a number of significant features, for example, the North Atlantic and North American Midcontinent faunas were clearly of about the same size throughout the interval depicted, although at every level compared the number of North Atlantic species is slightly larger. Only in the lower part of the *Amorphognathus tvaerensis* Zone is the number of species significantly larger in the North Atlantic than in the Midcontinent faunas.

A second feature of note is the modest contribution of cosmopolitan species to either fauna. At no level compared do such species constitute more than 10 percent of the total number of species in either fauna and, for the most part, the two or three cosmopolitan species recognized are the same ones throughout the entire interval shown.

Finally, about the same number of North Atlantic and Midcontinent species were apparently able to migrate periodically into areas dominated by the opposite fauna, but, except in the lower part of the *Amorphognathus tvae-*

rensis Zone, immigrant species constitute a somewhat larger percentage of the total Midcontinent fauna than they do in the North Atlantic fauna. Furthermore, from a level in the upper part of the *A. tvaerensis* Zone upward, it is always the same complex of North Atlantic species that contributes to the Midcontinent fauna, not a random assortment of the 19 to 22 that make up the North Atlantic faunas in this interval. A similar observation can be made about emigrants from the Midcontinent faunas. That is, "fibrous" conodonts, which are rare in the Midcontinent in faunas younger than Fauna 7, are the principal North American contributors to North Atlantic faunas in the lower part of the *A. tvaerensis* Zone but, above that level, Midcontinent immigrants into the North Atlantic Province belong mostly to single species of *Plectodina, Phragmodus,* and *Belodina,* not to a more varied assortment of the 11 to 16 species characteristic of Midcontinent faunas in this interval.

At essentially all levels compared in figure 5, at least 60 percent of the total numbers of species recognized in either the Midcontinent or the North Atlantic provinces were apparently indigenous to, and never strayed from, those

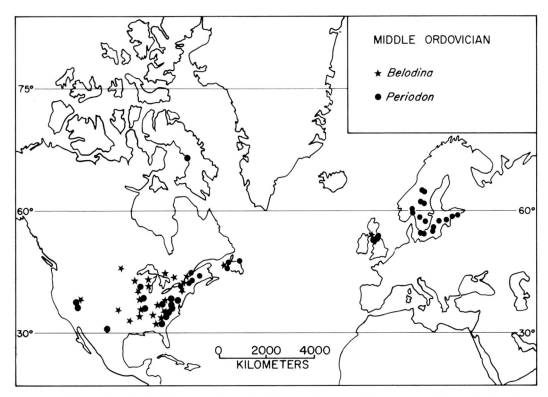

Fig. 4—Distribution of *Belodina* (stars), a typical Midcontinent conodont genus, and *Periodon* (dots), a genus characteristic of the North Atlantic conodont province.

provinces. Within each province, however, most characteristic species had a wide geographic distribution. Thus the conodont provinces we recognize were truly areas in which more than 50 percent of the species were endemic and, in this respect, fit Woodward's (1856) definition of a province, which is widely followed by biogeographers. Because of the high degree of endemism, it is small wonder that correlations based on conodonts between Ordovician rocks of the North Atlantic and Midcontinent Provinces is so difficult, particularly if it is borne in mind that immigrant species in one or the other of these provinces very rarely account for more than 10 percent of the total number of specimens collected, even though at some levels they may represent as much as 40 percent of the total number of species in the provincial fauna. Also, except for species of *Amorphognathus,* immigrant species have rather extensive vertical ranges and this makes them of limited use in detailed correlation. Lists of the species on which the numbers for figure 5 are based would serve little useful purpose in a general discussion. However, our experience as taxonomists lead us to believe that these numbers approximate biologic realities and that

there were two remarkably distinct conodont faunas in Middle and Late Ordovician seas of the present-day northern hemisphere.

Additional evidence is provided by figure 6, which shows the location of all the principal localities or areas from which conodonts of North Atlantic and North American Midcontinent type have been collected. As might be expected, conodonts of Midcontinent type are best known from various levels in the Middle and Upper Ordovician at numerous localities in North America, but the few Lower Ordovician forms described from the same geographic region are also distinctive and the localities from which they have been collected are included as indicators of the Midcontinent Province. In North America, the Midcontinent Province stretched at least from Hoved Island in Ellesmereland on the north (Weyant, 1968) to the Mina Plomosos area of Chihuahua, Mexico (Bridges and DeFord, 1961) on the south, and from northern Newfoundland (Barnes and Tuke, 1970) and the Appalachians (Rust, 1968; Drahovzal and Neathery, 1971) on the east to Nevada (Langenheim et al., 1962; Ethington and Schumacher, 1969; Ross, 1970) on the west.

MIDCONTINENT	M	C	AT		M	C	AT	NORTH ATLANTIC	N. AM. STAGES	BRIT. SERIES
Fauna 12	16	2	5	→ ←	4	3	22	*Amorphognathus ordovicicus* Zone	RICHMONDIAN	ASHGILLIAN
									MAYSVILLIAN	
Fauna 11	15	2	5	→ ←	5	2	18	*Amorphognathus superbus* Zone	EDENIAN	—?—
Fauna 10									SHERMANIAN	CARADOCIAN
Fauna 9	11	2	7		2	2	19		KIRKFIELDIAN	
Fauna 8								*Amorphognathus tvaerensis* Zone	ROCKLANDIAN	
									BLACK	
Fauna 7	19	2	2	→	9	2	29		RIVERAN	

FIG. 5—Tabulation of the numbers of species composing the Midcontinent and North Atlantic conodont faunas in the Upper Middle and Upper Ordovician. In column headings, M = Midcontinent species; C = cosmopolitan species; and AT = North Atlantic species (i.e., the conodont fauna of the *A. ordovicicus* Zone in the North Atlantic Province is composed of 29 species, 22 of which are of North Atlantic type, 4 of which are immigrants from the Midcontinent, and 3 are cosmopolitan). Heavy black arrows indicate times at which there were notable influxes of species characteristic of one provincial fauna into the realm of the other.

Ordovician conodonts of North American Midcontinent type are not restricted in their distribution, however, to North America. Collections from the Lower Ordovician part of the Durness Limestone of Scotland (Higgins, 1967) are largely of Midcontinent type, and Moskalenko (1967, 1970) has reported collections dominated by conodonts of Midcontinent aspect from Lower and Middle Ordovician rocks of the Siberian Platform. Philip (1966) and Packham (1967) record *Belodina compressa, Phragmodus undatus,* and other typically North American Midcontinent species from New South Wales, Australia, and the Lower Ordovician conodonts recently described from Queensland by Druce and Jones (1971) are, for the most part, strikingly similar to those in the few collections that have been described from the North American Midcontinent Province. In addition, the Queensland Lower Ordovician collections contain representatives of several forms (e.g., *Acanthodus, Chosonodina*) that have never been recorded in North Atlantic Lower Ordovician collections, but are well known from rocks in the North American Midcontinent (Ethington and Clark, 1971). Lower Ordovician collections from South Korea described by Müller (1964) include *Chosonodina* and other forms that suggest Midconti-

nent affinities. Lee (1970), on the other hand, thought that the Korean conodonts he described from the post-Tremadoc Lower Ordovician were dominantly of North Atlantic affinities. However, Lee's collections have no suggestion of the ramiform-element genera that characterize post-Tremadoc Lower Ordovician faunas in the North Atlantic Province and many of the simple-cone species he recognized have counterparts in North American Midcontinent faunas but are unknown in North Atlantic faunas. On balance, the Korean Lower Ordovician conodonts described by Müller (1964) and Lee (1970) are more like presumably contemporaneous Midcontinent types than North Atlantic ones. Korea is thus shown to be part of the Midcontinent Province in figure 6.

Conodonts representative of the North Atlantic fauna are similarly widespread in Ordovician rocks. As indicated in figure 6, North Atlantic-type conodonts are known from numerous localities in Scandinavia and the British Isles, and they have also been reported from scattered sections on the European continent, from the Ukraine (Drygant, 1970), Bulgaria (Spasov, 1970) and Turkey (Dean and Monod, 1970) on the east, to Brittany (Lindström and Pelhate, 1971) and Spain (Fuganti and Serpagli, 1968) on the west. North Atlantic cono-

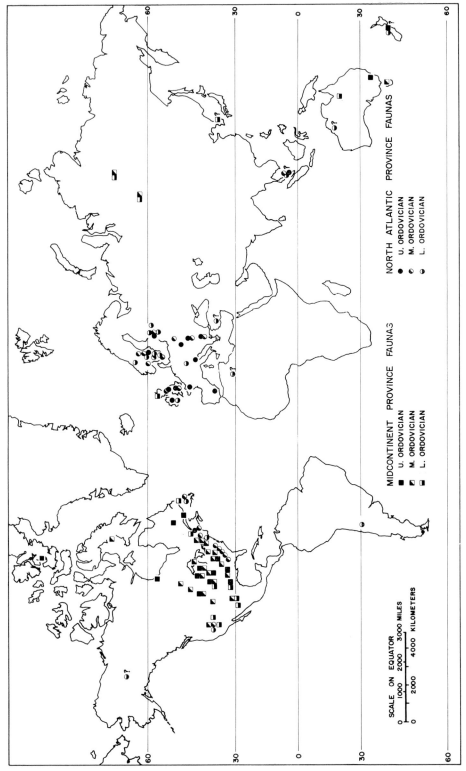

Fig. 6—Distribution of sections from which conodonts of North American Midcontinent and North Atlantic-type have been derived. In most cases, symbols represent more than one section. Question marks indicate that conodonts are of uncertain faunal affinities.

donts also dominate collections from Ordovician rocks of the central and eastern Appalachians, from Newfoundland on the northeast to Alabama on the southwest (Bergström, 1971). In the western Appalachians, rocks yielding primarily North Atlantic-type conodonts are separated by only a few miles from strata with conodonts of Midcontinent affinities.

Undescribed collections from Lower Ordovician rocks in Nevada and from Middle Ordovician rocks in the Yukon, together with described Middle Ordovician material from central Nevada (Ethington and Schumacher, 1969) and reported Lower Ordovician material from east-central Alaska (Churkin and Brabb, 1965) indicate that a fauna of North Atlantic type may also have dominated the northwestern part of North America during at least parts of Ordovician time. Much more information will be needed to clarify the distribution of North Atlantic-type conodonts in northwestern North America. However, the few localities from which conodonts of this sort are currently known must be considered in any interpretation of the causes of distribution of the North Atlantic and Midcontinent conodont faunas.

In addition to North American and European occurrences, figure 6 shows a single South American occurrence of conodonts apparently largely, although not entirely, of North Atlantic type in northwest Argentina (Hünicken and Gallino, 1970; Hünicken, 1971). North Atlantic-type conodonts may also dominate as-yet-undescribed collections from northwestern Australia, but the over-all affinities of conodonts in those collections are still uncertain (Lindström, 1964).

The faunal affinities of conodonts from two areas are uncertain: one in Malaya, the other in North Africa, and the affinities of these sections are questioned on figure 6. Some of the Lower Ordovician conodonts from the lower part of the Setul Limestone of Malaya described by Igo and Koike (1967, 1968) have a Midcontinent aspect, but others, and many of the younger Ordovician forms described, are not identifiable with species known now from either Midcontinent or North Atlantic faunas. Specimens described from North Africa by Bazoche (1960) are unrecognizable from her illustrations or descriptions, which is a pity for these are thus far the only Ordovician conodonts known from that entire continent. Undescribed collections from the Middle Ordovician of central Australia and Tasmania are characterized by species largely unknown in either the Midcontinent or North Atlantic Provinces, which led Bergström (1971) to postulate that an Australian

conodont faunal province could be recognized in that part of the southern hemisphere in Middle Ordovician time.

Although there is some question about the affinities of a few of the Ordovician conodonts described to date, the vast majority of known forms associate quite readily with one or another of the two major faunas so sharply delineated in Europe and North America. Reconstruction of the geographic distribution of these two faunas is undoubtedly quite incomplete, particularly in Asia and the southern hemisphere, however, figures 1 through 6 adequately demonstrate that in the Ordovician at least two conodont faunas existed in the present northern hemisphere and these maintained their biologic integrity and geographic separation through a substantial part of that period. Further, studies during the last few years (Bergström and Sweet, 1966; Kohut and Sweet, 1968; Bergström, 1973) have revealed subprovincial distribution patterns within each of these provinces.

SEPARATION OF FAUNAS

It is far easier to demonstrate the existence and chart the distribution of the North Atlantic and North American Midcontinent faunas in the Ordovician than to explain the long-term and apparently rather complete separation of these distinctive groups of conodont species. However, the problem of explaining the faunal, and thus provincial, segregation of Ordovician conodonts is somewhat simplified by two important limiting factors. Conodonts were undoubtedly marine animals and most, if not all of them, were planktonic or nektonic in habit. Thus speculation about the causes of provinciality in Ordovician conodonts needs to consider only the factors that govern distribution of pelagic faunas.

Hedgpeth (1957, p. 369–377) noted that "temperature has been considered the most important single factor governing [marine] distribution." Further, in considering distribution of the major pelagic realms of the upper or photic layer, he pointed out (p. 367; fig. 8) that "these major divisions roughly correspond to the latitudinal climatic belts of the sea, with a number of broad transitional areas." There are, of course, many perturbations of the general distributional pattern that Hedgpeth and others regard as the general model. Also, the exact role that temperature plays in determining the patterns observed in modern seas is seldom direct and varies considerably from one group of organisms to another. However, it is a reasonable postulate that conodont faunas distinctive of the Midcontinent and North Atlantic Provinces were developed and distributed in different, but adjacent, pelagic realms in Ordovician seas. We agree with Barnes and others (1973 and Bergström (1973) that at least the endemic components of these two faunas were probably segregated by water temperature, even though the more proximate causes of separation may have been salinity differences, temperature-dependent repopulation mechanisms, or the like.

If the Midcontinent and North Atlantic conodont faunas are taken as indicators of adjacent pelagic realms, it is not inconsistent with modern evidence to postulate that those realms coincided with temperature-defined water masses in Ordovician seas, as is roughly the case now. For about 1,500 miles in eastern North America the boundary between areas with Midcontinent conodonts and areas with North Atlantic conodonts is relatively sharp and we have discovered no distinct transition zone. This could indicate that the boundary between the water masses, to which each fauna was adapted, was similarly sharp in the Ordovician. The provincial boundary in eastern North America coincides, however, with a belt along which Ordovician rocks have been thrust an unknown distance northwestward. Such tectonic movements in post-Ordovician time undoubtedly narrowed any transition zone between faunal realms and may have buried such a zone entirely thus making the provincial boundary much sharper than was originally the case.

In the framework of the "fixist" model, so eloquently defended by Meyerhoff (1970a, 1970b) and Meyerhoff and Meyerhoff (1972), the North Atlantic conodont fauna would represent the warm-temperate pelagic realm and the Midcontinent fauna the boreal realm, if the distribution of these pelagic aggregations followed temperature-defined water masses in Ordovician seas. Northeastward deflection of the North Atlantic fauna to 65°N in and northeast of the Atlantic Basin, and into Alaska and the Yukon, would thus be explained as a result of oceanic circulation patterns of the sort that now translate warm water far north in the Atlantic and Pacific Basins. Southward deflection of the Midcontinent fauna to somewhat below 30°N in southwestern North America would be explained by translation of cooler water southward along the western continental margin in a cold ocean current. Interpretation of the Korean conodonts as Midcontinent (or boreal) forms probably would have to be regarded as a mistake for low warm-temperate North Atlantic forms should surely have been

dominant there in the Ordovician, as is now the case. The inscrutable Malayan fauna would turn out to be our only record of tropical Ordovician conodonts. Most of the southern hemisphere would probably have to be ignored for lack of detailed information, but, the Midcontinent-type conodonts of Australia might represent an anti-boreal fauna, and North Atlantic forms from Argentina might be interpreted as representatives of a southern warm-temperate pelagic realm. If so, conodonts of North Atlantic rather than Midcontinent type should appear in New South Wales and Tasmania, where south-flowing warm currents should have carried warm-temperate rather than boreal or anti-boreal species. The collections examined from those areas are not of North Atlantic type, however.

Unfortunately, there is no known way to distinguish between warm and cold-water conodont faunas from a study of conodonts alone. Several extrinsic factors suggest that the interpretation derived from the "fixist" model is incorrect. The Midcontinent Province outlined by the distribution of distinctive conodont faunas includes all the Ordovician evaporites known in North America and probably those from Siberia, as well. Conodonts typical of Midcontinent faunas are known from rocks laterally equivalent to and not far away from Lower Ordovician evaporites of the Ellenberger and Arbuckle of Texas and Oklahoma, Middle Ordovician evaporites of the Joachim Formation, and Upper Ordovician evaporites of the Williston and Moose Basins. Furthermore, conodonts of Midcontinent type do not disappear from parts of the section that intervene between evaporite deposits. On the contrary, Midcontinent faunas seemed firmly established in the Midcontinent throughout the Ordovician; they did not invade it just at times of evaporite maxima. But the fact that Midcontinent conodonts evidently were adapted to the warm waters from which evaporites could be deposited when other conditions were suitable, suggests that those conodonts were warm-water forms and that the Midcontinent Province was within a warm-water pelagic realm even when evaporites were not forming in it.

The Midcontinent Province, as outlined by conodont distribution, includes a vast area in which Ordovician sediments are largely carbonates. Bahamitic carbonates are widely distributed in this area but are rare in the realm of the North Atlantic Province, except along its Appalachian margin (Dr. Valdar Jaanusson, personal communication, 1972). Bahamitic carbonates suggest deposition in water above 20°C.

Interestingly, at times during the Middle and Late Ordovician when deposition of bahamitic carbonates spread briefly into the North Atlantic Province, so did typical Midcontinent conodonts. A striking illustration of this is the occurrence of Midcontinent conodonts in the Mjøsa Limestone of Norway and in Oandu strata (Vasalemma and Saku facies) of Estonia, which are the only beds of bahamitic type known in the Middle Ordovician of the Balto-Scandic area (Jaanusson, 1972).

The provincial differentiation so strikingly displayed by Ordovician conodonts seems to have ended, at least in the present northern hemisphere, late in the Ordovician or early in the Silurian. Silurian seas were inherited primarily by condont stocks of Midcontinent origin, although derivatives from the two North Atlantic stocks that made the most frequent sorties into the Midcontinent during the Ordovician are also found in Silurian and later rocks. Practically all of the indigenous components of the North Atlantic Ordovician faunas, such as *Prioniodus*, apparently disappeared without issue. Such a disappearance or

great diminution of pelagic provinciality, should be associated with poleward spread of warm, equable climate, not the reverse. If that was what happened in the latest Ordovician and Early Silurian, perhaps with disappearance of the Saharan ice sheets, the Midcontinent fauna must have been the warm-water one and the North Atlantic fauna the cooler-water one, not the reverse as suggested by the "fixist" model.

If condont faunas of the Midcontinent and North Atlantic Ordovician Provinces are interpreted as warm-water and cooler-water faunas, respectively, as the extrinsic evidence just mentioned suggests, some latitudinal rearrangement of continents seems to be required. In figure 7 a rearrangement of North America and Europe is suggested that brings Ordovician evaporite areas, main carbonate belts, and the sites from which Midcontinent-type conodonts are known into a belt straddling the equator. In such a reconstruction, sites from which North Atlantic-type conodonts are known in eastern North America and Europe define a warm-temperate realm in the southern hemisphere and sites from which similar conodonts

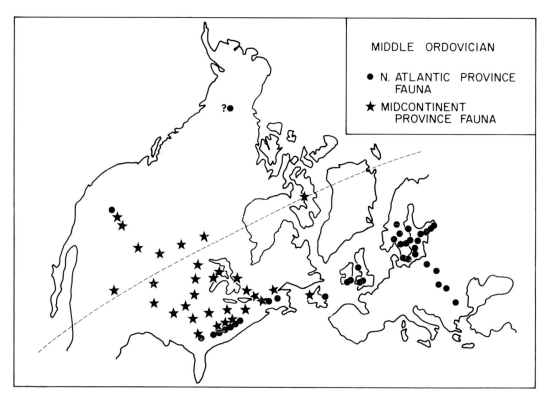

Fig. 7—Rearrangement of North America and Europe to bring Ordovician evaporite areas, main carbonate belts, and the sites from which Midcontinent-type conodonts are known into a belt straddling the equator (dashed line).

are known in northwestern North America suggest a similar warm-temperate realm in the northern hemisphere.

SPECIAL ASPECTS OF THE CONODONT FAUNAS

North Atlantic and Midcontinent Province conodonts differed markedly throughout the Ordovician. In the Early Ordovician, simple-cone species were abundant and varied, but very few of these were common to both provinces. Simple-cone species apparently dominated the Midcontinent faunas to the virtual exclusion of other types, whereas in the North Atlantic Province, species with ramiform-element apparatuses were conspicuous, if in most cases subordinate members of the Early Ordovician faunas.

Middle and Upper Ordovician faunas of the Midcontinent were composed largely of "fibrous" conodonts and nonfibrous species of ramiform-element genera. Only one apparently indigenous Midcontinent species (*Polyplacognathus ramosus*) developed platform-type skeletal elements. By contrast, North Atlantic Middle and Upper Ordovician faunas seem to

have lacked indigenous counterparts of the Midcontinent ramiform-element "fibrous" conodonts, and included a far greater variety of species with platform-type skeletal elements.

Despite the clear differences just indicated, there were also a number of curious similarities between Midcontinent and North Atlantic faunas, particularly between those of Middle and Late Ordovician age. These similarities, which we regard as examples of vicarism, suggest that Midcontinent and North Atlantic faunas may have had a broadly comparable structure and they may also prove to be quite significant in evaluating various models for conodont phylogeny. The more striking examples include the following.

Among the ramiform-element conodonts that dominated Midcontinent faunas of the Middle and Late Ordovician, species of *Phragmodus* and *Plectodina* were particularly common. More advanced species of *Phragmodus* (fig. 8A) are strikingly similar in skeletal architecture to species of *Periodon* (fig. 8B), a characteristic North Atlantic genus and an occasional immigrant into the Midcontinent Prov-

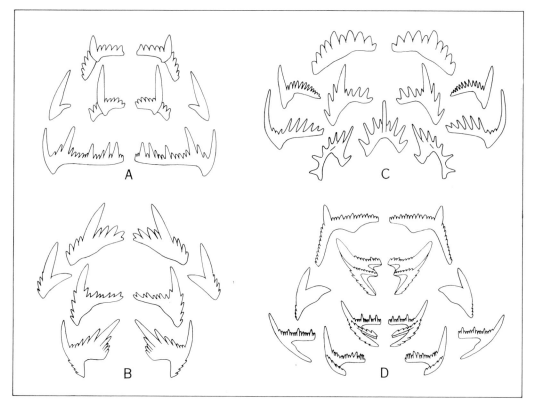

FIG. 8—Elements of the skeletal apparatuses of A, *Phragmodus;* B, *Periodon;* C, *Plectodina;* and D, *Prioniodus.* Elements are arranged in such a way that presumably analogous structures are in the same relative positions in each cluster.

ince. The skeletal apparatus of *Plectodina* (fig. 8C), on the other hand, is reminiscent of that of *Prioniodus* (fig. 8D), which seems never to have invaded the Midcontinent but dominated contemporaneous North Atlantic faunas through much of the Ordovician. In many respects, later species of *Plectodina* mimic North Atlantic *Microzarkodina* (a probable descendant of *Prioniodus*), although known species of *Plectodina* are entirely younger than those of *Microzarkodina*.

Parallel development, indicated by vicarious components of the Midcontinent and North Atlantic faunas, may indicate not only that the two faunas were of similar structure but that they had common ancestors before, or early in, the Ordovician. Those ancestors are unidentified, but the descendant history of the two faunas is fairly clear. Our interpretation of the evidence (Sweet and Bergström, 1972) is that *Plectodina* and *Oulodus* of the Midcontinent Ordovician faunas gave rise to *Ozarkodina* and *Delotaxis,* respectively, which are regarded by Lindström (1970) as early members of the Polygnathacea and Prioniodinacea, from which the great majority of post-Ordovician conodonts seem to have developed. The North Atlantic fauna, on the other hand, seems to have contributed much less to the later history of conodonts. Virtually all indigenous elements of that fauna seem to have become extinct in the Middle and Late Ordovician. Only *Amorphognathus, Icriodella,* and *Belodella* among compound forms, and *"Acodus" mutatus,* among simple-cone types, have Silurian descendants and the icriodontids, initiated by *Icriodella,* survived through the Devonian when they had worldwide distribution. Apparently all but a few of the stocks that are important in the later history of conodont evolution had Midcontinent origins, and it may be significant that post-Ordovician lineages founded by North Atlantic species arose from the segment of the North Atlantic faunas that most frequently migrated to the Midcontinent Province in the Middle and Late Ordovician.

SUMMARY

Regional distribution of Ordovician conodonts in the present northern hemisphere defines two distinct provinces, within which more than 50 percent of the species were endemic. These provinces are interpreted as features of adjacent pelagic realms in Ordovician seas and their long-term separation is explained as a result of adaptation by the respective conodont faunas to waters of different temperature. Vicarism between elements of the Midcontinent and North Atlantic conodont faunas suggests a common origin for and a parallel development of the faunas in the Ordovician. Conodonts of Midcontinent type were ancestral to most post-Ordovician lineages and, in the Ordovician, flourished in a vast area that also includes evaporites and bahamitic carbonate rocks. North American Midcontinent conodont faunas thus are taken as indicators of the Ordovician tropical-subtropical pelagic realm and North Atlantic faunas as indices to adjacent warm-temperate and colder-water realms in the northern and southern hemispheres. Much more needs to be known about Ordovician conodonts of the present-day southern hemisphere before a complete model for distribution of Ordovician pelagic realms can be devised.

ADDENDUM—In a paper published while the present study was in press, Barnes and others (1973) discuss some aspects of the provincial distribution of Ordovician conodonts. Lack of space prevents a detailed review here of their paper but we feel it is appropriate to point out that some of the conclusions expressed by these authors are contradicted by data available in the literature. For instance, they claim that on the basis of their restricted occurrence in a particular paleotectonic regime, Ordovician conodonts can be grouped into a series of faunal associations or communities, each characteristic of a particular tectonic setting from the shelf to the eugeosyncline. We question that on a regional scale these faunal associations, if they can even be recognized, are characteristic of, or restricted to, areas of particular geotectonic settings. For example, we feel it is misleading to label the genera *Pygodus, Prioniodus, Eoplacognathus,* and *Amorphognathus* as "eugeosynclinal" when all of them have their principal distribution and greatest abundance, as far as known, in epicontinental deposits on the Baltic Shield, at least some of which can be shown to have accumulated in very shallow water.

REFERENCES CITED

BARNES, C. R., C. B. REXROAD, AND J. F. MILLER. 1973. Lower Paleozoic conodont provincialism. Spec. Pap. geol. Soc. Am. 141:157–190.

———, AND M. F. TUKE. 1970. Conodonts from the St. George Formation (Ordovician), northern Newfoundland. Bull. geol. Surv. Can. 187:79–97.

BAZOCHE, D. 1960. Découvertes de conodontes dans l'Ordovicien inférieur du Sondage el Gassi No. 1 (Gi 1). Revue Micropaléont. 3:183–186.

BERGSTRÖM, S. M. 1971. Conodont biostratigraphy of the Middle and Upper Ordovician of Europe and eastern North America. *In*, SWEET, W. C., AND S. M. BERGSTRÖM, Eds. Symposium on conodont biostratigraphy. Mem. geol. Soc. Am. 127:83–157.

———. 1973. Ordovician conodont biostratigraphy. *In*, HALLAM, A., Ed. Atlas of palaeobiogeography. Elsevier, Amsterdam. p. 47–58.

———, AND W. C. SWEET. 1966. Conodonts from the Lexington Limestone (Middle Ordovician) of Kentucky and its lateral equivalents in Ohio and Indiana. Bull. Am. Paleont. 50(229):271–441.

BRIDGES, L. W., AND R. K. DeFORD. 1961. Pre-Carboniferous Paleozoic rocks in central Chihuahua, Mexico. Bull. Am. Ass. Petrol. Geol. 45:98–104.

CHURKIN, M., JR., AND E. E. BRABB. 1965. Ordovician, Silurian, and Devonian biostratigraphy of east-central Alaska. Ibid. 49:172–185.

DEAN, W. T., AND O. MONOD. 1970. The lower Palaeozoic stratigraphy and faunas of the Taurus Mountains near Beysehir, Turkey. I. Introduction to stratigraphy. Bull. Br. Mus. nat. Hist. Geol. 19:413–426.

DRAHOVZAL, J. A., AND T. L. NEATHERY. 1971. Middle and Upper Ordovician stratigraphy of the Alabama Appalachians. *In* DRAHOVZAL, J. A., AND T. L. NEATHERY, Eds. The Middle and Upper Ordovician of the Alabama Appalachians. Ala. geol. Soc. Guidebook Ninth Ann. Field Trip, Dec. 3–4, 1971, p. 1–62.

DRUCE, E. C., AND P. J. JONES. 1971. Cambro-Ordovician conodonts from the Burke River structural belt, Queensland. Bull. Bur. Miner. Resources Aust. 110:1–167.

DRYGANT, D. M. 1970. Stratigraphic distribution of conodonts in the Middle Ordovician limestones of the north-western Volyn (in Ukranian). Dopov. Akad. Nauk URSR. Ser. B, 10:891–894.

ETHINGTON, R. L., AND D. L. CLARK. 1971. Lower Ordovician conodonts in North America. *In*, SWEET, W. C, AND S. M. BERGSTRÖM, Eds. Symposium on conodont biostratigraphy. Mem. geol. Soc. Am. 127:63–82.

———, AND D. SCHUMACHER. 1969. Conodonts of the Copenhagen Formation (Middle Ordovician) in central Nevada. J. Paleont. 43:440–484.

FUGANTI, A., AND E. SERPAGLI. 1968. Geological remarks on Urbana Limestone and evidence for its Upper Ordovician age by means of conodonts–eastern Sierra Morena, south Spain. Boll. Soc. geol. ital. 87:511–521.

HEDGPETH, J. W., Ed. 1957. Treatise on marine ecology and paleoecology. Mem. geol. Soc. Am. 67:1296 p.

HIGGINS, A. C. 1967. The age of the Durine Member of the Durness Limestone Formation at Durness. Scott. J. Geol. 3:382–388.

HÜNICKEN, M. A. 1971. Sobre el hallazgo de conodontes en las calizas de la formacion San Juan (Ordovicico, Llanvirniano) Quebrada Potrerillos, Sierra de Yanso, Dpto. Jachal (Prov. de San Juan). Ameghiniana. 8(1):37–51.

———, AND E. J. GALLINO. 1970. Los conodontes de la formacion San Juan (Llanvirniano). Revta Fac. Cienc. Exactas, Fis. nat. Ser. Geol., Univ. Cordoba, 7:5–14.

IGO, H., AND T. KOIKE. 1967. Ordovician and Silurian conodonts from the Langkawi Islands, Malaya. Part I. Contr. Geol. Paleont. Southeast Asia. 3:1–29.

———, AND ———. 1968. Ordovician and Silurian conodonts from the Langkawi Islands, Malaya. Part II. Ibid. 4:1–21.

JAANUSSON, V. 1972. Aspects of carbonate sedimentation in the Ordovician of Balto-Scandia. Lethaia 5:217–237.

KOHUT, J. J., AND W. C. SWEET. 1968. The American Upper Ordovician standard. X. Upper Maysville and Richmond conodonts from the Cincinnati region of Ohio, Kentucky, and Indiana. J. Paleont. 42:1456–1477.

LANGENHEIM, R. J., JR., B. W. CARSS, J. B. KENNERLY, V. A. McCUTCHEON, AND R. H. WAINES. 1962. Paleozoic section in Arrow Canyon Range, Clark County, Nevada. Bull. Am. Ass. Petrol. Geol. 46:592–609.

LEE, HA-YOUNG. 1970. Conodonten aus der Choson-Gruppe (Unteres Ordovizium) von Korea. Neues Jb. Geol. Paläont. Abh. 136(3):303–344.

LINDSTRÖM, M. 1964. Conodonts. Elsevier, Amsterdam. 196 p.

———. 1969. Faunal provinces in the Ordovician of the North Atlantic areas. Nature. 225:1158–1159.

———. 1970. A suprageneric taxonomy of the conodonts. Lethaia. 3:427–445.

———, AND A. PELHATE. 1971. Présence de conodontes dans les calcaires de Rosan (Ordovicien Moyen a Supérieur, Massif Armoricain). Colloque Ordovicien-Silurien, Brest. Mém. Bur. Rech. Géol. Min. 73:89–91.

MEYERHOFF, A. A. 1970a. Continental drift, I: Implications of paleomagnetic studies, meteorology, physical oceanography, and climatology. J. Geol. 78(1):1–56.

———. 1970b. Continental drift, II: High-latitude evaporite deposits and geologic history of Arctic and North Atlantic Oceans. Ibid. 78(4):406–444.

———, AND H. A. MEYERHOFF. 1972. "The new global tectonics": major inconsistencies. Bull. Am. Ass. Petrol. Geol. 56(2):269–336.

MOSKALENKO, T. A. 1967. Conodonts from the Chunya Stage (Lower Ordovician) of the Rivers Moyero and Podkamennaya Tunguska. *In*, New data on the lower Paleozoic biostratigraphy of the Siberian Platform. Inst. Geol. Geofiz. sib Otd. (Akad. Nauk SSSR) p. 98–116; 161–162.

———. 1970. Conodonts of the Krivaya Luka Stage (Middle Ordovician) of the Siberian Platform. Trudy Inst. Geol. Geofiz. sib. Otd (Akad. Nauk SSSR) 61:1–116.

MÜLLER, K. J. 1964. Conodonten aus dem unteren Ordovizium von Südkorea. Neues Jb. Geol. Paläont. 119(1):93–102.

PACKHAM, G. H. 1967. The occurrence of shelly Ordovician strata near Forbes, New South Wales. Aust. J. Sci. 30:106–107.

PANDER, C. H. 1856. Monographie der fossilen Fische des silurischen Systems des russisch-baltischen Gouvernements. K. Akad. Wiss., St. Petersburg. i–x, 1–91.

PHILIP, G. M. 1966. The occurrence and palaeogeographic significance of Ordovician strata in northern New South Wales. Aust. J. Sci. 29 :112–113.

PULSE, R. R., AND W. C. SWEET. 1960. The American Upper Ordovician standard. III. Conodonts from the Fairview and McMillan Formations of Ohio, Kentucky, and Indiana. J. Paleont. 34 :237–264.

RÕÕMUSOKS, A. 1968. On the relation between the brachiopod faunas of northern Estonia, Scandinavia, Bohemia, Britain and North America. 23d Int. geol. Congr. Prague. Sec. 9, p. 21–29.

ROSS, R. J., JR. 1970. Ordovician brachiopods, trilobites, and stratigraphy in eastern and central Nevada. Prof. Pap. U.S. geol. Surv. 639 :1–103.

RUST, C. C. 1968. Conodonts of the Martinsburg Formation (Ordovician) of southwestern Virginia. Abstr. geol. Soc. Am. 1968 Ann. Mtg. p. 258.

SCHOPF, T. J. M. 1966. Conodonts of the Trenton Group (Ordovician) in New York, southern Ontario, and Quebec. Bull. N.Y. St. Mus. 405 :1–105.

SEDDON, G., AND W. C. SWEET. 1971. An ecologic model for conodonts. J. Paleont. 45 :869–880.

SPASOV, CHR. 1970. Conodonts of the limestone fragments of the Carboniferous conglomerate near Falkovetz (NW Bulgaria) : Spis. bŭlg. geol. Druzh. 31(3) :177–186.

SWEET, W. C., AND S. M. BERGSTRÖM. 1962. Conodonts from the Pratt Ferry Formation (Middle Ordovician) of Alabama. J. Paleont. 36 :1214–1252.

———, AND ———. 1966. Ordovician conodonts from Penobscot County, Maine. Ibid. 40 :151–154.

———, AND ———. 1972. Multielement taxonomy and ordovician conodonts. In, Symposium on conodont taxonomy. Geol. Palaeont. Sonderb. 1 :29–39.

———, R. L. ETHINGTON, AND C. R. BARNES. 1971. North American Middle and Upper Ordovician conodont faunas. In, SWEET, W. C., AND S. M. BERGSTRÖM, Eds. Symposium on conodont biostratigraphy. Mem. geol. Soc. Am. 127 :163–193.

———, C. A. TURCO, E. WARNER, JR., AND L. C. WILKIE. 1959. The American Upper Ordovician standard. I. Eden conodonts from the Cincinnati region of Ohio and Kentucky. J. Paleont. 33 :1029–1068.

WEBERS, G. F. 1966. The Middle and Upper Ordovician conodont faunas of Minnesota. Minn. Geol. Surv. Spec. Publs. SP-4 :1–123.

WEYANT, M. 1968. Conodontes Ordoviciens de l'Ile Hoved (Archipel Arctique Canadien). Bull. Soc. linn. Normandie, ser. 10. 9 :20–66.

WOODWARD, S. P. 1856. A manual of the Mollusca : A treatise on recent and fossil shells. Virtue Bros, London. i–xiv, 542 p.

GEOGRAPHY AND FAUNAL PROVINCES IN THE TREMADOC EPOCH

H. B. WHITTINGTON AND C. P. HUGHES

Sedgwick Museum, Cambridge, England CB2 3EQ

ABSTRACT—Analysis of lists of genera of trilobites, compiled for 37 different areas in the world, suggests that three faunal provinces existed during early Tremadoc time and two during late Tremadoc. In early Tremadoc time the *Rasettia* Province extended over much of present North America; the Tsinaniid Province over eastern Australia, South Korea, northeast China and North Vietnam, and the Olenid Province over western South America, southern Mexico, Nova Scotia, eastern Newfoundland, Europe, the Urals and central Asia. Faunas from northwest Siberian Platform are different from all others and may represent a separate fourth province. This distribution suggests that the Tsinaniid faunas inhabited shallow warm seas of one margin of Gondwanaland and the Olenid faunas cooler waters on the other margin. Adjacent to this continental mass is placed southern Mexico, a European mass which extended east to the Urals, and much of central and southeastern Asia. Late Tremadoc faunal distributions are basically similar, with the *Highgatella* Province being the equivalent of the *Rasettia* Province. An equivalent to the Tsinaniid Province is not discernible, and the Ceratopygid Province is equivalent in geographical spread to the Olenid and Tsinaniid Provinces. The Tremadoc Epoch considered as a whole, by using all the samples, gives a three-fold faunal distribution as in the early Tremadoc. The distributions lead to acceptance of a Protoatlantic in the Tremadoc as in Early Ordovician, but there is no evidence for the Mid-European Ocean of Ordovician times.

The rapid evolution of trilobites during the Tremadoc and Early Ordovician is shown by the successive replacements of families that occurred.

INTRODUCTION

In a previous study we compiled lists of trilobite genera and families known from particular areas and localities in the world in each of four divisions of the Ordovician System (Whittington and Hughes, 1972). For each division, dissimilarities between all possible pairs of faunas were calculated, and these dissimilarities analyzed. Each analysis showed more or less well defined groupings of the faunas, and each group was interpreted as a faunal province. If the geographical distribution of these provinces is plotted on a present-day map, a province appears as disjunct fragments distributed over parts of one or more continents. It would be more enlightening to plot such provinces on the appropriate world paleogeographical map. Only parts of such a map had been proposed previously, for example, an Atlantic map by Wilson (1966) and a Gondwanaland assemblage by McElhinney and Luck (1970). We used these proposals, current views on paleomagnetism and lithosphere plates, and the assumption that a faunal province originally extended around parts of a single continental mass, to propose four world maps for successive portions of Ordovician time. The present paper is an attempt along the same lines to propose a world paleogeographical map for the Tremadocian, in British terms latest Cambrian, in North American terms Trempealeauian and early Canadian (latest Cambrian and earliest Ordovician). This map, like the others, is a concoction intended to stimulate critical comment. The faunal provinces plotted are based on analyses (figs. 1–3) of a larger number of samples than is available for any division of the Ordovician System. Many of these faunas are from sequences in which a two-fold subdivision into lower and upper Tremadoc is recognized. The time terms, early and late Tremadoc, used here, correspond to this two-fold subdivision. Analyses of both subdivisions can be made (figs. 1, 2), as well as one for the undivided Tremadoc (fig. 3). The map (fig. 4A, B), plotted on the two polar hemispheres, shows our conception of geography during the epoch, possible changes within this time span are discussed in the text. Examination of our sources of data will show that a numbered paragraph may include a single locality or several sections or localities in a larger area such as a state.

This paper is therefore a broad study of major differences between faunas in seas surrounding continental masses. It takes no account of the relatively local effects of environment within a particular province, such as those discussed by Palmer (1969) or Lochman-Balk (1970) for North America. The stratigraphical correlations we have adopted are likewise generalized and may be open to question, particularly whether all, part, or none of the Trempealeau is equivalent to the early Tremadoc. We have adopted the first alternative, rather than the second (Jones, Shergold and Druce, 1971), since for many samples no unequivocal subdivision of the Trempealeau can be made. The third alternative (Lochman, 1965,

p. 471) that the Trempealeau is entirely pre-Tremadoc in age, is not accepted.

We are indebted to Dr. A. Gilbert Smith, Geology Department, Cambridge University, for helpful discussion of the map, to Mr. John Lewis for his skill in preparing the figures, and to Dr. N. Jardine, Cambridge University, for critical comments on the analytical procedures.

PROCEDURES

Procedures were discussed at length in our earlier work (Whittington and Hughes, 1972, pp. 237–241); here we give only the modifications we have made subsequently. Sources of data, stratigraphical correlations adopted, and taxonomic procedures are given in the final section. In our previous work we assessed dissimilarity between any two samples using the index of Simpson (1960, p. 304, equation 6), that is $1 - C/N_1$, where C is the number of taxa in common to two samples and N_1 the number of taxa in the smaller sample. Hughes (1973) has pointed out that this index may give unstable results particularly when one of the two faunas is small. We recognized this problem in our earlier study (Whittington and Hughes, 1972, p. 238), and attempted to overcome it by omitting from consideration small samples. This entailed an arbitrary decision that eight or ten taxa constituted a small fauna, and meant that some information was omitted from the analyses. Such omissions were undesirable, particularly because of their arbitrary basis, and because available data were sparse to begin with. To overcome this problem we use here Dice's coefficient (Dice, 1945), calculated as $1 - 2C/(N_1 + N_2)$, where C is the number of taxa in common to the two faunas and N_1 and N_2 the number of taxa present in the two samples. The triangular matrix of dissimilarity coefficients for a series of samples has been analyzed using nonmetric multidimensional scaling (figs. 1–3), as previously. This method, originally developed by Shepard (1962) and Kruskal (1964a, b) has recently been discussed in relation to the analysis of faunas by Hughes (1973). Dissimilarity at the generic level only has been analyzed here, since our previous study indicated that analyses at the family level give a similar but less precise result. The analyses were carried out in two stages. First, the data were analyzed to determine the major groupings. Taxa in common to all groups revealed by this initial analysis, that is, cosmopolitan genera, were then deleted and the analysis rerun. This procedure was adopted because dissimilarity coefficients for faunas, particularly small ones with any but a low percentage of cosmopolitan forms, are of little significance.

Assessment of dissimilarity is made from lists of genera, and takes no account of relative abundances, that is, a species represented by ten or hundreds of specimens in a collection has no more effect on the assessment than the single rare specimen. This is one reason why we suggest that such an assessment minimizes the influence of environment, and of course such assessments take no account directly of the type of rock or rocks from which a particular collection came. The generic lists summarize taxonomic work by a variety of authors, published in the main during the last twenty years, though some lists, particularly those from southeast Asia, are based on considerably earlier work. Figures 1–3 show that the *Rasettia* Province of the early Tremadoc of North America is as well defined as any during the Tremadoc. This presumably reflects, in part at least, the relatively recent taxonomic studies of most of the samples by workers between whom there is much common ground and understanding. These points emphasize some of the difficulties inherent in attempting to analyze a complex problem of this kind using the data currently available.

The paleogeographical map of the Tremadoc Epoch (fig. 4A, B) is modified from our map proposed for the succeeding Ordovician Arenig and Llanvirn Series (Whittington and Hughes, 1972, fig. 3). The reasons for adopting particular continental masses, and names for oceans and provinces were given previously (Whittington and Hughes, 1972, pp. 239–241). No oceanic areas are newly named here, but names are proposed for the new provinces. At present there appears to be little uniformity between paleontologists over the naming of faunal provinces. Geographical names have been used, for example, Scoto-Appalachian (Williams, 1973), but the continental assemblages of the lower Paleozoic may not provide suitably concise names. Further, different types of organism have differing tolerances and means of dispersal, so that, for example, the boundaries of trilobite faunal provinces may not correspond with those of brachiopods or echinoderms. It is preferred here to refer to provinces by typical or distinctive taxa, though this has the disadvantage that as faunas evolve the name of a province may change, for example, the *Rasettia* and *Highgatella* provinces of the early and late Tremadoc.

The use of outlines of present continents in the map is defended as an aid to understanding, but it may be argued that these outlines have no meaning in the Tremadoc and are misleading. We have, therefore, made the outlines diagrammatic, but not so as to obscure their supposed relation to present continents. The computer programs of Smith and Hallam (1970) have been used to plot the map in north and south polar projections. It is assumed that a faunal province extended through shallow seas around a continental mass, and was bounded by barriers to migration that were either oceanic or temperature controlled. The great majority of trilobites appear to have been benthonic animals, inhabitants of shelf seas, so that relatively wide or deep oceans were barriers to their dispersion.

EARLY TREMADOC FAUNAL PROVINCES

The analysis of twenty-five faunas at the generic level (fig. 1) shows three groupings which are considered to represent faunal provinces. The fauna of each province is listed in table 1, which shows cosmopolitan genera, families endemic to a province, and numbers of endemic genera of more widespread families. Best defined of these is that which extended over much of present North America. Of the families that are endemic to the province, genera of Lecanopygidae are most widespread, more so than Catillicephalidae which are unknown in western areas. The lecanopygid *Rasettia* is selected as name bearer, because it occurs in all the faunal samples except from the central Appalachians (25), its presence is questionable only in the undescribed fauna from the southern Rocky Mountains of Canada (24). Other endemic families of the province are known only from localities in the central and northeastern Appalachians (25, 28, 31, 32). Families not confined to the province, but containing two to five genera endemic to it, are widespread within it, except that Dikelocephalidae are confined to central and western regions (23, 26, 27, 29), and Marjumiidae to the northeastern region (25, 28, 31).

A second grouping revealed by the analysis (fig. 1) is that including Australian (33) and east Asian (35–37) faunas. The name Tsinaniid is selected for the province because the family Tsinaniidae is endemic to it, and has the most widespread distribution, one or more of the included genera being present in Australia (33), south Korea (37) and northeast China (36). The anomocariid genus *Haniwa* is known throughout the province, but also outside it in the Tienshan (21). Several genera endemic to the Tsinaniid Province, belonging to families not confined to the province, such as the Ptychaspididae and Saukiidae, are widespread within it, but Asaphidae are represented doubtfully only in Australia (33). Faunas in the Tsinaniid Province are linked to certain faunas in the *Rasettia* Province because genera of the Saukiidae are common to them, and because one genus of Dikelocephalidae is present in northeastern China (36).

The remaining faunal samples, from South America, Eurasia and North Africa, are linked at varying levels and are considered to constitute a third grouping here named the Olenid Province because genera of this family are widespread. The strongest link is that between southern Mexico (14) and Argentina (2), the former also linked to the German fauna (10) by the presence in both of two olenid genera, the calymenid *Pharostomina* and "*Shumardia*." The German (10) and British (8) faunas have in common *Hospes*, "*Shumardia*," *Proteuloma*, *Macropyge* and *Niobella*. These links are between faunas containing 18 to 37 genera, and so are reasonably well based. Lower Tremadoc faunas, excluding cosmopolitan forms, of Norway and Sweden (16), Colombia and Bolivia (5), Morocco (15) and southern France (9) are of two to four genera, so that a link between any one of them and any other fauna is based generally on a single genus. The faunas from Kazakhstan (11) and Tienshan (21) are larger, 20 and 12 genera respectively, and linked by the presence of *Lotagnostus*, *Hysterolenus* and *Hedinaspis* in both. However, olenids, ceratopygids and asaphids are prominent in these central Asian faunas, but are absent from the Tsinaniid Province, except for *Asaphellus* in Australia (33) and a doubtful ceratopygid in northeast China (36). On balance, therefore, the Kazakhstan and Tienshan faunas are placed in the Olenid Province. This placement is supported by the analysis of all Tremadoc faunas (37 samples) which shows (fig. 3) well-defined *Rasettia* and Tsinaniid Provinces and a better defined Olenid Province with the Tienshan (21) and Kazakhstan (11) faunas clearly linked to it. Families unique to the Olenid Province generally occur either in southern Mexico and Argentina or in Europe, only the calymenids, best known from Europe, being represented in southern Mexico by *Pharostomina*. Endemic genera of Asaphidae, Ceratopygidae, Nileidae, Olenidae and Remopleurididae are widespread in the province.

A fauna recently described from the northwest part of the Siberian Platform (20) contains nine genera of Acrocephalitidae, Illaenuridae, Plethopeltidae and Saukiidae, all endemic so that it is isolated by the analysis. It is possible that it represents the only known

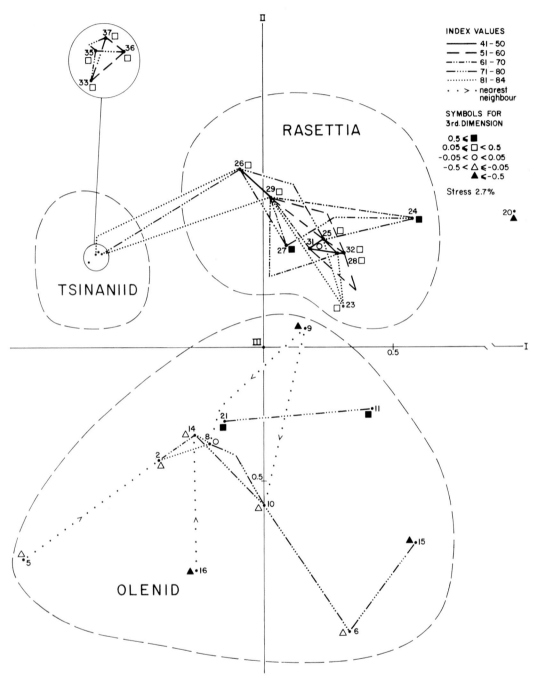

Fig. 1—Early Tremadoc: faunal provinces based on trilobite genera. Three-dimensional plot (third axis perpendicular to page) of analysis of dissimilarity indices between samples. Selected dissimilarity index values (Dice's coefficient) superimposed, each province outlined and named. Relationships between faunas of Tsinaniid Province shown in inset. Key to faunas: 2, Argentina; 5, Colombia; 6, Czechoslovakia; 8, England and Wales; 9, France (Montagne Noire); 10, Germany (Frankenwald); 11, Kazakhstan, USSR; 14, Mexico (Oaxaca); 15, Morocco (Anti-Atlas Mountains); 16, Norway and Sweden; 20, northwest Siberia, USSR; 21, Tienshan and Kuruk Tagh, USSR; 23, Alaska; 24, Alberta; 25, central Appalachians; 26, Minnesota and Wisconsin; 27, Montana and Wyoming; 28, Quebec; 29, Texas; 31, Vermont; 32, western Newfoundland; 33, western Queensland, Australia; 35, North Vietnam; 36, northeast China; 37, South Korea. Coordinates of fauna 20 are 1.47; 0.50. Stress ('goodness of fit') value 2.7% is rated as between 'good' and 'excellent' by Kruskal (1964a, p. 3).

TABLE 1.—FAMILIES AND GENERA OF THE OLENID, TSINANIID, AND *RASETTIA* PROVINCES DURING EARLY TREMADOC TIME[1]

Family	Province		
	Olenid	Tsinaniid	*Rasettia*
Agnostidae	1		2 (1)
Anomocariidae	1	2 (1)	
Asaphidae	8 (?7)	?1	1
Calymenidae	3 (3)		
Catillicephalidae			4 (4)
Ceratopygidae	8 (7)	1	
Cheiruridae	1 (1)		
Dikelocephalidae		1	4 (3)
Dokimocephalidae	1 (1)	1 (1)	1 (1)
Dorypygidae		1 (1)	
Entomaspididae			1 (1)
Eulomidae	2 (2)		
Eurekiidae	1		3 (2)
Geragnostidae*	2 (1)		1
Hapalopleuridae	1 (1)		
Harpidae	1 (1)		
Harpididae	2 (1)		2 (1)
Hungaiidae	2 (2)	1 (1)	1 (1)
Idahoiidae			1 (1)
Illaenuridae			2 (2)
Kaolishaniidae		2 (2)	
Kingstoniidae		1 (1)	1 (1)
Lecanopygidae			4 (4)
Leiostegiidae	2 (2)	1	2 (1)
Lichidae	2 (2)		
Loganellidae			2 (2)
Lonchocephalidae			3 (3)
Marjumiidae	1 (1)		3 (3)
Myindidae	2 (2)		
Nileidae	4 (4)		1 (1)
Norwoodiidae			1 (1)
Olenidae*	18 (17)		3 (2)
Pagodiidae		2 (2)	
Plethopeltidae*			3 (3)
Pseudagnostidae*	1 (1)		1 (1)
Pterocephaliidae			1 (1)
Ptychaspididae		7 (7)	5 (5)
Raymondinidae			1 (1)
Remopleurididae	6 (4)		3 (1)
Saukiidae*		8 (4)	4
Shirakiellidae		1 (1)	
Shumardiidae	3 (2)	1	1 (1)
Solenopleuridae	2 (2)	1 (1)	
Tsinaniidae		3 (3)	

[1] Only fully identified genera included in each number, the number in parentheses indicating the genera endemic to the province. Cosmopolitan genera, omitted from the figures, are *Geragnostus, Bienvillia, Plethometopus, Pseudagnostus,* and *Saukia;* families including cosmopolitan genera are indicated by asterisks. Illaenuridae, though apparently endemic to the *Rasettia* Province, are also known from the Siberian platform (not included in table).

sample of a fourth province which included the Siberian Platform (see fig. 4A, B).

LATE TREMADOC FAUNAL PROVINCES

Analysis of 23 faunas of late Tremadoc age (fig. 2) at the generic level shows two main groupings considered to represent faunal provinces. One of these extends over the present area of North America (excluding southern Mexico and certain eastern seaboard regions). The faunas are well linked, but not so strongly as in the early Tremadoc. Only the Quebec sample consists of relatively few genera. The ptychopariid *Highgatella* is selected as name bearer for the province as it is one of the few genera of endemic families to have a reasonably widespread distribution within the province, being present in central Texas (29), northern Vermont (31), Utah, Nevada (30) and possibly western Newfoundland (32). Other endemic families (table 2) are represented by one or two genera, the majority present in only one sample. Endemic genera of certain families present in both provinces, Asaphidae, Bathyuridae, Hystricuridae and Leiostegiidae, are well dispersed within this province, particularly *Symphysurina* (Asaphidae).

The remaining faunas show a different grouping from that of the early Tremadoc, in that faunas from Argentina (2) and Mexico (14), western Europe (6, 8, 16), Morocco (15), Pay Khoy (18), the Urals (22), Kazakhstan (11), Pamir (17), northeast China (36) and South Korea (37) are well linked, that is, there is no separate Australian–east Asian grouping corresponding to the Tsinaniid Province. Among endemic families (table 2) genera of Ceratopygidae, Hungaiidae and Orometopidae are widespread, those of all other endemic families being restricted to single samples except Calymenidae (*Pharostomina*) in Czechoslovakia (6) and Argentina (2) and Cyclopygidae in Britain (8) and Norway and Sweden (16). Because Ceratopygidae are present throughout the province, in South America, Europe, Asia and Australia, it is named the Ceratopygid Province. Both Ceratopygidae and Hungaiidae, present in Europe (16) and Asia (17, 37), occur in the lower Tremadoc, but continue to be important in the upper Tremadoc. Of endemic genera of widespread families, only *Asaphellus, Symphysurina* (Asaphidae) and *Symphysurus* (Nileidae) are recorded from geographically scattered localities. Weakly linked to the main group of the Ceratopygid Province are faunas from southern France (9), the Tienshan (21), Australia (33) and Colombia (5). These samples are small and poorly known, so that their placement is tentative. The Colombia (5) sample does not contain either ceratopygids or hungaiids, but does include *Symphysurus*, widespread in the province, with two asaphid genera and an olenid

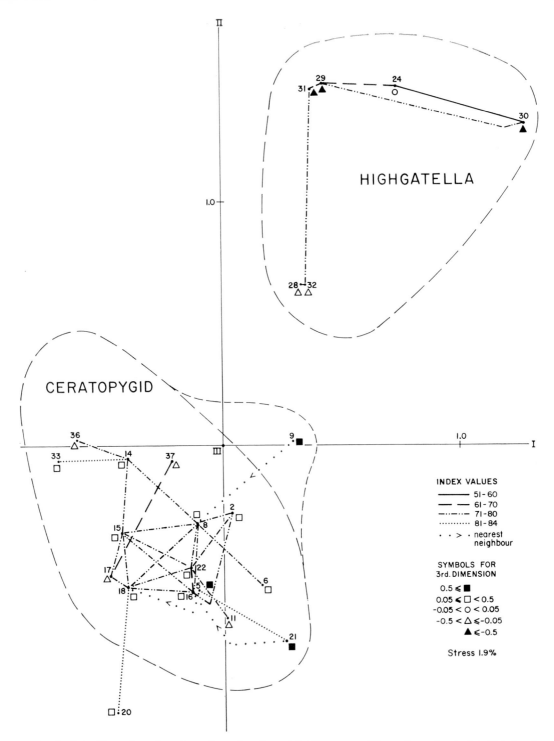

Fig. 2—Late Tremadoc: faunal provinces based on trilobite genera. Three dimensional plot (third axis perpendicular to page) of analysis of dissimilarity indices between samples. Selected dissimilarity index values (Dice's coefficient) superimposed, each province outlined and named. Key to faunas: 2, Argentina; 5, Colombia; 6, Czechoslovakia; 8, England and Wales; 9, France (Montagne Noire); 11, Kazakhstan, USSR; 14, Mexico (Oaxaca); 15, Morocco (Anti-Atlas Mountains); 16, Norway and Sweden; 17, Pamir (Tadzhikistan), USSR; 18, Pay Khoy, Arkhangelskaya, USSR; 20, northwest Siberia, USSR; 21, Tien-shan and Kuruk Tagh, USSR; 22, southern Urals, Aktuba region, USSR; 24, Alberta; 28, Quebec; 29, Texas; 30, Utah and Nevada and parts of Colorado and Montana; 31, Vermont; 32, western Newfoundland; 33, western Queensland, Australia; 36, northeast China; 37, South Korea. Stress ('goodness of fit') value of 1.9% is rated as 'excellent' by Kruskal (1964a, p. 3).

TABLE 2.—FAMILIES AND GENERA OF THE CERATOPYGID AND *HIGHGATELLA* PROVINCES DURING LATE TREMADOC TIME[1]

Family	Province	
	Ceratopygid	*Highgatella*
Agnostidae		1
Alsataspididae	1	
Asaphidae*	11	3
Bathyuridae	1	4
Calymenidae	2	
Ceratopygidae	3	
Cheiruridae*	4	1
Cyclopygidae	2	
Encrinuridae	1	
Entomaspididae		1
Eulomidae*	1	1
Geragnostidae*	2	
Harpidae	1	
Hungaiidae	5	
Hystricuridae*	1	7
Illaenidae	1	
Kingstoniidae	2	
Komaspididae	1	
Lecanopygidae		1
Leiostegiidae*	1	2
Lichidae	1	
Missisquoiidae		1
Monkaspidae	1	
Nileidae*	5	1
Norwoodiidae		2
Olenidae*	12	3
Orometopidae	2	
Plethopeltidae		1
Pliomeridae*	2	
Pseudagnostidae		1
Ptychopariidae		1
Remopleurididae*	4	1
Shumardiidae*	2	
Typhlokorynetidae		1

[1] Only fully identified genera included in each number. Cosmopolitan genera, omitted from the figures, are *Bellefontia Niobella, Pilekia, Euloma, Geragnostus, Harpides, Loganopeltis, Hystricurus, Leiostegium, Borthaspidella, Bienvillia, Hypermecaspis, Parabolinella, Plicatolina, Pliomeroides, Protopliomerops, Apatokephalus, Kainella, Pseudokainella, Remopleuridiella,* and *Conophyrs;* families including cosmopolitan genera are indicated by asterisks.

and shows closest affinity to the fauna from the Tienshan (21). The most widely scattered weakly linked fauna on the plot (fig. 2) is that from the northwest Siberian Platform (20), from which only two genera are recorded. The faunal affinities of this sample are equivocal, and though slightly less problematical than that from the lower Tremadoc, this fauna is not placed in either province.

FAUNAL PROVINCES OF THE TREMADOC (UNDIVIDED)

The analysis made for the undivided Tremadoc (fig. 3) revealed similar groupings to those obtained for the upper and lower Tremadoc separately, which are referred to here by com-

pounding their equivalent late and early Tremadoc province names. This analysis was made in order to be able to include the data from faunas which have not been dated as early or late Tremadoc. Such faunas, from Afghanistan (1), eastern China (4), the Sayan Altai (19), the Kilien Shan (12), the Kuznetskiy Alatau (13) and eastern Newfoundland (7), clearly group with the faunas of the Olenid-Ceratopygid Province. Notable is the strong difference between eastern and western Newfoundland faunas, the latter lying in the *Rasettia-Highgatella* Province. Faunas linked rather loosely into this province include those from central and southwest China (3), Kazakhstan (21) and Tienshan (11), and the small faunas from Colombia (5) and southern France (9). Reference has already been made to the position of the Kazakhstan and Tienshan faunas and, although they are not well linked, they clearly belong to this group. Extremely weakly linked (dissimilarity coefficient, 0.92) is the sample from the northwestern Siberian Platform, which thus is not included in the province. Its position is not quite so isolated as in the early Tremadoc, but slightly more so than in the late Tremadoc.

The *Rasettia-Highgatella* Province is well defined, with the Alaska (23) sample, entirely of early Tremadoc age, the most detached. The Tsinaniid Province is clearly defined and a small fauna listed from Iran (34) appears to belong closer to it than to any other province.

GEOGRAPHY OF THE TREMADOC EPOCH

A pioneer attempt by Wilson (1957) to assess and explain the world-wide distribution of Upper Cambrian (including Tremadoc) trilobites led him to emphasize the importance of facies and tectonics as factors controlling this distribution. Factors which Wilson did not consider are those resulting from the paleogeography of the time, since he used a present day map on which to plot his results. Current views on paleomagnetism and lithosphere plates indicate that Cambrian geography was quite different from the present (Smith, Briden and Drewry, 1973). We have proposed (Whittington and Hughes, 1972, p. 239–241, figs. 3, 6, 9, 12) a series of four world paleogeographical maps for the Ordovician. These maps were based on the assumption that a Gondwanaland continental mass existed much as proposed by Smith and Hallam (1970), the pole being situated in western north Africa. It was further assumed that a faunal province extended through contiguous shallow waters around a

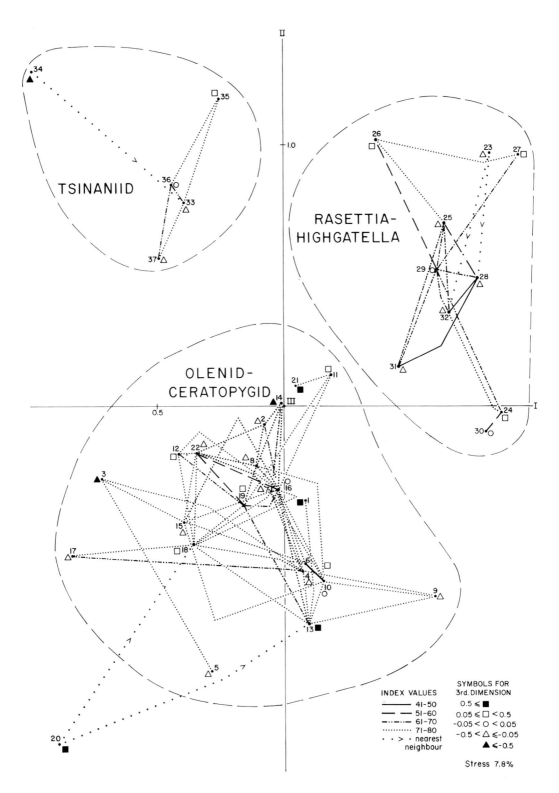

TABLE 3.—NUMBERS OF FAMILIES KNOWN, BECOMING EXTINCT, AND APPEARING FOR THE FIRST TIME DURING THE TREMADOC AND ORDOVICIAN[1]

	Families present	Families becoming extinct at end	New Families appearing
Late Cambrian			
Early Tremadoc	48	22	17
Late Tremadoc	36	14	10
Ordovician			
Arenig and			
Llanvirn	39	6	17
Llandeilo	34	1	1
Caradoc	33	6	0
Ashgill	32	17	5

[1] Figures based on records summarized in tables 1 and 2 and tables 1, 3, 5, and 6 of Whittington and Hughes, 1972. Data from Moore, 1959, used to determine families which appeared first in Tremadoc rocks or in older rocks. The number of "families present" in each interval is the total of those known to be in existence, that is, it includes families known in older and younger rocks but not recorded from that interval. Thus the number does not agree with the total number listed in a particular table. An example is the occurrence of Komaspididae in pre-Tremadoc rocks, and in the upper Tremadoc but not the lower Tremadoc. Komaspididae are included as a family present in lower Tremadoc rocks for the purposes of this table, which is intended to give a measure of rate of evolutionary change.

continental mass, and was bounded by barriers determined by oceanic climate (i.e., depth, width, temperature and/or circulation). The present North American and Eurasian continents were divided into portions, assembled and positioned using the latter assumption together with other geological evidence. We proceed in the same way here, and suggest a world Tremadoc paleogeography (fig. 4A, B). Since no proposal along these lines for pre-Tremadoc paleogeography has been made, the Tremadoc map is compared and contrasted only with the succeeding map for the Early Ordovician, Arenig-Llanvirn Series (Whittington and Hughes, 1972, fig. 3).

In figure 4A, B, a southeast Asia block is placed close to the Australian margin of Gondwanaland, to give a contiguous Tsinaniid Faunal Province in presumed warm, tropical waters on one margin of Gondwanaland. Possible divisions of Asia constitute a special difficulty, and it will be seen that the Olenid-Ceratopygid Faunal Province is tentatively considered to have extended into east central China as well as central and southwest China. The Tsinaniid Province, presumably a descendant of an earlier Late Cambrian province, is recognized in South Korea and northeast China, and possibly North Vietnam and even Iran. This suggests that our southeast Asia mass may not have been a single block. Further, there is structural evidence in Australia suggesting that eastern Australia may have been detached from the remainder of Australia, and thus from Gondwanaland, in the lower Paleozoic. If so, the Tsinaniid Province (of eastern Australia and parts of southeast Asia) may have extended over a mass detached from Gondwanaland. This is a tentative suggestion and the possibility is not indicated on the map (fig. 4A, B).

On the opposite margin of Gondwanaland is the Olenid-Ceratopygid Province, in cooler waters, extending over western South America, Morocco and Europe eastwards to the Urals. There is no evidence of different faunas in northern and southern Europe, as there is in Arenig and Llanvirn time, so that a Mid-European Ocean does not appear to have existed during the Tremadoc Epoch. How extensive a Proto-Tethys (between Europe and Gondwanaland) may have been, and whether there is indeed any evidence for such an ocean, is an open question. Since southern Mexico faunas

FIG. 3—Undivided Tremadoc: faunal provinces based on trilobite genera. Three-dimensional plot (third axis perpendicular to page) of analysis of dissimilarity indices between samples. Selected dissimilarity index values (Dice's coefficient) superimposed, each province outlined and named. Key to faunas: 1, Afghanistan; 2, Argentina; 3, central and southwest China; 4, China (Chekiang province); 5, Colombia; 6, Czechoslovakia; 7, eastern Newfoundland and Cape Breton, Nova Scotia; 8, England and Wales; 9, France (Montagne Noire); 10, Germany (Frankenwald); 11, Kazakhstan, USSR; 12, Kilien Shan, Kansu, China; 13, Kuznetskiy Alatau, USSR; 14, Mexico (Oaxaca); 15, Morocco (Anti-Atlas Mountains); 16, Norway and Sweden; 17, Pamir (Tadzhikistan), USSR; 18, Pay Khoy, Arkhangelskaya, USSR; 19, Sayan Altai mountain region, USSR; 20, northwest Siberia, USSR; 21, Tienshan and Kuruk Tagh, USSR; 22, southern Urals (Aktuba region); 23, Alaska; 24, Alberta; 25, central Appalachians; 26, Minnesota and Wisconsin; 27, Montana and Wyoming; 28, Quebec; 29, Texas; 30, Utah and Nevada and parts of Colorado and Montana; 31, Vermont; 32, western Newfoundland; 33, western Queensland, Australia; 34, Iran; 35, North Vietnam; 36, northeast China; 37, South Korea. Stress ('goodness of fit') value of 7.8% is rated between 'fair' and 'good' by Kruskal (1964a, p. 3).

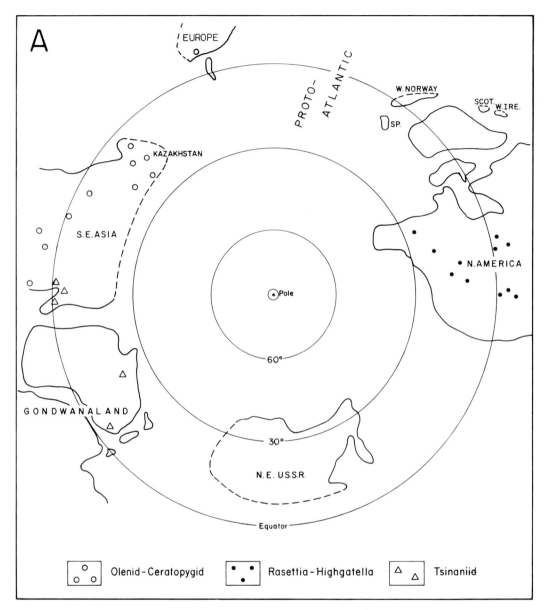

Fig. 4—Stereographic projections of the northern (A) and southern (B) hemispheres showing paleo-geography and trilobite faunal provinces for the undivided Tremadoc (see text for differences between early and late Tremadoc provinces). Abbreviations for geographical areas: E. Ire., southeastern Ireland; E. Newf., eastern Newfoundland; Eng., England and Wales; Fla., State of Florida, U.S.A.; Marit.-N.

belong in this province, we have added an appropriate continental fragment to Gondwanaland in a tentative position. A peculiarity of the distribution of this province, as compared to the present, is the wide latitudinal spread which may indicate that Tremadoc latitudinal temperature belts were less well defined than today.

A Protoatlantic Ocean was accepted for the Early Ordovician (Whittington and Hughes, 1972, p. 240), and evidence given for placing western Newfoundland, western Ireland, northern Scotland and parts of western Norway adjacent to a North American mass. On the opposite side of the Protoatlantic, adjacent to Europe, were placed eastern Ireland and England, eastern Newfoundland, a Maritme States-New England fragment, and part of the

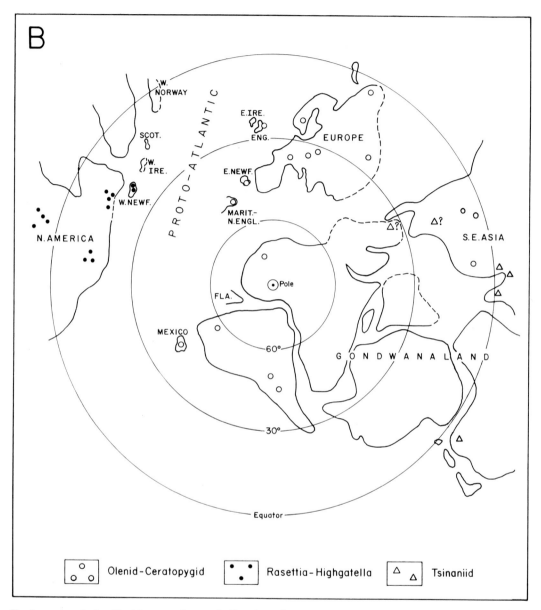

Engl., parts of the Maritime provinces of Canada and New England states of U.S.A.; Scot., Scotland; Sp., Spitsbergen; W. Ire., northwestern Ireland; W. Newf., western Newfoundland; W. Norway, western Norway. See text for discussion of affinities of single fauna known from northeastern USSR.

State of Florida. During the Tremadoc Epoch there is a marked contrast between faunas from western Newfoundland and eastern Newfoundland and Nova Scotia (fig. 3), and on this basis a similar line is adopted for this division though trilobite evidence from western Ireland, Scotland and western Norway is wanting. Bird, Dewey and Kidd (1971) have also put forward convincing arguments in favor of a Proto-atlantic of this nature throughout Cambrian time. The distinctive faunas of the *Rasettia-Highgatella* Province (fig. 4A, B) extended over large areas of the North American mass.

Whittington and Hughes (1972, p. 245) have given reasons for placing a northeast Asia mass (which included Kazakhstan) adjacent to North America during Arenig and Llanvirn time. The small Tremadoc faunas described from the northwestern Siberian Platform occupy isolated positions in all the analyses (figs. 1–3), especially in the lower Tremadoc. Faunas from Kazakhstan appear to belong in the Olenid-Ceratopygid Province. Tentatively we place Kazakhstan as part of the southeast Asia block, and a northeast Asia block is shown isolated from North America and Gondwanaland. The implications are not that Kazakhstan suddenly changed its position between Tremadoc and Arenig time, but that Kazakhstan, known to be structurally complex, may be made up of parts of at least two Paleozoic plates, the Early Ordovician faunas being from one fragment, the Tremadoc from another.

Some of the implications of comparisons between the proposed Tremadoc geography and that proposed for the Arenig and Llanvirn are:

a) the Protoatlantic Ocean was developed much as in the Early Ordovician;

b) the Mid-European Ocean did not begin to open until the late Tremadoc or early Arenig; during the Arenig and Llanvirn it appears to have opened rapidly;

c) parts of present Mexico should be added to Gondwanaland, adjacent to northern South America;

d) the nature and extent of the supposed Proto-Tethys requires elucidation; and

e) evidence for subdivisions of Asia, and the position of a division between Europe and Asia, is inadequate. There is no evidence during the Tremadoc Epoch for a northeast Asian mass having been adjacent to North America. Here, we have included as parts of a southeast Asia mass Afghanistan, the Pamir, and Kazakhstan. The marked dissimilarities between certain faunas on the southeast Asia mass suggest a possible line of division separating North Korea and northeast China from the rest of the mass, and placing them with eastern Australia to form a separate continental mass.

EVOLUTION OF LATE CAMBRIAN AND ORDOVICIAN TRILOBITES

This subject has been discussed by Whittington (1966), who drew attention to the great evolutionary changes that took place in trilobites during Late Cambrian and Early Ordovician times. Table 3 gives figures expressing these rapid replacements and shows the drop in the rate in post-Llanvirn time. The five new families which appeared in the Ashgill each contain a single genus.

The Bathyurid Province of the Arenig (Whittington and Hughes, 1972, table 1, fig. 3) is the successor to the *Highgatella* Province of the late Tremadoc in the North American mass. Twelve families (46%) of the Bathyurid fauna are unknown in earlier faunas, indicative of continued rapid evolution. None of the families unique to the *Highgatella* Province continues into the Ordovician. Families containing many endemic genera in the *Highgatella* Province include Asaphidae, Bathyuridae and Hystricuridae; these families continue to be important, with many endemic genera, in the Bathyurid Province. The ancestors of Cheiruridae and Pliomeridae, important for their endemic genera in the Bathyurid Province, are represented in the earlier *Highgatella* faunas.

The Ceratopygid Faunal Province of the late Tremadoc covered a vast area, which in the Arenig and Llanvirn was occupied by at least three distinct provinces—the *Asaphopsis* in South America, the *Selenopeltis* in North Africa and southern Europe, and the Asaphid in northern Europe (Whittington and Hughes, 1972, table 1, fig. 3). Faunas from the Pamir and China are of uncertain affinity during this time. Taking the faunas of the three Early Ordovician provinces together, 13 of the 34 known families (38%) are newly evolved. Of families unique to the Ceratopygid Province, Alsataspididae, Calymenidae, Cyclopygidae, Hungaiidae and Orometopidae have representatives in the three successor Ordovician provinces, but not in the Bathyurid Province. Other of the Ceratopygid Province species presumably ancestral to important groups in the three Ordovician provinces belong within Asaphidae, Cheiruridae, Encrinuridae and Nileidae.

Recently Valentine and Moores (1972) have suggested a relationship between distribution of continents and rates of evolution, attributing the spectacular rise in family diversity in Late Cambrian-Early Ordovician times to continued stabilization of general conditions after the break-up of a postulated Precambrian supercontinent. Although this may be so in a broad sense, the models suggested by us for the Tremadoc and Ordovician imply that the configurations of continents were far from stable. Further, our models are based in part on the view that distinctive faunal provinces evolved on newly isolated continental masses, for example, the Tsinaniid Province or the faunas of the northeast Asia block, or the Asaphid Province of the Early Ordovician which evolved its distinctive characters with the opening of the Mid-European Ocean. Such ideas offer a fruitful avenue for study, when the paleogeography of the late Precambrian and early Paleozoic is better understood.

SOURCES AND COMPILATION OF DATA

The data for the analyses consist of lists of families and contained genera of trilobites known from rocks of the Tremadoc Series in various areas or localities. The area or locality, and the sources of data, are listed below. We have accepted the correlation advocated by Whittington (1966, p. 700–701), that the Tremadoc of Europe is equivalent to the Trempealeau (lower Tremadoc) and lower Canadian, zones A–F of Utah-Nevada, Gasconadian and Demingian Stages (upper Tremadoc) of North America. Tables of Jones, Shergold & Druce (1971) have been used for correlations with Queensland, Australia, and northeast Asia, with the amendment that we regard their Payntonian Stage as early Tremadoc in age. Details of the stage and formation used for a particular list are given below. Where possible, we have used a division into lower and upper Tremadoc, as indicated in the lists. We have used the most recently published data, which in a few cases consist of a faunal list without description. Assignment of genera to families follows the Treatise (Moore, 1959) where it has not been emended by subsequent work. Exceptions to this practice include the following: Agnostida, family Agnostidae includes *Agnostus, Homagnostus;* family Geragnostidae, *Geragnostus* (subgenera *Gymnagnostus, Lotagnostus*), *Trinodus;* family Pseudagnostidae, *Litagnostus, Machairagnostus, Pseudagnostus;* other genera in uncertain family. Hungaiidae include *Asaphopsis, Birmanites, Dactylocephalus, Dikelocephalina, Hungaiia, Leimitzia, Temnoura, Warendia.* Cheiruridae, subfamily Pilekiinae, are classified following Lane (1971). Calymenidae includes *Bavarilla, Eulomina,* and *Pharostomina.*

In the following list, the number is the same as that used in figures 1–3 and in the text.

Olenid-Ceratopygid Province

1. Afghanistan: Wolfart, 1970; undivided.
2. Argentina: Harrington and Leanza, 1957; lower and upper.
3. Central and southwest China: Lu, 1959; Sheng, 1958; Kobayashi, 1969, p. 209–210; Panho and Tungtzu formations; undivided.
4. China, Chekiang province: Lu, 1959; Kobayashi, 1969, p. 209–210; Yinchufu Shale; undivided.
5. Colombia, South America: Harrington and

Kay, 1951; Henningsmoen, 1957; lower and upper.
6. Czechoslovakia: Vaněk, 1965; lower and upper.
7. Eastern Newfoundland and Cape Breton, Nova Scotia: Dean, 1970; Hutchinson, 1952, 1962; undivided.
8. England and Wales: Hutchinson and Ingham, 1967; Whitworth, P. H., personal communication; lower, *D. flabelliforme,* transition and *C. tenellus* zones; upper, brachiopod, *Shumardia* and *Peltocare* zones.
9. France, Montagne Noire: Sdzuy, 1958; Thoral, 1936; lower and upper.
10. Germany, Frankenwald: Sdzuy, 1955, 1961; Leimitz Shale, lower.
11. Kazakhstan, USSR: Ivshin and Pokrovskaya, 1968; Shidertian Stage, *Acerocare-Eurekia-Lotagnostus asiaticus* zone, lower and upper.
12. Kilien Shan, Kansu, China: Chang and Fan, 1960 (see also Kobayashi, 1969, p. 225–226); Yin Kou Group, supposed upper Tremadoc, treated as undivided.
13. Kuznetskiy Alatau, USSR: Rosova, 1968, table 4; undivided.
14. Mexico, Oaxaca: Robison and Pantoja-Alor, 1968; Tiñu Formation, lower and upper.
15. Morocco, Anti-Atlas Mountains: Destombes, 1967, lower Fezouata Formation, undivided; Destombes, 1970, same formation, lower and upper.
16. Norway and Sweden: Henningsmoen, 1959; Tjernvik, 1956; lower, *Dictyonema* Shale 2e α-δ; upper, *Ceratopyge* Limestone, 3a α-δ.
17. Pamir, Tadzhikistan, USSR: Balashova, 1966; upper.
18. Pay-Khoy, Arkhangelskaya, USSR: Burskyi, 1970; upper.
19. Sayan Altai mountain region, USSR: Petrunina et al., *in* Halfin, 1960, p. 409–433; undivided.
20. Siberia (northwest), USSR: Rosova, 1968, fig. 7, tables 3, 5; lower and upper.
21. Tienshan and Kuruk Tagh, USSR: Troedsson, 1937; Henningsmoen, 1957; Kobayashi, 1969; lower, localities 20L and 22L, with *Westergaardites;* upper, localities 20U, 22U.
22. Urals, Aktuba region at southern end, USSR: Balashova, 1961; upper.

Rasettia-Highgatella Province

23. Alaska: Palmer, 1968; lower (Trempealeau).
24. Alberta, Canada: Aitken and Norford, 1967;

lower, zone 1; upper, zones 2–9 (= zones A–F of Utah and Nevada).

25. Central Appalachians: Rasetti, 1959; lower (Trempealeau).

26. Minnesota and Wisconsin: Nelson, 1956; Raasch, 1951; lower (Trempealeau).

27. Montana and Wyoming: Trempealeau of Williston Basin, Lochman-Balk, 1964; Lochman-Balk and Wilson, 1967; Trempealeau of Montana and Wyoming, Grant, 1965.

28. Quebec, Canada: Lévis Conglomerate, boulders of Trempealeau age; Rasetti 1944, 1945, 1963; faunas of early Canadian age (upper Tremadoc); Rasetti, 1943, 1954.

29. Texas: Lower Tremadoc (Trempealeau), Wilberns Formation, San Saba Member, Longacre, 1970; Winston and Nicholls, 1967; upper Tremadoc, Wilberns Formation, *Mississquoia* and *Symphysurina* zones, Winston and Nicholls, 1967; boulders in west Texas, Wilson, 1954; Henningsmoen, 1957.

30. Utah and Nevada, parts of Colorado and Montana: upper Tremadoc, zones A–F; Berg and Ross, 1959; Lochman, 1964, 1965, 1966; Hintze, 1953; Ross, 1951, 1958, 1970; Ross *in* Whitworth, 1969.

31. Vermont: lower Tremadoc, "Gorge Formation," Rasetti, 1944, p. 231; upper Tremadoc, "Gorge Formation," Shaw, 1951, 1955; Highgate Formation, Shaw, 1966.

32. Western Newfoundland: lower Tremadoc (Trempealeau), Kindle and Whittington, 1958, 1959; upper Tremadoc, Whittington, 1970, table 4–1; Rasetti, 1954.

Tsinaniid Province

33. Australia: Western Queensland, Jones, Shergold and Druce, 1971; lower Tremadoc, Payntonian and Datsonian; upper Tremadoc, Warendian. Victoria, Digger Island Formation, upper Tremadoc, Jones, Shergold & Druce, 1971, p. 23.

34. Iran: Tremadoc undivided; Mila Formation, member 4, Stocklin, Ruttner and Nabavi, 1964; Derenjal Formation, Ruttner, Nabavi and Hajian, 1968.

35. North Vietnam: Saurin, 1956, Lower Tremadoc, zones 17, 18; upper Tremadoc, zone 19.

36. Northeast China: lower Tremadoc, Fengshanian of Liaoning and Hopeh, Shakuotun-Chiushukou fauna, Kobayashi, 1966b, p. 245–6, 275, 282; upper Tremadoc, lower part of Yehli Limestone and Wanwanian, Kobayashi, 1966b, p. 262; Chang, 1966.

37. South Korea: lower Tremadoc, Kasetsu Formation, *Dictyites* and *Eoorthis* zones, Kobayashi, 1966a, p. 34–36; upper Tremadoc, Dongjeom Quartzite, Tomkol Shale, Mungog Formation, Kobayashi, 1966a, p. 36–38, 54–55.

REFERENCES CITED

AITKEN, J. D., AND B. S. NORFORD. 1967. Lower Ordovician Survey Peak and Outram Formations, southern Rocky Mountains of Alberta. Bull. Can. Petrol. Geol. 15(2):150–207.

BALASHOVA, E. A. 1961. Some Tremadocian trilobites of the Aktyubinsk region. Trudy geol. Inst. Leningr. 18:102–145, pls. 1–4.

———. 1966. Trilobites from the Ordovician and Silurian beds of Pamir. Trudy uprav. geol. sov. Minist. Tadzhik. 2:191–262. (In Russian).

BERG, R. R., AND R. J. ROSS. 1959. Trilobites from the Peerless and Manitou Formations, Colorado. J. Paleont. 33:106–119, pls. 21, 22.

BIRD, J. M., J. F. DEWEY, AND W. S. F. KIDD. 1971. Proto–Atlantic Ocean crust and mantle: Appalachian/Caledonian ophiolites. Nature Phys. Sci. 231:28–31.

BURSKYI, A. Z. 1970. Early Ordovician trilobites of central Pay-Khoy. *In* Opornyy razrez ordovika Pay-Khoya, Vaygacha i yuga Novoy zemli. Nauchno-issled. Inst. Geol. Arkt. p. 96–138.

CHANG, W. T. 1966. A few Lower Ordovician trilobites from eastern Shansi. Acta Palaeont. sin. 14(1):6–8.

——— AND C. S. FAN. 1960. Class Trilobita of the Ordovician and Silurian Periods of the Ch'i-lien Mountains. *In*, Geol. Gaz. Ch'i-lien Mountains. Peking, 1–162. (Only translation seen.)

DEAN, W. T. 1970. A new Lower Ordovician trilobite faunule from Random Island, eastern Newfoundland. Geol. Surv. Pap. Can. 70–19:1–10.

DESTOMBES, J. 1967. Distribution et affinités des genres de trilobites de l'Ordovicien de l'Anti-Atlas (Maroc.). C. r. somm. Seanc. Soc. géol. Fr. 4:133–134.

———. 1970. Cambrien moyen et Ordovicien. Notes Serv. géol. Maroc. 229:161–170.

DICE, L. R. 1945. Measures of the amount of ecologic association between species. Ecology. 26:297–302.

GRANT, R. E. 1965. Faunas and stratigraphy of the Snowy Range Formation (Upper Cambrian) in southwestern Montana and northwestern Wyoming. Mem. geol. Soc. Am. 96:1–171.

HALFIN, L. L., Ed. 1960. Biostratigraphy of the Paleozoic Sayan-Altai Mountain region, I, Lower Paleozoic. Trudy sib. nauchno-issled. Inst. Geol. Geofiz. miner. Syr. 19:1–498.

HARRINGTON, H. J., AND M. KAY, 1951. Cambrian and Ordovician faunas of eastern Colombia. J. Paleont. 25(5):655–668, pls. 96, 97.

HARRINGTON, H. J., AND A. F. LEANZA. 1957. Ordovician trilobites of Argentina. Spec. Publs. Univ. Kans. Dept. Geol. 1:1–276.

HENNINGSMOEN, G. 1957. The trilobite family Olenidae. Skr. norske Vidensk-Akad. 1 Mat.-Naturv. Kl. 1:1–303, 31 pls.
———. 1959. Rare Tremadocian trilobites from Norway. Norsk geol. Tidsskr. 39:153–173, 2 pls.
HINTZE, L. F. 1953. Lower Ordovician trilobites from western Utah and eastern Nevada. Bull. Utah geol. Miner. Surv. 48:1–249, 28 pls.
HUGHES, C. P. 1973. Analysis of past faunal distributions. In, TARLING, D. H., AND S. K. RUNCORN, Eds. Implications of continental drift to the Earth Sciences. Academic Press, New York. 1:220–230.
HUTCHINSON, R. D. 1952. The stratigraphy and trilobite faunas of the Cambrian sedimentary rocks of Cape Breton Island, Nova Scotia. Mem. geol. Surv. Can. 263:1–124, 7 pls.
———. 1962. Cambrian stratigraphy and trilobite faunas of southeastern Newfoundland. Bull. geol. Surv. Can. 88:1–156, 25 pls.
HUTCHINSON, R., AND J. K. INGHAM. 1967. New trilobites from the Tremadoc Series of Shropshire. Palaeontology. 10:47–59.
IVSHIN, N. K., AND N. V. POKROVSKAYA. 1968. Stage and zonal subdivision of the Upper Cambrian. 23d Int. geol. Congr. Prague, Rep. 9:97–108.
JONES, P. J., J. H. SHERGOLD, AND E. D. DRUCE. 1971. Late Cambrian and Early Ordovician stages in western Queensland. J. geol. Soc. Aust. 18(1):1–32.
KINDLE, C. H., AND H. B. WHITTINGTON. 1958. Stratigraphy of the Cow Head region, western Newfoundland. Bull. geol. Soc. Am. 69:315–342, 8 pls.
———. 1959. Some stratigraphic problems of the Cow Head area in western Newfoundland. Trans. N.Y. Acad. Sci. Ser. 2. 22:7–18.
KOBAYASHI, T. 1966a. The Cambro-Ordovician formations and faunas of South Korea, Part X, Sect. A, The Chosen Group of South Korea. J. Fac. Sci. Tokyo Univ. Sec. II, 16(1):1–84.
———. 1966b. The Cambrian and Ordovician faunas of South Korea, Part X, Sect. B, The Chosen Group of North Korea and northeast China. Ibid. Sec. II, 16(2):209–311.
———. 1969. The Cambro-Ordovician formations and faunas of South Korea, Pt. X, section D, The Ordovician of eastern Asia and other parts of the continent: Ibid. Sec. II, 17(2):163–316.
KRUSKAL, J. B. 1964a. Multidimensional scaling by optimising goodness of fit to a non-metric hypothesis. Psychometrika. 29:1–27.
———. 1964b. Nonmetric multidimensional scaling: a numerical method. Psychometrika. 29:115–129.
LANE, P. D. 1971. British Cheiruridae (Trilobita). Palaeontogr. Soc. Monogr. London. p. 1–95.
LOCHMAN, CHRISTINA. 1964. Basal Ordovician faunas from the Williston Basin, Montana. J. Paleont 38(3):453–476, pls. 63–67.
———. 1965. Lower Ordovician (Zone D) faunules from the Williston Basin, Montana. J. Paleont. 39(3): 466–486.
———. 1966. Lower Ordovician (Arenig) faunas from the Williston Basin, Montana and North Dakota. J. Paleont. 40(3):512–548.
LOCHMAN-BALK, C. 1970. Upper Cambrian faunal patterns on the craton. Bull. geol. Soc. Am. 81:3197–3224.
——— AND J. L. WILSON. 1967. Stratigraphy of Upper Cambrian-Lower Ordovician subsurface sequence in Williston Basin. Bull. Am. Ass. Petrol. geol. 51(6):883–917.
LONGACRE, S. A. 1970. Trilobites of the Upper Cambrian ptychaspid biomere, Wilberns Formation, central Texas. J. Paleont. 44(supp. to I):1–70.
LU, Y. H. 1959. Subdivision and correlation of the Ordovician rocks of south China. Geol. Press, Peking. 113 p.
McELHINNEY, M. W., AND G. R. LUCK. 1970. Paleomagnetism and Gondwanaland. Science. 168:830–832.
MOORE, R. C., Ed. 1959. Treatise on invertebrate paleontology. Pt. 0:1–560.
NELSON, C. A. 1956. Upper Croixan stratigraphy—upper Mississippi Valley. Bull. geol. Soc. Am. 67:165–184.
PALMER, A. R. 1968. Cambrian trilobites of east-central Alaska. Prof. Pap. U.S. geol. Surv. 559B:1–115.
———. 1969. Cambrian trilobite distributions in North America and their bearing on Cambrian paleogeography of Newfoundland. In, KAY, G. M., Ed. North Atlantic—geology and continental drift. Mem. Am. Ass. Petrol. Geol. 12:139–144.
RAASCH, G. O. 1951. Revision of Croixan Dikelocephalidae. Trans. Ill. St. Acad. Sci. 44:137–151.
RASETTI, F. 1943. New Lower Ordovician trilobites from Lévis, Quebec. J. Paleont. 17(1):101–104.
———. 1944. Upper Cambrian trilobites from the Lévis Conglomerate. Ibid. 18:229–258, pls. 36–39.
———. 1945. New Upper Cambrian trilobites from the Lévis Conglomerate. Ibid. 19:462–478; Corrections. Ibid. 20:88.
———. 1954. Early Ordovician trilobite faunules from Quebec and Newfoundland. Ibid. 28:581–587, pls. 60, 61.
———. 1959. Trempealeauian trilobites from the Conococheague, Frederick, and Grove limestones of the central Appalachians. Ibid. 33:375–398, pls. 51–55.
———. 1963. Additions to the Upper Cambrian fauna from the conglomerate boulders at Lévis, Quebec. Ibid. 37(5):1009–1017, pls. 129, 130.
ROBINSON, R. A., AND J. PANTOJA-ALOR. 1968. Tremadocian trilobites from the Nochixtlán region, Oaxaca, Mexico. Ibid. 42:767–800.
ROSOVA, A. V. 1968. Biostratigraphy and trilobites of the Upper Cambrian and Lower Ordovician of the northwest Siberian Platform. Trudy. Inst. Geol. Geofiz. sib. Otd. 36:1–196.
ROSS, R. J. 1951. Stratigraphy of the Garden City Formation in northeastern Utah, and its trilobite faunas. Bull. Peabody Mus. nat. Hist. 6:1–161, 36 pls.
———. 1958. Trilobites in a pillow-lava of the Ordovician Valmy Formation, Nevada. J. Paleont. 32:559–570, pls. 83–84.

————. 1970. Ordovician brachiopods, trilobites and stratigraphy in eastern and central Nevada. Prof. Pap. U.S. geol. Surv. 639 :1–103.

RUTTNER, A., M. H. NABAVI, AND J. HAJIAN. 1968. Geology of the Shirgesht area (Tabas area, east Iran). Rep. geol. Surv. Iran. 4 :1–133.

SAURIN, E. 1956. Le Cambrien en Indochine. XXth Int. Geol. Congr. Mexico. El Sistema Cambrico I :393–415.

SDZUY, K. 1955. Die Fauna der Leimitz-Schiefer (Tremadoc). Senckenbergiana. 492:1–74. 8 pls.

————. 1958. Fossilien aus dem Tremadoc der Montagne Noire. Senckenberg. leth. 39 :255–285. pls. 1–3.

————. 1961. Neue Funde aus den Leimitz-Schiefern (Tremadoc). Ibid. 42(314) :227–243. pls. 1, 2.

SHAW, A. B. 1951. The paleontology of northwestern Vermont, 1, new Late Cambrian trilobites. J. Paleont. 25 :97–114, pls. 21–24.

————. 1955. The paleontology of northwestern Vermont, 4, a new trilobite genus. Ibid. 29 :187.

————. 1966. Paleontology of northwestern Vermont, XII. Fossils from the Ordovician Highgate Formation. Ibid. 40(6) :1312–1330.

SHENG, S. F. 1958. The Ordovician trilobites of southwestern China. Acta Palaeont. sin. 6(2) :183–204, pls. 1–7.

SHEPARD, R. N. 1962. The analysis of proximities: Multidimensional scaling with an unknown distance function. I and II. Psychometrika. 27 :125–139, 219–246.

SIMPSON, G. G. 1960. Notes on the measurement of faunal resemblance. Am. J. Sci. 258A :300–311.

SMITH, A. G., J. C. BRIDEN, AND G. E. DREWRY. 1973. Phanerozoic world maps. In, HUGHES, N. F., Ed. Organisms and continents through time. Spec. Pap. Palaeontology. 12 :1–42.

————, AND A. HALLAM. 1970. The fit of the southern continents. Nature. 225 :139–144.

STÖCKLIN, J., A. RUTTNER, AND M. NABAVI. 1964. New data on the lower Paleozoic and pre-Cambrian of North Iran. Rep. geol. Surv. Iran 1 :1–29.

THORAL, M. 1936. Contribution a l'étude paléontologique de l'Ordovician inférieur de la Montagne Noire et revision sommaire de la faune cambrienne de la Montagne Noire. Thèses Fac. Sci. Univ. Paris. ser. A. 1541:1–362. 35 pls.

TJERNVIK, T. E. 1956. On the Early Ordovician of Sweden, stratigraphy and fauna. Bull. geol. Instn. Univ. Upsala. 36 :107–284. 11 pls.

TROEDSSON, G. T. 1937. On the Cambro-Ordovician faunas of western Quruq tagh, eastern T'ien-shan. Acta Palaeont. sin. n. s. B, no. 2, 74 p., 10 pls.

VALENTINE, J. W., AND E. M. MOORES. 1972. Global tectonics and the fossil record. J. Geol. 80 :167–184.

VANĚK, J. 1965. Die trilobiten des mittelböhmischen Tremadoc. Senckenberg. leth. 46(4/6) :263–308.

WHITTINGTON, H. B. 1966. Phylogeny and distribution of Ordovician trilobites. J. Paleont. 40(3) :696–737.

————. 1970. Zonation and correlation of Canadian and early Mohawkian Series. In, ZEN, E. A., W. S. WHITE, J. B. HADLEY AND J. B. THOMPSON, Eds. Studies of Appalachian geology: northern and maritime. Wiley, New York. p. 49–60.

————, AND C. P. HUGHES. 1972. Ordovician geography and faunal provinces deduced from trilobite distribution. Phil. Trans. R. Soc. B. 263:235–278.

WHITWORTH, P. H. 1969. The Tremadoc trilobite *Pseudokainella impar* (Salter). Palaeontology. 12(3) : 406–413.

WILLIAMS, A. 1973. Distribution of brachiopod assemblages in relation to Ordovician palaeogeography. In, HUGHES, N. F., Ed. Organisms and continents through time. Spec. Pap. Palaeontology. 12 :241–269.

WILSON, J. L. 1954. Late Cambrian and Early Ordovician trilobites from the Marathon Uplift, Texas. J. Paleont. 28 :249–285, pls. 24–27.

————. 1957. Geography of olenid trilobite distribution and its influence on Cambro-Ordovician correlation. Am. J. Sci. 255 :321–340.

WILSON, J. T. 1966. Did the Atlantic close and then reopen? Nature. 211 :676–681.

WINSTON, D., AND H. NICHOLLS. 1967. Late Cambrian and Early Ordovician faunas from the Wilberns Formation of central Texas. J. Paleont. 41(1) :66–96.

WOLFART, R. 1970. Fauna, Stratigraphie und Paläogeographie des Ordoviziums Afghanistan. Beih. geol. Jb. 89 :1–125.

INDEX[1]

[1] The editor was greatly assisted in the completion of the index and many related matters by the secretarial assistance of Mrs. Patricia Hamilton and Mrs. Joan Roley, Western Washington State College.